MW00604763

MEDICAL PRACTICE MANAGEMENT
Body of Knowledge Review

OPERATIONS MANAGEMENT

VOLUME 1

MGMA
104 Inverness Terrace East
Englewood, CO 80112-5306
877.275.6462
mgma.org

Medical Group Management Association® (MGMA®) publications are intended to provide current and accurate information and are designed to assist readers in becoming more familiar with the subject matter covered. Such publications are distributed with the understanding that MGMA does not render any legal, accounting, or other professional advice that may be construed as specifically applicable to individual situations. No representations nor warranties are made concerning the application of legal or other principles discussed by the authors to any specific factual situation, nor is any prediction made concerning how any particular judge, government official, or other person who will interpret or apply such principles. Specific factual situations should be discussed with professional advisors.

Library of Congress Cataloging-in-Publication Data

Business operations.
 Operations management.
   p. ; cm. -- (Medical practice management body of knowledge review (Third edition) ; volume 1)
 Preceded by Business operations. c2009.
 Includes bibliographical references and index.
 ISBN 978-1-56829-446-9
 I. MGMA (Association), issuing body. II. Title. III. Series: Medical practice management body of knowledge review (Third edition) ; v. 1.
 [DNLM: 1. Practice Management, Medical. W 80]
 R728
 610.68--dc23
                     2015007872

Item: 8820
ISBN: 978-1-56829-446-9

Printed in the United States of America

10 9 8 7 6 5 4 3 2

Body of Knowledge Review Series — Third Edition

VOLUME 1 Operations Management

VOLUME 2 Financial Management

VOLUME 3 Human Resource Management

VOLUME 4 Organizational Governance and
Patient-Centered Care

VOLUME 5 Risk and Compliance Management

Contents

Introduction

Managing the day-to-day operations, from facility maintenance to technology implementation to the improvement
of administrative processes, is at the heart of what a medical practice manager contributes to the healthcare system.
And while many of the same competencies are required for
managers in any organization, there are particular nuances
specific to the delivery of healthcare in a clinic setting that differentiate the medical practice administrator from his or her
peers in other business or healthcare delivery environments.
The chapters in this volume follow the blueprint designed
by practicing medical practice executives to describe the key
competencies, knowledge, and skills required to develop and
maintain effective operations in the medical practice.

The major areas of competence, as identified by Medical
Group Management Association® members, required for
effective operations management in a medical practice are:

1. Design and implement a process improvement
   program;

2. Analyze, develop, implement, and provide feedback on
   the strategic plan;

3. Evaluate present needs, forecast future needs, and
   locate appropriate opportunities for purchasing and
   asset management;

4. Develop, adapt, and maintain facilities to provide a
   high-quality and safe environment;

5. Identify, select, and utilize outsourced business services
   and external expertise;

6. Identify, develop, and manage information technology;

7. Develop and manage communications, marketing, and community relations plans;

8. Establish, communicate, implement, and maintain productivity and compensation benchmarks for physicians and staff; and

9. Monitor physician conduct and performance expectations in coordination with the practice's governing body.

Within each chapter, these major competencies are further delineated according to the key knowledge and skills required to *demonstrate* competency as an operations manager. A few examples of these supporting skills are the ability to develop policies for physician standards of conduct, the knowledge to implement an allocation system of revenues and expenses to support physician compensation, the skill to create a marketing plan, and the ability to provide a safe environment for patients and employees. These skills and many others are explored in detail in the pages that follow.

Chapter 1

Designing and Implementing a Process Improvement Program

ALL BUSINESSES LIVE OR DIE by their processes, and developing a program to consistently improve those processes is needed to achieve sustainable growth, account for changes in the external environment, and keep up with changes within the business itself. The practice that does not constantly test its own organization's core processes and develop and implement ways to improve the operation will stagnate and eventually be unable to meet the clinical and business challenges of the future. The key knowledge and skills necessary to effectively manage the process improvement efforts of a medical practice include identifying organizational needs and desired outcomes, applying quality assessment techniques, developing policies and procedures, enforcing corrective action, and establishing continuous process improvement review.

Process improvement means challenging the way that things have always been done. Not all process improvement programs will meet their goals, but all will produce a positive gain for organizations willing to take some risk to improve themselves. Through the use of audits, outside reviews, compliance reviews, and just standing back and asking "Why do we do this process this way?," an organization can identify the key areas where improvements in the operation and sustainability of the practice can be made. Process improvement also requires an investment of time and thought to evaluate a system and determine a better way to do the job, and an investment in education and training so employees learn new processes, leaders can implement them, and their outcomes can be monitored and evaluated.

In the realm of clinical practice, areas for review that may result in process improvement include coding documentation, risk assessments, chart audits, and auditing of compliance with regulatory and payer regulations. Within these areas, specific types of audits, reviews, and assessments can include:

- Reviewing medical records to evaluate completeness of documentation and to identify those providers whose documentation does not support the procedural or visit code used or who are using a procedural or visit code that is lower than the documentation can support;

- Determining if the diagnosis coding has the highest level of specificity that matches the clinical documentation;

- Comparing the compliance requirements of the various regulatory agencies and third-party payers that use guidelines and policies to ensure the practice meets the expectations and coverage determinations for medical necessity of these outside entities; and

- Reviewing and analyzing the historical data of the organization (e.g., malpractice claims, patient complaints, and external evaluations) to identify trends and areas for additional review and analysis.

All of these reviews can be used as part of larger outcome-based quality assurance programs, which in turn give rise to and support many process improvement initiatives. Structures, processes, and outcomes are the vital components of a quality assurance program, which provide the operational focus for it.

Clearly, no one method of measurement has yet evolved as a gold standard. In most cases, these areas are first addressed through the use of the various audits and assessments. Within larger organizations, these audits can be done internally, assuming qualified personnel exist within the practice. In other cases, these reviews can be contracted out to qualified consultants who can provide the same data to the practice.

The findings, which reflect on the current structure, process, and outcomes of the services of the organization, are often presented to senior clinical and administrative management for review and corrective action. Without proper and effective communication to all stakeholders, the value of these findings is greatly diminished. To be most effective, communication of these findings should be provided in written format, but within the context of a face-to-face meeting where discussion can take place.

These findings, if used properly, become the basis for implementing the various methodologies that may be applied to improve the processes within the organization, including:

- Flowcharting the process being reviewed to identify possible redundancies or dead ends within the process;

- Reviewing historical data that may exist from previous assessments, such as chart audits, coding reviews, and assessments, and comparing those data to current data to identify variations and possible trends that will spotlight concerns and issues; and

- Completing surveys of patient, referring physician, and employee satisfaction levels to identify issues of concern to these groups of stakeholders.

These methodologies are useful in identifying issues, areas for improvement, and possible systemic changes related to the processes in effect. It is often advisable to implement pilot programs before executing changes on an organization-wide basis. Through application on a limited scale, an organization is able to test the proposed changes to ensure that there are no unanticipated ramifications. After these changes are proven through a pilot program, they can be safely applied throughout the organization.

To properly apply and maximize the effect of these reviews within the organization, it is necessary to create teaching models and techniques that effectively impart this knowledge to the staff of the organization. These models vary significantly, based on several factors, including the size of the organization, existing staff mix, complexity of the changes that are being envisioned, and amount of time that can be made available for training and education purposes.

In small organizations, this training can consist of staff meetings, with senior physicians and management providing the training through the use of lectures and roundtable discussions. In larger practices, this training and education may be expanded to include department-specific classes, use of online training and outside consultants or vendors, and sending staff members to off-site courses and seminars. Without this training and support from senior management and physicians, it is difficult or even impossible to obtain staff buy-in to these new process improvements. It is through this investment in time and resources that an organization will be able to realize improvements in their processes and clinical outcomes.

::: Structuring for Quality Improvement

In the past, organizing for delivery of quality was not a central theme for the medical group. Many structural and operational considerations took precedence over quality of care because quality was taken for granted. The lack of standardization, absence of any formal adherence to best practices, and dearth of formalized quality improvement for programs all contribute to a failure of progress in this area.

Medical group structures are often not designed to facilitate quality initiatives. The short-term focus on financial performance is a chief culprit. Groups do not invest enough, either financially or in the training needed to carry out large-scale improvement initiatives. Investment dollars come only from the shareholders' pockets, a prospect that has long curtailed the development of modern medical groups. In his book *Out of the Crisis*, W. Edwards Deming asks a question that should serve as the cornerstone of any group's quality initiative: "What are you doing about the quality that you hope to provide to your customers four years from now?"[1]

The issue of quality in the U.S. healthcare system is becoming increasingly important as we gain more understanding about it. For most of history, quality has been virtually undefined. As Plato might have said, "Quality is in the eye of the beholder." However, that is changing dramatically and will continue to do so as measures and expectations of healthcare service quality continue to evolve.

Quality Management

Quality management is used to reduce errors and improve patient care. Knowing that patient experience influences outcomes, we are inherently motivated to reassess processes that enhance care delivery, and we find that these efforts increase provider satisfaction and improve practice culture. It starts with quality management processes and rolls outward.

Quality management initiatives help professionals design, implement, and maintain quality initiatives, measurement activities, and administrative policies and procedures that ensure patient safety and the consistent delivery of quality care. In practical terms, that means:

- Using analytical processes, such as Lean or total quality improvement programs, to improve interaction and communication between clinical teams;

- Creating internal tracking so that medical practice groups can compare their practices with others on quality, safety, and cost benchmarks; and

- Establishing, evaluating, and enforcing standards for quality.

Examples range from something as simple as taking a new approach to enforcing hand-washing requirements to a complex retooling of referral processes to reduce patient scheduling wait times. No area should be neglected because the return on investment from financial and emotional standpoints is powerful. Practices benefit from increased productivity and improved patient outcomes, increased physician buy-in, and enhanced partnerships for administrators and providers. As you reassess your processes, it is important to ask, "Is this the type of care that I'd want for my family member?" Working toward that goal lets your practice set a new standard for care delivery and encourages everyone to be proud of the work they do.

Population Health Management

A great example of this is the number of members who are tapping into patient data to extract actionable information and improve patient health and patient experience as outlined in the population health management (PHM) series of the Medical Group Management Association® (MGMA®). The PHM series in MGMA magazines and the MGMA *In Practice* blog illustrates how simple it is to have a positive effect on the health of your patient population, yet the MGMA 2013 Population Health Management Study shows that fewer than half of the respondents use these data tools.

Medicine is a complex business, and some processes are rigid by design. But there are still simple ways to make a difference in the lives of your patients, and PHM is one of them. The acronym refers to a patient population, but in reality, it's a group of your patients — the people you see in your waiting rooms and talk with in the exam rooms. You can make a difference in their lives by assessing and changing processes.

MGMA frequently reminds industry members that medical paperwork represents people, a reality that gets lost in the shuffle of files. Kearin Schulte, MS, CMPE, gained buy-in for positive change by reminding her staff that each file represented a patient. "When you talk with team members about the people who they take care of, they are quiet. They take notice," she asserts. "It's not just paper. They're real people."

The 2013 Workgroup for Electronic Data Interchange report includes 10 recommendations to increase the effectiveness and efficiency of our healthcare system. Here are four representative examples:

1. **Patient engagement:** Identifying ways to enable patient engagement through improved electronic access to critical healthcare information;

2. **Payment models:** Identifying business, information, and data exchange requirements that will help enable emerging payment models;

3. **Data harmonization and exchange:** Identifying ways to better align administrative and clinical information capture, linkage, and exchange; and

4. **Innovative patient encounter models:** Identifying business cases for innovative encounter models that use existing and emergent technologies.

These elements of the report touch on the quality management domain because they refer to changes to administrative processes that affect patient care. They help eliminate wasteful administrative processes that detract from high-quality patient care and help practices focus on their true mission of supporting the delivery of high-quality patient care.

⠿ Streamlining a Process Using Lean: A Case Study

What does it take to make a process better in a physician's office? Who has time to fix anything these days? With ICD-10, meaningful use, physician quality reporting systems, reductions in payments, and increases in costs, how are we supposed to focus on the patient? How are we supposed to maintain the highest quality of care and the continuous improvement of processes?

The answers are teamwork, passion, and using the right tools. It takes a team of incredible people to make a practice run smoothly, each with different skill sets. But what are the right tools?

Defining Lean

Lean is a fundamental change in how people within an organization think and what they value, thus transforming how they behave. The basic principles of Lean are to:

- Specify value;
- Engage the staff;
- Eliminate waste;
- Establish pull (customer demand); and
- Seek perfection.

To specify value, your practice must determine which activities or services are offered and provided every day that are of value to your patients, that is, value-added activities and services that are necessary to patients and for which they are willing to pay. For example, the Carolina Skin Surgery Center, PA (Charlotte, N.C.) profiled later in this chapter performs Mohs micrographic surgery, which is a value-added service. An example of a non-value-added service would be Clinical Laboratory Improvement Amendments, which are important to the practice, but oblivious to all but the most informed patients.

Engaging the staff is best accomplished through training. Lean incorporates many methods for process improvement, including:

- **Plan, do, study, act (PDSA).** This commonly used tool involves planning a change, trying out the change, studying the change to see how it worked, and implementing the change as the new protocol.

- **Value stream map (VSM).** This provides the "big picture" of a process and lets you draw it out to identify areas for potential change.

- **Kaizen event.** The term *kaizen* (which is both a concept and a structured approach) means change for the good (*kai* means change; *zen* means good). With a kaizen event, small, continuous steps are documented and measured to improve a process.

- **Gemba walk.** This requires someone to follow a colleague as he or she focuses on one process and time each step. (*Gemba* is a Japanese term meaning the place where value is created.) The information gathered is used to help identify opportunities for process improvements and efficiencies.

Eliminate waste refers to the process of eliminating problems, such as overproduction, patient wait times, extra work for staff that serves no value, and motion waste. Examples include:

- How many times is one sheet of paper passed back and forth for a signature?

- How many supplies are being ordered — too many or too few?

- Are patients waiting to see a doctor for more than 30 minutes?

- Do staff members have to constantly stop what they are doing to fix a printer because it will not work?

Identifying the roots of these issues leads to solutions that are often easy, but just as often overlooked in a busy practice.

Establish pull refers to the ability to respond to customer demand. This step reiterates the importance of only producing what the patient wants and creating processes to maintain the highest quality of services offered.

The final principle, seek perfection, focuses on relentless, continuous improvement by everyone. To paraphrase Henry Ford: Failure is only the opportunity to begin again more intelligently.

Using Lean

The Carolina Skin Surgery Center learned about Lean during a clinical quality program sponsored by the North Carolina Medical Society Kanof Institute for Physician Leadership. Their staff members had not heard of Lean before this program, but Lean principles helped the practice operate more efficiently.

To implement Lean, the practice held biweekly team meetings where they discussed what processes needed to be improved, including the micrographic surgery process.

When they started Lean training, their objective was to streamline the process of scheduling Mohs surgery patients. Most patients prefer to have a consultation and the procedure completed the same day. To do this, they need patients to fully understand the procedure. Most patients think it is as simple as a biopsy taken at a dermatologist's office, but it is more detailed, precise, and potentially more invasive. The practice needs to gather time-consuming medical histories and ask their patients questions such as:

- Do you have a pacemaker or artificial joints?
- Have you had major surgeries?
- What medications are you taking?
- Do you have medication allergies?
- Do you smoke? (Patients who smoke need to stop smoking before and after the surgery.)
- Do you have vacation plans? (Patients need to stay in town for at least one week after the surgery for their safety.)

Depending on the surgery, patients might also need a driver.

All of this takes far more time than most patients realize, and the practice needed to create a way to convey that information to their patients.

To identify opportunities for process improvement, the practice started with a gemba walk. The surgery coordinator was followed and timed for each task related to patients who scheduled a consult and procedure on the same day. The gemba walk was done for several patients because each patient is unique: Some have more medications than others and some have more questions than others.

After completing this process, the gathered information was entered into a current-state VSM, which showed the process as a whole and allowed the practice to identify areas for improvement. By using a VSM, they were able to determine that, on average, it takes 1 day, 2 hours, 41 minutes, and 8 seconds to schedule a patient for surgery.

Next, the practice looked at the VSM to determine where improvements were needed. To better serve the patients, they needed to improve the way they received information and communicated with referring doctors. They were not receiving all of the necessary information, such as demographics, insurance information, and pathology reports, which delayed the process. Without a demographic page, they could not call a patient. Without insurance cards, they could not ascertain whether the practice was in-network with a potential patient's insurance, and without the pathology report, they could not perform surgery.

The practice was spending a lot of time discussing all of this information with patients. It took 15 to 30 minutes to discuss the surgery in detail, give pre-op and post-op instructions, take past medical histories, gather medication and allergy information, and provide special instructions. Worse, it was not billable time. They wanted to know what they could do to shorten this time while ensuring that all the necessary information would be collected.

The practice was also spending a lot of time documenting conversations with patients. Their policy was to document in the chart every conversation with each patient and everything that was discussed: 30-minute discussions meant a lot of transcription was necessary. It was also time-consuming to enter the information into the electronic health record (EHR) system. At the time, the system was slow and entering data was tedious.

Once improvement areas were discovered, the practice started to perform PDSAs, after which they were able to streamline the process, which was improved by 98 percent.

Making Specific Changes

The first change the practice made was to launch a new Website that lets referring physician offices securely upload patient paperwork. The Website provides instructions and details to patients about the information the practice needs. To ease the transition to this new process, referring physicians were called and told what patient information was necessary. They were also asked for feedback about additional features that would make the information transfer process seamless and convenient for them.

Next, a new e-mail process with patients was implemented that cut down phone time by more than half. The practice uses the e-mail address received from the referring physician to send an e-mail (without protected health information) to the patient, which asks how the patient would like to schedule and if the patient would like a consult on a separate day or on the same day as the procedure. If the patient wants to skip a separate consult, the practice provides steps to schedule the procedure, which include:

- Watching a slide show, created and posted on the practice's YouTube channel, which discusses what to expect before and after Mohs surgery;

- Visiting the practice's Website to review information about the procedure;

- Reviewing the detailed video about Mohs surgery on the American College of Mohs Surgery Website (using the link provided on the practice's Website); and

- Completing the paperwork posted on the practice's Website and sending it to the office via fax, e-mail, or mail.

Once these steps are completed, the patient is asked to call the office and speak with the surgery coordinator, who provides a date and time for surgery and will answer any remaining questions. The surgery is reviewed briefly using the teach-back method, which includes asking questions to ensure that the patient understands the procedure.

The new e-mail process inevitably improved documentation time. By reducing the time spent gathering medical histories and explaining surgical procedures, there was less information to document. The practice also created master templates to use for organizing notes.

The final step was changing EHR systems. Entering patient information in the new system is much easier, and the system includes a patient portal so that patients can enter the information themselves when it's convenient for them, which saves the practice much time during the visit.

Implementing Lean had a positive impact. The practice can now schedule patients faster and more efficiently, and it can ensure that patients fully understand Mohs surgery, which reduces the number of last-minute cancellations and rescheduled appointments.

The practice continues to improve this process. The key to using Lean is that you never stop improving, even if you think you are finished. The secret to getting started is breaking complex, overwhelming tasks into small, manageable tasks and then starting on the first one.

::: Lean Implementation in Your Practice

There are many barriers to successful Lean implementation that must be overcome, including:

- Lack of understanding;
- Poor handoffs;
- Inadequate skills; and
- Lack of leadership.

Practice professionals owe patients value, quality, safety, and respect. They owe practice owners a return on their investment, vision, loyalty, accountability, and results. There are several ways to measure experience for patients, including:

- Tracking patient wait times;
- Measuring the size and cleanliness of waiting rooms; and
- Offering television and/or reading material.

For Lean to succeed long-term in your practice, tap into the emotional energy of your providers and staff and assess alignment and engagement. Determine whether you have the right people in the right jobs, whether there is an emotional connection to the work, and how you can tap into personal motivation for change.

Lean is revered for its ability to reduce waste identified using process maps and charts; it promises to streamline processes and improve efficiency. Yet you will still rely on people to implement a new plan and might discover that they take some of the same issues with them to the new system. According to Roger Gerard, PhD, executive business partner at ThedaCare, an integrated health system in Appleton, Wis., to use Lean effectively, your practice's employees might need a refresher in simple communication, a willingness to see processes through the eyes of the people who implement them, and unique ideas to effectively redesign those processes.

Asking for Input

Gerard, who helped lead Lean techniques at ThedaCare, which added $12 million to the bottom line in six months, points out that lucrative business practices and high-quality patient care are not mutually exclusive concepts and that the future success of a practice relies on a willingness to engage in honest and open dialogue and to champion its love of numbers.

"Be proud of it when someone says, 'All you care about are numbers,'" states Gerard. "If you don't, there will be a question of survival. There's nothing to apologize for there, and that's lost on a lot of people in healthcare."

Kenneth Hertz, FACMPE, principal consultant at MGMA Health Care Consulting Group, agrees: "Number crunchers have always gotten a bad rap. In reality, the ability to crunch numbers and...to speak the number-data language is a critical skill that will be needed in the future, in evidence-based medicine, bundled payments, [and] episodes of care."

At a time when payers are complementing the fee-for-service atmosphere with value-based models, Gerard asserts that healthcare professionals need to invest in nonrevenue-generating activities that affect future operations and patient care. For example, how do you encourage physician use of EHRs and transitioning to ICD-10?

Providers must also start using words like "customers" when referring to patients, a switch that represents more than semantics and epitomizes what Gerard calls "dangerous paradigms" that prevent some professionals from reaching their full potential.

"How do we know they're customers?" he asks. "They paid," he answers. "We don't like to treat them like customers, but they're customers. They pay your paycheck. If you used the word *more*, maybe you'd have more respect for them instead of being so patronizing."

Take, for example, a case where patients waited an average of 64 days for referrals to the neuroscience department at the University of Colorado Hospital, Aurora. The reason was because of 16 workflow sheets with various options to process requests.

"We had a problem and knew it was time to show our warts," says Kearin Schulte, MS, CMPE, MGMA member, neurosciences practice manager. "We weren't making anyone happy anywhere," including patients, referring doctors, practicing doctors, and employees.

Using Lean techniques, Schulte worked with Laura Strom, MD, medical director of the neurology department, to assess the process. In one year they whittled the 64-day wait time to 4 days. "It was mind-blowing," affirms Schulte.

"It's what it should be to ensure access to care for patients," adds Strom, who participated in most monthly meetings that lasted two to four hours. She stresses that the key is engaging different sets of employees at different stages of the process. "They're the ones doing the job every day," she explains. "We didn't want to make assumptions."

When implementing Lean concepts at ThedaCare, Gerard's colleagues mapped one process and discovered that there were 14 minutes of real work spread out over an hour and a half. One of the solutions was retooling the surgical center so that all tools and supplies were within reach of the doctor or surgical staff. It eliminated the need for surgeons or surgical nurses to find and retrieve necessary tools. The room is now more efficient, and, according to Gerard, "It yields a less stressful environment where there is a higher quality of care. You can have higher quality and financial improvements simultaneously."

Engaging Staff

To start this process, you must ensure that the staff and leadership are ready for change and are aware of what the process entails. The next step is to engage staff members in dialogue to gain a better understanding of what they do, then identify system roadblocks and ways to motivate change.

A baseline understanding is that people seek pleasure and try to avoid pain. Gerard explains that you must remember *that* when you try to change provider behavior, whether it pertains to using an EHR, meaningful use incentives, or schedules.

Gerard states, "You can't go into a Lean process with a physician and say you're trying to improve financial performance. That is not a source of high emotional energy and not the real point.

"You could, however, point out that 'We are trying to make your life easier so you can get what you want and patients get what they want.'"

Focus on points of frustration and emphasize how solutions will alleviate them. The words you use are also important. Try saying *vision* instead of *plan* and *working smarter* vs. *operating effectively*, which turns people off. Gerard adds, "It has to be an emotionally anchored process if the Lean process is going to work."

Conversation: The Missing Link

"Great things happen when people come together in conversation," asserts Gerard. In the process, which entails inquiry and disclosure, you can often expose waste in the system. He calls the process "opening the kimono" because it requires vulnerability and can uncover personnel issues that erode morale and reduce productivity levels.

"If you're not addressing issues with marginal performers, in 90 days you have marginal leaders," stresses Gerard.

Hertz agrees and notes the importance of having the right people in the right jobs, not just filling empty slots. "In many of the practices I work with, there is often a shortage of capable candidates for a position, so the thought is to keep the marginal one because having somebody is better than having nobody," he explains. "The practice is almost always better having nobody in a position than having a marginal performer. The real issue here is the lack of training most practices provide for new employees...training at all levels — culture, policies, procedures, customer service, expectations. Without clear expectations, adequate training, and holding people accountable to meet those expectations, practices continue to have marginal performers — and oftentimes, dealing with the marginal staff takes away time from mentoring and coaching the better performers to star-level quality."

Gerard advises conducting a cultural assessment for readiness after you have had the conversation to identify issues that can, if not resolved, stymie efforts to implement Lean. As you move through this process, Gerard encourages participants to slow down, facilitate dialogue, and identify fears, which can be the source of most resistance.

This is where a root-cause analysis, which gets all the issues on the table, can be helpful. It allows team members to make choices together and encourages an environment of engagement vs. compliance. The difference, Gerard says, is that engaged employees have emotional connections to their work, and compliant employees will follow instructions or stated directions while the boss is watching. To establish a culture of engaged employees, leaders must have humility, candor, and respect. He adds, "If any one of those ingredients is missing, you're done."

Gerard recommends asking staff to write purpose and vision statements and to identify three priorities. These priorities will vary from practice to practice, but common examples include:

- Ensure financial viability;
- Support staff as they transition to hospital employees;
- Help my team focus on value, quality, and cost;
- Create a positive, nurturing environment where everyone can accomplish more; and
- Create an efficient, stress-free environment.

One of the reasons Gerard suggests asking employees to list these priorities, or areas of focus, is to deselect. "If you do not deselect, you are not prioritizing," Gerard points out. "And," he adds, "You begin to look incompetent because you're not doing things well."

Tapping Your Human Resources

Running practices requires an assessment of business performance, which includes profitability and productivity. Although staff members often represent the most valuable and costly resource, they are typically overlooked when professionals reach for Lean tools to improve patient care and staff morale.

Instead of imposing an organizational structure, Gerard suggests approaching staff members to identify and test solutions to issues they identify. Outlining the dangers of becoming a problem solver for staff, he emphasizes that although it is not a manager's job to do the work of staff or know the intricate details of that work, it is a common trap. "When we try to solve other people's problems, we create victims," he says.

Gerard stresses that the ability to solicit suggestions and listen to what employees tell you empowers and engages them in different ways that generate positive energy. It demonstrates your belief in their ability to make improvements to processes across an organization, which can position them for future growth.

It also taps a rich resource of information, affirms Owen Dahl, FACHE, CHBC, LSSMBB, independently contracted consultant at MGMA Health Care Consulting Group, who achieved a black belt in Lean Six Sigma: "The premise of using staff to make the process improvement concept work is critical, and it requires a culture of improvement with support from leadership — doctors! The key, though, is to recognize that employees see, know, and have ideas about improvements that aren't necessarily communicated or even encouraged by leadership."

"None of us lives in boxes," says Gerard, alluding to organizational charts. "We are complex creatures...Lean is not about simple processes. It's about respect for people."

"There are still managers who believe that the issue in process problems is the people, not the process," says Hertz. "For those who believe that, it is difficult to make the journey to understand that the issue is more likely the process — and that to solve it, the people must be involved with the analysis and solution development. Absent, it will not work, nor will it ever take hold."

When instituting process improvement, benchmarking can uncover areas with the most potential for improvement. In most instances, benchmarking can be considered a method for comparing similar or best practices. In addition, benchmarking is an excellent tool for uncovering different processes and clinical and administrative activities and factors. Benchmarking also provides valuable, and, in most cases, quantitative support to aid in communication, decision making, and developing buy-in. In summary, benchmarking can be used to evaluate, observe, analyze, determine best in class, and convince others of a need for change.[2]

::: Conclusion

Process design and improvement skills lay the foundation for medical practice success. Process improvement requires a strong ability to use tools and techniques, but also the ability to engage staff and leadership to continuously focus on improving the quality of patient care. The best tools and plans are ineffective without the ability to provide the leadership needed to make necessary and potent changes. An administrator who is able to effectively improve practice processes will inevitably advance his or her own career as well as the success of the practice.

Notes

1. W. Edwards Deming, *Out of the Crisis* (Cambridge, MA: Massachusetts Institute of Technology, Center for Advanced Engineering Studies, 1990), 166.
2. Deming, *Out of the Crisis*, 166.

Chapter 2

The Strategic Plan

STRATEGIC PLANNING is a complex and ongoing process of organizational change. It is "a disciplined effort to produce fundamental decisions and actions that shape and guide what an organization is, what it does, and why it does it, with a focus on the future."[1]

Planning is required when the future state we desire involves a set of interdependent decisions, that is, a system of decisions.[2] The key knowledge and skills necessary to effectively develop and implement strategic plans include identifying organizational goals and needs, setting goals and assigning responsibility, aligning business plans with the mission and strategy of the organization, and monitoring the effectiveness of the plans.

Strategy determines and reveals the organizational purpose by defining long-term objectives, action programs, and resource allocation priorities. It attempts to achieve a long-term sustainable advantage in each of its businesses by responding appropriately to the opportunities and threats in the firm's environment and the strengths and weaknesses of the organization. It identifies the distinct managerial tasks at all levels of your business and lets you apply a coherent, unifying, and integrative pattern of decisions. It defines the nature of the economic and noneconomic contributions it intends to make to its stakeholders, is an expression of the strategic intent of the organization, and is aimed at developing and nurturing the core competencies of the firm. It also serves as a means for investing selectively in tangible and intangible resources that can give your organization a sustainable competitive advantage.[3]

Planning used to be based on a 5- to 10-year timeline. Not anymore. The rate of healthcare change continues to accelerate. From new payment strategies and business models to mergers and acquisitions and new clinical pathways, the industry seems to be shifting underneath our feet. Mix these changes with an aging workforce, projected tsunami of Medicare patients, provider shortage, and general economic issues and asset deterioration, and you quickly realize why planning 5 or 10 years out is no longer a viable option. Detailed planning is more likely to be relevant and accurate for a one- to two-year period.

Here are a few areas to focus on to ensure planning success, continued relevance, and sustainability.

Know your practice. Develop a compelling and well-articulated mission and vision for your practice. To paraphrase Yogi Berra: if you don't know where you're going, there's a good chance you won't get there. Determine what is important to your physicians in the future, whether that's independence or financial security and freedom from management issues through merger, acquisition, or sale.

Master your business. Rigorous business discipline and financial management is more important than ever. Benchmark your performance, and study the group and industry trends. Lead and manage at the highest level possible. Develop a budget and employ it as a management tool. Leverage technology and your top-performing personnel.

Educate yourself and your leadership. Network with your colleagues. Attend meetings. Read magazines, e-zines, and blogs, and share information with physicians and administrative leadership. Ensure that your practice staff is aware of the ever-changing environment and its potential effect on your group.

Consider quarterly goals. Typical strategic planning is done in annual time increments. Change the time horizon from annual to quarterly to take advantage of increased currency and relevance and the ability to act on and react to external forces and regulations.

Abandon the annual retreat. Many practices conduct strategic planning retreats every two or three years. What would happen if you conducted quarterly mini-retreats? In lieu of waiting 12, 24, or 36 months to tackle strategic issues, coordinate quarterly mini-retreats (extended four-hour planning meetings) with quarterly strategic goals.

What if? That's the world we live in. What used to be obvious no longer is. Consider options in your planning process. What is the most likely result? What is the best- and worst-case scenario? Ensure different points of view in the discussions. Employ all of the resources available to you. Scenario planning is an increasingly useful tool for practices to consider.

⁚⁚⁚ Differences between Conventional Planning and Strategic Planning

One of the major differences between conventional planning and strategic planning is that "conventional planning tends to be oriented toward looking at problems based on current understanding, or an inside-out mind-set. Strategic planning requires an understanding of the nature of the issue, and then finding of an appropriate response, or an outside-in mind-set."[4]

Long-range planning is a projection from the present or an extrapolation from the past. It tends to be numbers driven. Strategic planning, conversely, builds on anticipated future trends, data, and competitive assumptions and tends to be idea driven. It also seeks to provide a clear organizational vision or focus. If, for example, a medical practice finds through its planning research that its community is fast becoming a mecca for retiring seniors, the group would be wise to strategically add certain types of staff or services over the coming years that would be attractive to this population.

The Strategic Planning Process: Who, What, Why, When, Where, and How?

Before initiating the planning process, the organization must plan to plan. Key concepts, such as *who* should be involved in the planning process, *what* the goal or direction of the planning process is, *why* the organization is planning, *when* and *where* planning should take place, and *how* it will all be accomplished, need to be addressed prior to beginning the planning process.

Who?

One of the most detrimental mistakes a medical group practice can make is putting the planning process solely in the hands of the administrator, with little involvement from other stakeholders within, or even outside of, the organization. The administrator and board chair should be included in the planning group and should drive the development and implementation of the plan, but their buy-in and participation, although essential, should take on the role of facilitator vs. active participant. Demonstrated support through encouragement and motivation, meeting attendance, and resource allocation (time, space, and/or financial) are the main roles of the administrator and board members.

The coordination and facilitation of strategic planning in general should be designated as the responsibility of a key stakeholder, and development of the strategy should be a line job, with each stakeholder responsible for the strategic implications of his or her decisions.[5] The rationale for this is that the managers and staff members are more in touch with the activities that take place within their areas because they are firsthand responders. Who better to identify areas of change than those who have identified the need for it?

However, in some cases, consideration should be given to hiring a facilitator or consultant from outside of the organization to lead the strategic planning process before resting the leadership responsibility on one of the managers or staff members. If any of the following is a concern, outside assistance may be warranted:

- This is the organization's initial attempt at conducting strategic planning;

- Planning efforts have been unsuccessful in the past;

- There appears to be a wide range of ideas and/or concerns among organization members about strategic planning and current organizational issues to be addressed in the plan;

- The members believe there is no one in the organization who has sufficient facilitation skills;

- No one in the organization is committed to facilitating strategic planning for the organization;

- Leaders believe that an inside facilitator will either inhibit participation from others or will not have the opportunity to fully participate in planning themselves; and/or

- Leaders want an objective voice (e.g., someone who is not likely to have strong predispositions about the organization's strategic direction issues and ideas).[6]

Once it has been determined who will facilitate the strategic planning process, the planning team should be formed. The first step in establishing the team is to identify its membership. For example, determine who will be directly involved in planning, who will provide key information to the process, who will review the plan, who will authorize the plan, and who will lead implementation of the plan. There should be at least one person appointed to the team who ultimately has authority to make strategic decisions (i.e., to select which goals will be achieved and how). The composition of the team should also ensure that as many stakeholders as possible, internal and external, are involved in the planning process. Internal stakeholders, such as physicians and clinical and clerical staff members, should be well represented. Each will bring a different perspective to the process. It is also likely that external stakeholders, such as patients and contract staff members, may have valuable input at some point in the planning process, so it is a good idea to include them when that point arises. Exercise caution, because many of these external stakeholders may also share this type of relationship with the organization's competitors. Sometimes, it may be wise to communicate the confidentiality of meetings and possibly ask participants to sign nondisclosure agreements.

There is no ideal number of members for the strategic planning team. If the organization is very small, all employees may be involved; if the organization is large, a representative from each division, area, or department may be selected. Therefore, team membership could range from 2 to 50 representatives. Subcommittees should be used to manage the team when it grows larger than 20 members. This will ensure that all voices are heard throughout the process.

What and Why?

Once the planning team has been established, it is important to ensure that the team understands what its charter is, why the team has been tasked with it, and why the charter is important to and valued by the organization. There must be buy-in from all involved to ensure a successful planning process and the development and implementation of a plan that will assist the organization in managing change and in its decision making for the future. Instilling a sense of ownership in the organization and bringing together everyone's best and most reasoned efforts have important value in building consensus about where an organization is going. It also provides a clearer focus of organization, producing more efficiency and effectiveness to increase productivity.

When and Where?

The next step is to determine the number of meetings the committee should have. This will depend on whether the organization has done planning before, how many strategic issues and goals the organization faces, whether the culture of the organization prefers short or long meetings, and how much time the organization is willing to commit to strategic planning.[7]

Most organizations attempt to complete the strategic planning in two to three months, with meetings every few weeks. This is a good range; if any longer, then the momentum will possibly be lost and the planning effort may fall apart. An effective way to initiate the planning process is to host an off-site retreat for one or two days, as it provides a change of pace and encourages participants to think outside the box or outside the office. Dedicating this much time up front reinforces the importance of the process and the support by administration. It also allows the equivalent of months of one-hour meetings to be conducted in one or two days in an uninterrupted fashion.

How?

The final step in the planning-to-plan process is to provide the team with the tools and resources it needs to develop, implement, and maintain the plan. Adequate resources in the form of supplies (white board, markers, flip charts, paper, etc.), time, money, and creative freedom need to be dedicated to this task. If this is a new undertaking within the organization, dedicating funds to be used for hiring a facilitator or consultant, or sending staff to training, is recommended. The leader of this initiative needs to understand the steps involved and needs to be able to facilitate the completion of each step in the process.

Components of the Strategic Plan

The strategic plan, as defined earlier, is "a disciplined effort to produce fundamental decisions and actions that shape and guide what an organization is, what it does, and why it does it, with a focus on the future."[8] To accomplish this goal, several activities must take place in a sequential order, related to mission, vision, values, goals, and objectives.

Mission

The first step in the strategic planning process is to define the medical group practice's mission, which is its purpose or reason for being. This is usually illustrated in a mission and/or vision statement for the practice, the values of the practice, and in the practice's goals and objectives. If the practice cannot clearly articulate what its purpose is, what it values, and in what direction it is headed in the future, then the remaining steps in the planning process cannot be addressed. In other words, *all* planning for the organization hinges on the mission statement.

The mission of an organization is the organization's precise statement of purpose. It helps keep management focused on preserving or strengthening the organization's unique competitive niche. It helps transform ideas into action. It can also prevent panic and unwise marketing or spending responses to meet an indirect thrust by competitors. Most organizations have limited resources, and a mission statement is a constant reminder of where those limited resources should be focused. Another advantage of a mission statement is that it promotes unity within the organization: It elicits an emotional, motivational response in company employees. This, in turn, creates a culture that is less resistant to change. Focusing on the most important purposes of an organization also brings clarity to expectations, again strengthening the culture of the organization. Developing a mission statement is a challenging process; however, the benefits realized make it worth the effort.

The best mission statements use simple speech with no technical jargon and no embellishment and can be transferred into individual action every day. For example, the mission statement of the Medical Group Management Association® (MGMA®) is "To elevate the performance of medical practice leaders and their organizations by connecting members, building partnerships, setting the standards for certifications, advocating for physician practice and providing innovative solutions,"[9] in which MGMA comes right out and says something. So does Merck: "To provide innovative, distinctive products and services that save and improve lives and satisfy customer needs, to be recognized as a great place to work, and to provide investors with a superior rate of return";[10] and Disney: "The mission of the Walt Disney Company is to be one of the world's leading producers and providers of entertainment and information. Using our portfolio of brands to differentiate our content, services, and consumer products, we seek to develop the most creative, innovative, and profitable entertainment experiences and related products in the world."[11]

The most successful missions are measurable, definable, and actionable project statements with emotional appeal that everyone knows and can act on. A mission such as "to be the best healthcare provider in the world" sounds good for a medical group practice, but a simple mission statement, such as the one PepsiCo used at one point — "Beat Coke!" — is even better because it is a statement that can be measured every day by every employee. Mission statements can also affect company strategies and tactics. If Pepsi were to change its mission to "Beat Czech Cola," different strategies would be called for, along with different geographic tactics in sales, advertising, and distribution.

Formulating a mission statement is best accomplished by asking the planning team a few key questions: What is our main function? What business are we in? Why do we exist? Whom do we serve? What do we value? How are we unique? As these questions are evaluated, a mission statement will start to evolve.

Vision

The vision statement of an organization outlines what an organization wants to be. It is future oriented, inspirational, and ambitious; however, it is also realistic and achievable. Typically a vision is "more important as a guide to implementing strategy than it is to formulating it."[12] This is because strategy development is driven by what the organization is trying to accomplish, which is the organization's purpose. A vision is more encompassing than the mission. It answers the question: What does the organization look like as it effectively carries out its mission? It is the pursuit of this image of success that really motivates people to work together.

Building on the previous mission statement examples, the visions of those organizations are as follows:

- MGMA: "To be the foremost resource for members and their organizations in creating and improving systems that complement the delivery of affordable, quality patient care";[13]

- PepsiCo: "Our responsibility is to continually improve all aspects of the world in which we operate — environment, social, economic — creating a better tomorrow than today";[14]

- Merck: "We make a difference in the lives of people globally through our innovative medicines, vaccines, and consumer health and animal products. We aspire to be the best healthcare company in the world and are dedicated to providing leading innovations and solutions for tomorrow";[15] and

- Disney: "Generating the best creative content possible; fostering innovation and utilizing the latest technology; and expanding into new markets around the world."[16]

A vision should challenge and inspire the practice to achieve its mission, just as these examples have illustrated. A vision should orient the practice's energies and serve as a guide to action. It should also be consistent with the practice's values.

Values

Values represent the core priorities in the organization's culture, including what drives members' priorities and how they truly act in the organization. Values represent the organization's highest priorities and deeply held driving forces. They are statements about how the organization will value customers, suppliers, and the internal community. Value statements describe actions that are the living enactment of the fundamental values held by most individuals within the organization. Values are increasingly important in strategic planning, often driving the intent and direction for the planning team.[17]

In developing a values statement, team members may use methods ranging from highly analytical and rational to highly creative and divergent, such as focused discussions, divergent experiences around daydreams, and sharing stories.[18]

One effective alternative to focus groups or roundtables is the nominal group technique (NGT). NGT balances participation among members and produces a greater number of and more creative ideas than traditional interacting groups. The NGT process, as it applies to developing a statement of values for the organization, is presented in a flowchart in Exhibit 2.1.

No matter what method is chosen for formulating the values statement for the organization, four to six core values the organization would like to operate from should be selected. In selecting these values, internal (e.g., staff members, physicians) and external (e.g., patients,

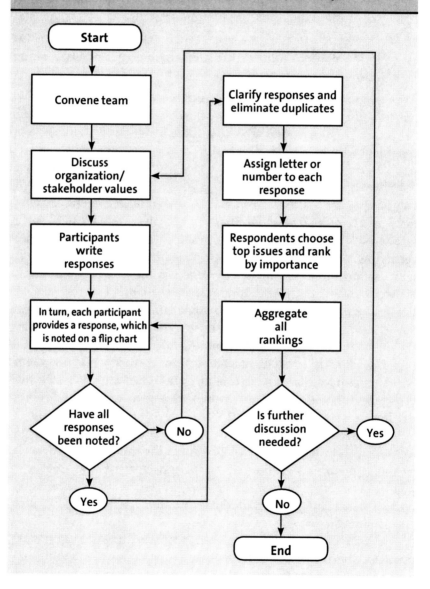

EXHIBIT 2.1

Flowchart of Nominal Group Technique Steps

payers, vendors, competitors, community) stakeholders' values should be considered. Attention should be given to any differences observed between the organization's preferred values and its true values (the values actually reflected by members' behaviors in the organization). For example, if patient service and satisfaction is a chosen value, is the front desk staff empowered to schedule appointments based on the patient's schedule or based solely on the physician's schedule? Are office hours convenient for working parents, including evening and weekend hours?

::: Strengths, Weaknesses, Opportunities, and Threats

Before the next steps of strategic planning can be developed, it is important to use a strengths, weaknesses, opportunities, and threats (SWOT) analysis to assess the organization's internal environment (strengths and weaknesses) and external environment (opportunities and threats). The SWOT process involves several steps and is often done in the context of a group meeting or retreat.

A SWOT analysis helps to find the best match between external environmental trends and internal capabilities, specifically:

- A strength is a resource or capacity the organization can use effectively to achieve its objectives.

- A weakness is a limitation, fault, or defect in the organization that will keep it from achieving its objectives.

- An opportunity is any favorable situation in the organization's environment. It is usually a trend or change of some kind or an overlooked need that increases demand for a product or service and permits the firm to enhance its position by supplying it.

- A threat is any unfavorable situation in the organization's environment that is potentially damaging to its strategy. The threat may be a barrier, a constraint, or anything external that might cause problems, damage, or injury.

The two key questions a SWOT analysis addresses are:

1. What are the significant issues that the group practice faces today?

2. How should the group practice attend to these issues?

An example of a SWOT analysis is presented in Exhibit 2.2.

EXHIBIT 2.2

Strategic Plan SWOT Analysis

INTERNAL FACTORS	EXTERNAL FORCES
Strengths	**Opportunities**
What does your practice do well? ■ In this cell, the internal strengths of the practice should be highlighted. Strengths can relate to the practice at large, to the environment, to perceptions, and to people. "People" elements include the skills, capabilities, and knowledge of participants.	*Where are the opportunities for your practice?* ■ In this cell, the external opportunities for the practice should be highlighted. Opportunities can entail socioeconomic, environmental, and demographic factors.
Weaknesses	**Threats**
What part of your practice needs improvement? ■ In this cell, the internal weaknesses of the practice are identified. This should include an honest appraisal of how things are in the practice. It is not uncommon for "people" problems to emerge as major weaknesses (e.g., poor communication, lack of leadership, little trust, etc.).	*What is happening in your area that could threaten your practice?* ■ In this cell, the external threats for the practice are identified. Threats are events that may, with a change of emphasis or perception, adversely affect the practice. The same factors may emerge as both a threat and an opportunity.

The SWOT analysis will reveal where the medical group practice should focus its resources, and the practice's goals and objectives (e.g., strategies) should arise from this. For example, if one of the practice's weaknesses is in providing geriatric care and a physician is retiring from the practice, a goal could be structured around the opportunity of recruiting a physician who specializes in geriatric care and expanding the practice to meet the needs of this growing population. The practice thus would be overcoming its weakness by pursuing an opportunity.

Goals and Objectives

The words *goal* and *objective* are often used interchangeably, but goals are strategic, long-term outcomes while objectives are tactical, mid- to short-term actions that are taken to accomplish a goal. For example, your practice might have a goal of decreasing overhead by 10 percent, with one related objective of creating an internal billing department to avoid high outsourcing costs. Despite their differences, goals and objectives for the practice should be SMART, which stands for specific, measurable, attainable, realistic, and tangible.

Specific goals and objectives are more likely to be accomplished than general ones. A general goal would be to "recruit a new physician." Using the previous example, a specific goal would be to "recruit a physician who specializes in geriatric medicine."

Without a means of measuring the goals and objectives (e.g., setting a deadline date, a percentage to improve, a number to achieve), knowing when they are accomplished can become difficult. For example, a goal that states "We will recruit two new physicians — one geriatric specialist and one generalist — by March" is more likely to be understood and accomplished than a goal that simply states "We will recruit new physicians for the practice."

When goals and objectives are attainable and realistic, they are set at a level that practices can and will work toward achieving.

Goals and objectives are tangible when they can be experienced with one of the senses — taste, touch, smell, sight, or hearing. When goals and objectives are tangible, making them specific and measurable, there is a better chance of attaining them.

Analysis of the Medical Practice

A number of methods to analyze costs, benefits, and risks are associated with any decision or plan, including cost-benefit analysis and group self-assessment.

Cost-Benefit Analysis

The procedure always involves the following steps:

1. Define the plan or the decision and the process by drawing a flow-chart or list of all inputs, outputs, activities, and events, using the budget or other financial statements and information as guides;

2. Calculate the cost and benefit of each service (include, if possible, direct, indirect, financial, and social costs and benefits);

3. Compare the sum of the costs with the sum of the benefits; and

4. Select the best choices if alternatives are being considered.

Risk can be considered by evaluating the likelihood of failure and assigning a weight to each alternative that has been identified in the analysis. By determining weighted average likelihood of success or failure for each alternative, a risk stratification of the alternatives is possible. For example, there are five alternatives, and the likelihood of failure is 10, 12, 30, 40, and 50 percent, respectively. Clearly, the first alternative has the greatest chance of success, and this information can be incorporated into the discussion.

Group Self-Assessment

Assessing service quality and patient outcomes is becoming essential to the modern medical group practice. The medical group's customers (patients and their families) have ever-increasing expectations of medical services, which have a direct correlation to the group's strategic and operational plans.

Michael Porter writes extensively about group competitiveness and has outlined three fundamental operational strategies:[19]

1. Focus;

2. Differentiation; and

3. Price.

In a medical practice, focus takes shape as a specialty focus or a service-line focus. Quality in services that meet or exceed customer expectations is a key differentiator for medical groups. There is little opportunity to deal with pricing issues in many medical practice settings. The presentation of these data by administration or committees to the board is essential.

Practices need their patients to be advocates for them in the ma place. It has been said that "if we take care of the patients, they will ta care of us." That becomes especially important as pay for performance and other stringent standards are introduced by the market. Pay for performance is a new element that integrates quality and customer issues into pricing strategies for many of the healthcare organizations' largest payers, including companies such as Medicare, UnitedHealthcare, and Aetna. It is necessary and required to provide technically competent service, but alone it is insufficient for the future medical group to be successful. Patient satisfaction is a key element, because value is established as a function of price and quality. Quality is an aggregate measure of patient satisfaction, technical competence, and medical quality.

Organizational Communication Pathways

Communication pathways may be formal or informal, as well as positive or negative. The pathway needs to fit the purpose of the communication and should be determined by the content to be presented. For example, one should not fire an employee in front of a large public group. Likewise, the best forum to announce a new product or service offered by a clinic is not through private one-on-one meetings. As a general rule, the more complex the message, the greater the need for high-involvement communications that are more succinct and structured and incorporate more documentation and follow-up. The complexity might be defined by the nature of the communication or its effect on the community or the group.

Good communications always require careful planning, appropriate channel selection, and a consistent, professional message.

Repetition and reinforcement of the message are also keys to having the audience "receive" and "remember" the intended message. Both formal and informal channels can be used to communicate a group's message.

Formal channels include:

- Memos;

- E-mail;

- Documents, such as letters;

- Meetings, small or large (private or public);

33

de:

- Word of mouth;
- Rumor mill; and
- Informal meetings.

E-mail and mass media can be both formal and informal. Mass media can be directed to individual groups as well as other groups on a more informal, indirect basis. E-mail can be sent to an individual or a few individuals in a rather informal way or be used to broadcast important policy or procedure changes and updates to the group at large.

::: Understanding Culture

What parts of the strategic planning process should involve physicians? Physicians are busy, patient-focused individuals, and the task of developing a process that successfully allows them to participate effectively and efficiently in strategic planning presents a major challenge.

A review of cultural differences between healthcare organizations and physicians offers some direction. Atchison and Bujak describe the difference in orientation between healthcare leaders and physicians in terms of an "affiliate" vs. an "expert" culture.[20] In the healthcare leaders' affiliate culture, roles are interdependent and thought processes are focused on long-term solutions that will benefit the greatest number of people. In the physicians' world, described as an expert culture, roles are hierarchical with the expert at the lead. Real-time clinical decision making using a linear thought process is paramount. An understanding of the differences between affiliate and expert cultures is an important factor in designing a physician-driven strategic planning process. Many times difficulties with healthcare planning processes can be traced to the fundamental differences between these two cultures.[21]

Healthcare organizations possess an affiliate culture. The leadership and staff have a sense of unity and embrace the mission, values, and vision of the organization. The messages embedded in each of these statements are important to healthcare professions that are dominated by the need to belong to a larger organization. Healthcare workers have been trained and rewarded by their professions to work in a collegial manner with others. Nurses, therapists, administrators, and most other support staff members embody these characteristics. These professionals embrace the mission, enjoy teamwork, trust each other, and tend to seek harmony in the work environment.[22]

Expert cultures are very different from the affiliate culture. Expert cultures are found in engineering firms, architectural firms, law firms, and in the profession of medicine. Expert cultures are characterized by individualized behavior. Unlike affiliate cultures, where affiliation is the major motivational influence, expert cultures are dominated by the motivational influences of personal accomplishment and self-reliance.[23]

⣿ Input vs. Outcomes

Healthcare leaders need to understand and respect the unique dynamics of both cultures. In designing a strategic planning process for a practice, special consideration needs to be given to the cultural orientation of physicians. One example of a difference between the expert and affiliate cultures is how decisions are made. Physicians tend to focus on outcome. The affiliate culture, conversely, focuses on a participative process where everyone has a voice.

What matters most is that the outcome is successful. It is essential that the process is inclusive. The need to be inclusive is time-consuming and may leave physicians impatient with the process. Traditional physicians' training and socialization focuses on rapid, independent decision making rather than consensus building, teamwork, and sacrificing self-interest for the greater good.[24]

The critical challenge is to align the goals of the individual physician with the larger needs of the organization. The key to meeting this challenge is designing a process that is sensitive to the personal interests of physicians while at the same time accomplishing the vision of the practice. A shared mission and values are largely irrelevant to the task of engaging physicians. In fact, emphasis on mission and values runs the risk of distracting from the process to the point that it may not succeed. Physicians are goal directed and as a consequence, they are not mobilized by mission statements. Alignment occurs when the vision for the clinical service line aligns with physicians' personal and professional goals. When the vision for the clinical service line is deficient, the individual physicians do not know where they fit in the future and tend to default to their own personal goals. The key cultural element for collaborating with physicians is a shared vision that benefits all parties.[25]

Healthcare leaders should be cognizant of the cultural orientation of physicians when designing a strategic planning process. Several key principles to consider are listed here.

- **Control over decisions that affect the physician:** It is important that physicians exert control over decisions that relate to their practices. Physicians respond well to processes when they have a sense of control over the decisions that most affect them.

- **Respect for the expert:** A variety of avenues should be used to solicit physician input throughout the development and implementation of the planning process. Examples include requests for e-mail comments, a special voicemail, and open forums. The goal is to aggressively pursue physician participation and create a feeling of respect for their ideas and suggestions.

- **Rapid decision-making processes:** Physicians regularly practice independent, rapid decision making. The typical strategic planning process is normally much more collaborative, deliberate, and prolonged. Techniques for expediting decision making need to be employed throughout the strategic planning process.

- **Structured decision making:** In the clinical environment, physicians use deductive decision making. An approach that mimics this style of decision making will facilitate the planning process. Whenever possible, key issues should be summarized and reduced to "yes/no" and "either/or" questions. This decision-making approach mimics the clinical decision-making style that is familiar to physicians.

An understanding of the expert culture lets healthcare leaders successfully engage physicians in a strategic planning process. Leaders must keep in mind that the main differences between the expert culture and the affiliate culture are the respective roles of vision and values.[26] Experts will support a planning effort where the vision includes a role for them and aligns with their personal goals and aspirations. Affiliates, conversely, are more concerned about shared values and the overall organization. Affiliates, like experts, want to see how they fit into the future, but more importantly, affiliates want to align with a group that has similar beliefs. Experts do not make shared values a prerequisite for engagement. When experts share the organizational values, the process has more synergy, but shared values alone will not engage experts. Healthcare leaders need to focus on a shared vision that is sensitive to the needs of the physician stakeholders and the organizational mission.

Physician Input for Improved Outcomes

To maximize the benefits of physician engagement with the strategic planning process, healthcare leaders need to employ an approach that maximally involves physician input from the onset. The leader needs to plan for the planning process.

An effective technique is to interview key physicians and gain insight regarding a customized planning process that will allow their participation. Leaders must be cognizant that physicians will find it difficult to carve out time for long-term strategic planning amid day-to-day patient care demands. A typical process is likely to take several months to complete and will incorporate multiple planning sessions, each consuming the better part of a day. Because of time constraints and the need to have balanced input, meetings must be well organized, purposeful, direct, and efficient. An agenda should be developed and adhered to for each meeting. Involving physicians in the entire planning process, while not an easy undertaking, results in more input and a more robust plan with widespread ownership and greater commitment.

Several key considerations should be kept in mind in designing a strategic planning process that will successfully engage physicians from the outset:

- Physician participants are busy with patient care activities and reluctant to participate in a bureaucratic strategic planning process. Physicians are unwilling to devote an inordinate amount of time to the process. The process must be efficient and respectful of physicians' time.

- Because of the intensive clinical training required to become a physician, most physicians have not developed business and planning skills.

- Leadership must ensure that the strategic planning process does not become too operational vs. visionary.

- Leadership needs to create measures to evaluate the success of goals and objectives. Expected outcomes should be listed and measurements for success should be created.

The journey is often more important than the end result for a strategic planning process. A written strategic plan is valuable as documentation of the discussion and the decisions made along the way, but it is often anticlimactic in comparison to the positive benefits of the process itself.[27] An effective process that incorporates the perspectives and desires of the key physician stakeholders into the emerging plan leads to ownership. People tend to own and support what they help create. Indeed, no undertaking can build physician engagement as effectively as an inclusive, efficient, and transparent strategic planning process. The strategic planning process includes key benefits such as physicians being recognized as the most credible voice in the strategic planning process when it comes to their needs and those of their patients. The process also unites physicians around a common good (patient care) that they care deeply about. It helps the physician participants understand how their personal expectations fit with the expectations of their colleagues, and how they can form a team.

The reflection involved with a strategic planning process provides a clear and current picture of the forces shaping the clinical practice and offers a platform for making proactive, rather than reactive, decisions about the future. It provides the impetus to seize opportunities for clinical and business improvements. It also:

- Clarifies the reasons why the practice exists and builds upon those qualities to attract and retain like-minded physicians;
- Helps the practice identify what it does best and how to capitalize on its unique strengths with developments in the scope, profitability, and effectiveness of its offerings; and
- Provides opportunities for the practice to prioritize its efforts and allocate limited resources in ways that are consistent with its goals.

A shared vision coupled with an effective strategic planning process creates alignment for a common destination and a shared view of how to get there. Physician input, ideas, and opinions should be solicited early and often in the planning process. An inclusive process can reduce anxiety and suspicion by demonstrating that the practice has a plan for the future, and the physicians are a major part of shaping that future.

⠇⠇ A Strategic Planning Example for Facility Design

Whether you are building a new facility, looking for one, or have a practice in an existing building, there are many strategic planning strategies you can use to get the most efficiency out of the space.

Finding new space for the expansion of clinical practices that improve patient experience is often cost prohibitive, but a structured approach to master facility planning can help practices turn a patient-focused vision into reality. Mayo Clinic in Rochester, Minn., developed a framework that enabled one department to double the volume of its outpatient program without expanding its footprint. The team developed a successful approach to designing patient-focused facilities by answering these key questions:

- What should be included in a master plan?
- How do we know when practices are using their space efficiently?
- How do we encourage innovation and how can we be realistic given financial constraints?

The resulting framework has been used by master planning teams throughout Mayo Clinic with tremendous results and gains in efficiency. For example, one clinical department revamped five floors to increase volumes in growing national programs by 50 percent without adding space, resulting in an improved net operating margin, increased efficiency, and better use of space.

The plans that have had the most success were supported by a strong business and clinical case. To win endorsement for its plan, the aforementioned clinical department proved it could grow its high-priority national outpatient programs.

A structured approach can be used for a range of projects, from simple plans to large-scale, complex efforts. The three critical stages for any master plan are project definition and strategy formulation, data and information gathering, and facility planning.

Project Definition and Strategy Formulation

When starting a master facility plan, first establish a project charter, which is a dynamic document that identifies the scope of planning, stakeholders, specific objectives to be measured, proposed timeline, project team, and vision. The vision statement should include your practice's future goals (7 to 10 years down the road) and incorporate direction from the organization's leaders. Review the charter throughout planning to maintain focus on the scope, responsibility, timeline, and stakeholders. Charters might need to be adjusted during the planning process for various reasons, including changes in physician leadership, which affect overall department strategy; and room utilization data that does not support the plan objectives, which can prompt the leadership to realize that less space is needed than originally anticipated. Be sure any changes to the process receive project team endorsement.

If this is a large-scale project affecting multiple departments or divisions, the project facilitator should meet with service-line leaders for practices that will be affected to communicate overall vision, what their responsibilities are, how the process works, and how they will be able to contribute. For example, in one successful master planning effort, leadership set the expectation that service-line leaders develop ways to reduce their clinical footprint, which led to exciting and engaging discussions about the real space needs in clinical areas. Leaders came together to see how they could share space. These collaborative interactions took place because everyone understood how they could contribute.

At this stage, it's critical to establish a common goal for the team, agree on a working approach, and clearly define everyone's role before moving forward. Many practices are tempted to minimize the importance of project definition and jump into data and information gathering. But it's important to ensure that the project is clearly defined. If the team skips or rushes through the steps in the project definition phase, they are more likely to backtrack later, which extends the timeline, sends unclear messages to stakeholders, carries a risk of team members operating under different assumptions, and can ultimately lead to failure. Space can be a sensitive issue, and it is important that the executive planning team takes the time to "get on the same page."

Data and Information Gathering

Collecting objective data will streamline the decision-making ability of practice professionals working to improve facility planning. Setting standards for how this data should be collected is important so that decision makers can have a picture of what is occurring across the organization. There are four steps for successful data and information gathering:

1. Begin with the end result in mind. Understand what the team and its charter aim to accomplish. Careful planning will prevent

unneeded data collection. All data collected should clearly contribute to the outcome. One example of unneeded data collection could be surveying utilization of patient rooms for four weeks when there aren't practice variations in volume. If volumes are consistent, what would those extra three weeks tell the team?

2. Before data collection begins, document the assumptions and methodology for collection. For example, if exam room utilization needs to be determined, you will need to answer and document the following questions:

   ■ Will extra time be allowed for room turnover?

   ■ Will lunch hours be included in the data?

   ■ How will seasonal variation be accounted for?

3. Communicate your goals. It is essential for key stakeholders to understand the methodology and assumptions in data collection before it begins. Identify those stakeholders early. If key people don't buy in to your methodology and assumptions, they might not trust the objective data you are working to collect. When considering stakeholders, don't forget frontline staff. The data collection will often involve unusual activity in the clinical area. Make sure staff members know why unfamiliar people might be in their workspaces. You might also want to leverage staff to collect certain types of data.

4. Collect the data and analyze it based on the assumptions you made at the beginning of the process. Examples of important data to collect include process flow analysis, such as spaghetti diagrams, utilization studies, scheduling analysis, volume trends, and projections; and financial analyses.

Facility Planning

In the final stage of the master planning process, inventory how staff members and patients operate in the existing space to determine whether clinical space constraints affect the practice. We call this review "existing space validation." It is not uncommon to find that space is being used inefficiently. Once you complete this review, you will have documented the square footage of the existing space and will understand how the space functions.

Using a space program lets you show the existing square footage being used, the amount of space requested by service-line leaders, and how much space the project team would like to allocate in the proposed plan.

Dedicate a column in this program to future space needs and requests. The needs of the service line should be considered and should be supported by data. This exercise helps you to rightsize patient and staff space based on use; function; industry standards; and the *Guidelines for Design and Construction of Health Care Facilities* (Facility Guidelines Institute), a reference manual endorsed by the American Institute of Architects; and institutional space standards. For example, Mayo Clinic has internal reference standards for office and workspace size and configuration based on work requirements.

After you've completed this exercise, ask the leadership team to review future space requests based on evaluation criteria developed at project initiation. Some space requests may be readjusted or removed from this document based on misalignment with evaluation criteria.

Following a final review, generate block diagrams based on the document, critical adjacency requirements, and revised process and patient flow analysis. The diagrams represent a high-level analysis of the feasibility of facility improvements. Construction phasing plans, timelines, and an initial cost estimate can be generated from the diagrams. Often complex plans will be multiphase and multiyear efforts to procure funding over time.

Using this standard framework for master facility planning allows practice professionals to find space for growth in their existing footprint, or it might prove that more space is needed.

Additional Recommendations

When undertaking a project of this size and scope, it is critical to consider every scenario imaginable before making a decision, including the following:

- All relevant facts should be gathered in an effort to make as informed of a decision as possible;
- You should not shy away from engaging outside expertise to assist with any part of the process;

- No matter how smooth it might seem that things should go, it is inevitable that politics of some sort will involve itself into the project;

- Most likely something will occur to delay the project at some point;

- The need to use attorneys and possibly an accountant will likely be unavoidable, and legal fees could be considerable;

- Budgeting for contingency funds is a must to be prepared for those unexpected costs or cost overruns;

- No matter how good your intentions are, some faction of the community will be against your project, and thick skin will be required to deal with outside influences and opinions that are out of your control; and

- Although it is fine to try to share your message, rather than trying to refute all negative thoughts in the media, simply take the high road and keep your focus on the ultimate goal.

It is easy (and understandable) to get caught up in the excitement and euphoria of the new project. However, one must not lose focus or forget about the day-to-day business and the most critical task, which is taking care of the patients. Leadership and staff members will need keep open minds because the only true constant will be change. Expect the unexpected!

⠿ Conclusion

Strategic planning skills place practice managers in a leadership role. Strategic planning requires a deep understanding of the business's strength and weaknesses as well as how to adjust to the opportunities and threats in the market. Effective strategic planning requires an executive to synthesize data from disparate inputs, formulate a plan, and communicate the plan to the stakeholders in the practice. The ability to communicate effectively with these stakeholders depends on the reputation the practice executive builds and ultimately the relationship the executive has with the physician stakeholders. The foundation of that relationship is built on the credibility, competency, consistency, ethics, and communication skills demonstrated in the practice every day. The interactions practice executives have every day will affect their effectiveness in the high-leverage decisions and projects that are often the result of strategic planning.

Notes

1. John M. Bryson, *Strategic Planning for Public and Nonprofit Organizations: A Guide to Strengthening and Sustaining Organizational Achievement* (San Francisco: Jossey-Bass, 2004).

2. Russell L. Ackoff, *A Concept of Corporate Planning* (New York: Wiley Interscience, 1970); Henry Mintzberg, *The Rise and Fall of Strategic Planning* (New York: Simon and Schuster, 1994), 11.

3. Arnoldo C. Hax and Nicolas S. Majluf, *The Strategy Concept and Process: A Pragmatic Approach* (Upper Saddle River, NJ: Prentice Hall, 1996), 14.

4. T.J. Rowley, "Moving beyond Didactic Ties: A Network of Stakeholder Influences," *Academy of Management Review* 22, no. 4 (1997): 887–910.

5. Linda E. Swayne, Peter M. Ginter, and W. Jack Duncan, *The Physician Strategist: Setting a Strategic Direction for Your Practice* (Chicago: Irwin Professional Publishing, 1996).

6. Carter McNamara, *Field Guide to Nonprofit Strategic Planning and Facilitation* Minneapolis, MN: Authenticity Consulting LLC, 2000).

7. McNamara, *Field Guide.*

8. Bryson, *Strategic Planning.*

9. "Mission, Vision and Values," Medical Group Management Association, www.mgma.org.

10. "Mission Statement," Merck & Co., Inc., www.merck.com/about/Merck %20Vision%20Mission.pdf.

11. "Mission Statement," The Walt Disney Company, http://thewaltdisney company.com/investors.

12. Bryson, *Strategic Planning.*

13. "Mission, Vision and Values," Medical Group Management Association.

14. "Our Mission & Values," PepsiCo, www.pepsico.com/Purpose/ Our-Mission-and-Values.

15. "Vision Statement," Merck & Co., Inc., www.merck.com/about/Merck%20 Vision%20Mission.pdf.

16. "Roger Iger Vision," The Walt Disney Company, http://thewaltdisney company.com/about-disney/leadership/ceo/robert-iger.

17. McNamara, *Field Guide.*

18. McNamara, *Field Guide.*

19. Michael E. Porter, *Competitive Strategy: Techniques for Analyzing Industries and Competitors* (New York: Free Press, 1980), 35.

20. Thomas A. Atchison and Joseph S. Bujak, *Leading Transformational Change: The Physician-Executive Partnership* (Chicago: Health Administration Press, 2001).

21. Atchison and Bujak, *Leading Transformational Change.*

22. Atchison and Bujak, *Leading Transformational Change.*

23. Atchison and Bujak, *Leading Transformational Change.*

24. Joseph S. Bujak, *Inside the Physician Mind: Finding Common Ground with Doctors* (Chicago: Health Administration Press, 2008).

25. Bujak, *Inside the Physician Mind.*

26. Bujak, *Inside the Physician Mind.*

27. D. Beckham, "Physician Involvement in Hospital Strategic Planning," *Trustee* 63, no. 6 (2010): 6–7.

Chapter 3

Purchasing and Asset Management

THE PURCHASING SYSTEM is a key component in the operation of any medical practice. It determines how well medical groups can procure and administer the right goods and services in the right place, at the right time, for the right price, and in the most efficient and effective way possible. Effective management of the purchasing function requires competence in identifying types of supplies and equipment needed, implementing an inventory control plan, establishing procurement procedures, managing effective vendor relationships, and establishing procedures for ordering and replenishing supplies and equipment.

::: Types of Supplies and Equipment

All operating costs or overhead except for W-2 employees' salaries and related payroll taxes are "purchasing system processed costs" and go through the practice's purchasing process. These include fixed assets, nonbillable supplies, and separately billable supplies, which have important distinctions for accounting and claims purposes.

Fixed Assets

Fixed assets include property, building structures, and equipment used in the business that is not sold to patients (computers, vehicles, furniture, etc.). These assets are classified as noncurrent because they cannot be easily converted into cash, and they are sometimes referred to as tangible assets. These costs reside on the practice's balance sheet until they are transferred to the income statement as operating costs through depreciation.

Nonbillable Supplies

Basic supplies that are assumed to be an integral part of a medical procedure or service cannot be billed for separately. The list of these supplies varies depending on the company or government agency processing the claim, but examples include cold packs, trays, sponges, clips, drains, IV pumps, and probes.

There are often other restrictions on what you can bill separately for. Reusable supplies and supplies that can be purchased over the counter are two examples that aren't likely to qualify for separate reimbursement. Be sure to bundle the costs of these types of supplies into the procedure or service cost itself or they will not be recaptured.

Note that bundling does not refer to the often illegal practice of creating kits filled with nonbillable supplies and then billing for the kits. Claims processors care only about the contents of such kits, which are ineligible for reimbursement if they contain nonbillable items.

Separately Billable Supplies

So what supplies can you bill for separately? These are generally any supplies that required an order by a doctor, are not purchasable over the counter, and were for a specific patient with documentation to prove it. Patient comfort items, such as slippers, are not included, nor are items sold in bulk where exact quantities are difficult to trace for billing purposes (cotton swabs, sanitary pads, lotion, etc.).

Lists of separately billable supplies should be obtained from every organization that processes the practice's claims. Check for updates at least annually to see if there are new items you should or shouldn't bill for.

⠿ Supply Costs

According to a recent cost survey report of the Medical Group Management Association® (MGMA®), the median operating costs of non-hospital-based single-specialty practices range roughly between

$250,000 and $400,000 per full-time-equivalent provider.[1] These costs account for 45 to 60 percent of this type of practice's total revenue.[2]

The cost categories that compose the operating costs are:

- Drug supplies;
- Medical and surgical supplies;
- Building and occupancy costs;
- Furniture and equipment;
- Administrative supplies and services;
- Clinical lab tests;
- Radiology and imaging costs;
- Management fees;
- Employee benefits and salaries; and
- Nonphysician provider benefits and salaries.

For practices with extensive lab test and outpatient treatment services, the costs can be much higher. The preceding report shows that the median purchasing system processed costs for hematology and oncology practices are approximately $2,800,000, or about 60 percent of total revenue.

Finally, these amounts and percentages are even higher when provider costs (except for compensation and payroll taxes) are included in purchasing system processed costs.

⠿ Who Is in Charge of Making Purchases?

Most medical practice business systems that account for a large amount of revenues or expenses are somewhat centralized in the practice, and physician-owners (or at least the administrators) play a critical role in their oversight and review. The segregation of oversight duties between owner and administrator is important to maintaining a strong internal control system. For example, billing system activities are usually initiated by physicians documenting their services and coding their own charges. Thus the physician-owners have a keen interest in reviewing the billing and collection reports because the content of these reports directly affects the physician's compensation.

EXHIBIT 3.1

Supply and Capital Expenditure Purchasing Decisions by Position[4]

Position	Medical / Surgical Supplies	Capital Expenditure
Practice administrator / CEO	23.1%	53.9%
Nurses	33.3%	0.0%
Office / Clinic manager	20.5%	5.1%
Administrative assistant	6.4%	0.0%
Health system personnel	7.7%	1.3%
Board of directors or board committee	0.0%	25.6%
Purchasing director / Manager / Clerk	5.1%	0.0%
Physician	1.3%	12.8%
All others	2.6%	1.3%
	100.0%	100.0%

As another example, the payroll system in most medical practices operates under a strict set of accounting controls; these include approval of pay rates and hours worked, security of internal or outsourced payroll processing, and signatures by the administrator or physician-owner on payroll checks. Other business systems are tightly controlled and have a high degree of executive oversight. These systems also have detailed written policies and procedures, such as password protection on vendor accounts and outside audits and oversight by a reputable CPA firm.

In many medical practices, the purchasing function is decentralized and fragmented throughout an organization, with responsibility assigned to both clinical and administrative staff. Critical day-to-day details, such as ordering and receiving goods and services, are often delegated to clerical staff members, with minimal required oversight. A recent study of spending behavior of physicians revealed that in medical practices with 4.0 to 5.9 practicing physicians, the ordering decisions for medical and surgical supplies and capital expenditures were made by employees in the positions shown in Exhibit 3.1.[3]

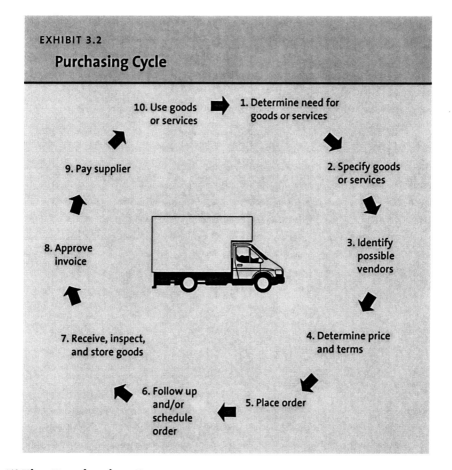

EXHIBIT 3.2

Purchasing Cycle

10. Use goods or services → 1. Determine need for goods or services

9. Pay supplier

2. Specify goods or services

8. Approve invoice

3. Identify possible vendors

7. Receive, inspect, and store goods

4. Determine price and terms

6. Follow up and/or schedule order

5. Place order

⸪ The Purchasing Process

Understanding a practice's purchasing function requires a working knowledge of the overall purchasing cycle, which is depicted in Exhibit 3.2.

The following sections describe each step of the purchasing process and identify potential financial and operating risks. They conclude with recommendations for practices to consider in improving their purchasing functions.

1. Determine the Need for Goods and Services

Determining the need for goods and services is often the responsibility of the person using and/or delivering them. For example, nurses and medical assistants determine what exam room equipment and supplies they need and the quantities to stock. For new services, the manager initiating the service usually identifies what supplies are needed. Equipment and other supply companies can help determine what is needed to implement a new service. The manager can also ask colleagues who provide a similar service what supplies and services they use.

For ongoing services, it is important to determine whether the practice's current supply list delivers the best result to the patient and value to the physician at the most reasonable cost. Over time, new products and services become available that deliver comparable or better results at a lower cost because of a reduction in the resource costs, patent expirations, and private label alternatives. Practices should periodically review their supply list for ongoing services to find potential cost reductions.

Recommendation summary:

- Consult with supply companies and other practices in determining what goods and services you need; and

- Periodically review the supply and service list to determine if current supplies are providing the highest level of quality and the best value.

2. Specify Goods or Services

Once the needed goods or services have been identified, a practice must specify, in detail, the goods or services to be ordered. Some practices use a standard order form known as a purchase order or purchase requisition. Purchase orders normally contain the following information:

- Date of purchase order;

- Purchase order number;

- Originator's name, department, and contact information;

- A complete and very detailed description of the goods or services;

- Quantity;

- Price;

- Date needed;

- Shipping address;

- Billing address; and

- Any special shipping instructions, such as refrigeration or receiver signature.

It is important to remember purchasing controls such as requests for proposal, standing orders, and group purchasing.

While few small practices actually use purchase orders because of the administrative burden, standard purchase orders can help ensure that goods and services are properly specified and delivered promptly. Precise specifications are critical for many clinical supplies.

Recommendation summary:

- Specify, in detail, what goods and services are to be ordered;

- Consider using sequentially prenumbered purchase orders; and

- Ask vendors about opportunities to make purchases online for ease and efficiency.

3. Identify Potential Vendors

Once a practice has determined what it needs and has described the goods and services and delivery requirements in detail, it must seek out possible vendors. Potential vendors can be identified through a variety of sources, including:

- Current suppliers;

- Equipment manufacturers;

- Other practices;

- Hospitals;

- Trade associations;

- The Internet; and

- Telephone book business directory.

Practices should keep a list of and maintain contact with MGMA resource guide backup vendors for the same goods and services in case the practice's primary dealer is unable to deliver. Group purchasing organizations (GPOs) are also a very good source of potential vendors and discounts; these organizations negotiate deals for the purchase of medical goods and services on behalf of their members, which include hospitals, nursing homes, medical practices, and other provider organizations.

Recommendation summary:

- Identify as many vendors as possible;
- Network with fellow MGMA members for feedback on potential vendors;
- Use all reasonable sources to identify potential vendors;
- Maintain relationships with several backup vendors; and
- Consider using GPOs.

4. Determine Price and Terms

Negotiating and maintaining the best price and terms of payment may be the most critical step in the purchasing cycle but is often the task for which medical practices are the least prepared. Physicians and administrators tend to have very little training in negotiation and are often uncomfortable doing it. Entry-level clinical employees are frequently tasked with ordering supplies and services and may not be skilled in negotiating the best deal.

Contrast this with medical equipment and other supply companies that employ highly trained sales professionals whose compensation is directly proportional to the dollar volume of goods sold and the profitability of each account. With all the training and experience that these sales professionals have, it is no wonder that medical assistants, medical technicians, nurses, administrators, and even physicians are often no match for these seasoned negotiators.

Negotiation through Competitive Bidding

One of the best ways to level the playing field and get the best value for the practice is to make salespeople work for you by soliciting competitive bids for all goods and services.

Implementing a competitive bidding process is not difficult. The first step is to list the items the practice buys for the type of goods and services it provides. Spreadsheets are great tools for compiling and manipulating such a list. If the practice currently buys from a small number of vendors, it can usually get a report of purchases over the last year from each vendor that shows detailed product descriptions, manufacturers, and volume. Many vendors will provide the list in a spreadsheet format. If a practice uses more than one vendor, it will have to combine the vendor lists.

Even if the practice cannot secure a purchase or product list from a vendor, it can build its own list by reviewing past invoices. If a complete list of purchases would take too long to develop, a list of the highest dollar-volume items is usually sufficient. Practices often find that a few specific items constitute the majority of their purchases.

In a large organization, after the lists are developed, it is time to call a bidders meeting, inviting all interested vendors identified earlier. This meeting is an effective way to communicate to the sales representative of each vendor that the practice is serious about implementing a competitive bidding process. At the meeting, the practice should distribute the supply bid list, provide any special shipping and billing requirements (by department or location), set a deadline for receiving the written bids (usually two weeks), and answer any questions the vendors may have.

In a small group, an e-mail bid request will typically be sent with an attachment identifying the products used in the practice. Suppliers should be encouraged to offer their best price because they will be bidding against their competitors.

The practice may require the bidders to provide the bids in the same spreadsheet format as the practice is using. Answering vendor questions in a public forum, such as a bidders meeting or a group e-mail to the suppliers, will ensure that all vendors get the same information. If the practice must provide information to a particular vendor after the meeting, it should make sure that all bidders receive the same information.

When the bids come back from the vendors, their prices can be inserted in the spreadsheet. Prior-year quantities can be multiplied by the new prices to project the supply costs for the coming year for each of the vendors. If the spreadsheet includes the prior-year prices, the practice can compare the costs from the competitive bidding process to the actual cost paid the prior year.

This competitive bidding process can be repeated as often as the practice wishes. It is prudent to rebid the prices at least every year or two.

The pricing component of the purchasing cycle is one of the biggest risk areas for fraud and irregularities. The practice must be careful about delegating purchasing authority to those employees who lack negotiating skills. Skilled, aggressive salespeople often woo these key decision makers with small gratuities such as movie passes, sporting event tickets, or gift cards to ensure their loyalty and convince them not to seek competitive bids or change vendors. In extreme cases, employees with purchasing authority may work in collusion with vendors, taking bribes or kickbacks, which could cost the practice thousands of dollars.

The control environment is an important consideration when evaluating a practice's purchasing cycle. A doctor or administrator accepting gifts, gratuities, and other favors from medical suppliers, insurance agents, or major equipment vendors sets the wrong example for the practice's employees. Control is now heavily regulated through the Sunshine Act and should not factor into the practice's purchasing cycle.

The practice's leaders must set an ethical and moral example for their employees. In addition, purchasing policies and procedures should be established so that unprepared or unethical employees are not in a position to make major purchasing decisions without oversight. These policies should clearly prohibit physicians and employees from accepting gifts or gratuities from any supply company.

Recommendation summary:

- Establish purchasing policies and procedures with appropriate involvement and oversight by the practice's owners and leaders;

- Provide negotiating and purchasing training to those employees involved in the purchasing process;

- Create a positive control environment with segregation of duties, ethical training, and practice leaders that set an ethical example for employees;

- Adopt policies that prohibit employees from accepting gifts or gratuities from suppliers;

- Engage in a competitive bidding process whenever possible; and

- Solicit new bids for goods and services every year or two.

5. Place the Order

A practice must make sure it has an adequate inventory of supplies on hand to fill the needs of its patients and providers, making it important to determine how much to order and when to place the order.

Ordering, distribution, and supply chain managers have used the latest technology to significantly reduce the time between placing an order and delivery of that order. Vendors also offer expedited delivery systems if a practice finds itself running short on supplies.

Sometimes vendors provide significant discounts for volume purchases. The challenge here is that medical practices seldom have a great deal of storage space. If discounts are significant, practices should consider acquiring additional space to store additional supplies if the materials will not expire or be dated and replaced by newer, improved consumables.

Medical groups must be practical about their ordering steps. Many groups order supplies using an ordering calendar at regular intervals such as weekly, biweekly, or monthly. A simple way to alert the practice when supply levels are low is to make a brightly colored mark in the practice's storage area indicating that when the stock is depleted to that mark it is time to reorder.

Another important step in the ordering process relates back to the internal control environment. To prevent the relationship between the purchaser and the vendor from getting too personal, practices should rotate the person who orders the supplies. For example, if a practice normally has a medical assistant or nurse order supplies, that task should be rotated among all of the nurses or medical assistants. In cases of collusion among the employees and a salesperson, rotation of duties can often expose these inappropriate relationships.

Finally, medical groups should set and enforce limits on the maximum dollar volume that employees at various levels can commit to on behalf of the practice. This policy ensures that more oversight is provided as orders become progressively more expensive. For example, a practice could adopt a policy that sets purchasing limits as shown in Exhibit 3.3. Be sure to adjust these limits based on the size of the practice.

Recommendation summary:

- Develop policies and procedures for ordering, such as using ordering calendars or an inventory alert system;

- Rotate the ordering responsibility among practice employees; and

- Enforce ordering policies that limit the dollar amount of goods and services that employees can order without additional approval.

EXHIBIT 3.3

Sample Purchasing Limits for a Medical Practice

Commitment Level	Authorized Employee
$500	Medical assistant or nurse
$1,000	Clinic or office manager
$2,500	Practice administrator or CEO
$5,000	Physician president or managing physician
$10,000	Board of directors
Over $10,000	Shareholders

6. Follow Up on and Schedule the Order

Supply orders should be routinely tracked to ensure that the goods are delivered when needed. In the past, follow-up was done exclusively by telephone, but today supply chain and delivery systems make it easy to track orders online.

When identifying possible vendors, it is important to get references on the delivery reliability of the vendor. If a vendor has problems delivering as scheduled, it should be willing to expedite a shipment at no additional cost. If a vendor is chronically late in its deliveries, it should be excluded from future purchases and bidding.

Expediting is applying pressure to a vendor or supplier to meet an accelerated delivery schedule or speed up the delivery of a late order or backorder. Expediting is usually done by telephone and sometimes requires going to the sales manager. Practices should have a system in place to elevate the expediting process when necessary.

Recommendation summary:

- Screen vendors based on delivery reliability;

- Implement a routine follow-up system; and

- Expedite late orders and do not be afraid to request the vendor to use a more expensive shipping method if the vendor does not deliver on time through its normal channels.

7. Receive, Inspect, and Store the Goods

A formal receiving process is important to confirm the placed order has arrived in good condition and in the correct quantity. The receiving process also directs the goods to the destination where they will be used or stored and ensures that the proper receiving documentation is reviewed, approved, and forwarded. Practices should plan storage close to where the goods and supplies are to be used.

To strengthen internal controls, an order should be received and checked by someone who was not responsible for placing the order. It is also important to make sure the quantity received is correct, because distributors will sometimes make partial shipments when the distributor is running low on stock. Occasionally, an order will be shorted but billed as a full order. Verify that shipping and handling of split orders is not increased if the separate orders are not at the practice's request.

Watch for Scams

Unscrupulous vendors target medical practices for fraud by calling to ask about equipment in the office and the names of people responsible for making purchases related to that equipment. Then they send unsolicited boxes of office supplies (often low-quality printer toner, paper, rubber gloves, or some other consumable that is routinely repurchased). The supplies are followed days or weeks later by invoices charging outrageous prices. The whole point is to dupe an unsuspecting employee into paying the invoice out of habit, or to get an employee to call the vendor to dispute the charge so the vendor can threaten them with legal action if the invoice is not paid or force them to pay for return shipping while charging an exorbitant restocking fee.

The Federal Trade Commission (FTC) offers a number of tips for avoiding this and other scams that target small businesses in its *Small Business Scams* publication:[5]

1. **Train your staff.** Educate your employees about how these scams work. In addition to your regular receptionist, talk to everyone who may pick up the phone. Put a copy of the FTC publication in employee mailboxes. Mention it in a staff meeting. Post it on the break room bulletin board or where employees clock in and out.

2. **Inspect your invoices.** Depending on the size and nature of your business, consider implementing a purchase order system

to make sure you're paying only legitimate expenses. At a minimum, designate a small group of employees with authority to approve purchases and pay the bills. Train your employees to send all inquiries to this group. Compile a list of the companies you typically use for directory services, supplies, and other recurring expenses. Encourage the people who pay the bills to develop a "show me" attitude when it comes to unexpected invoices from companies they're not familiar with, even if those invoices list one of your employee's names. Don't pay for products or services you're not sure you ordered.

3. **Verify to clarify.** If you get a message that looks to be from a bank, credit card company, or government agency, investigate before responding. Using a phone number you know to be legitimate, contact the office directly to ask if the inquiry is on the up and up. Furthermore, many business directory scam artists are headquartered in Canada or in other foreign countries but use post office boxes or mail drops to make it look like they are in the United States. Before paying, check them out for free at www.bbb.org, and read the Better Business Bureau (BBB)'s report on them.

4. **File a complaint.** If a scammer is sending you bogus bills, speak up:

   - File a complaint with the FTC at ftc.gov/complaint and with the BBB. Complaints help shape the FTC's law enforcement agenda, so it's important to sound off when you spot a scam. Are you concerned about business directory fraudsters' threats to tarnish your credit if you don't pay? Many will simply drop the matter and may even provide a refund if they know you've complained;

   - If you think you've been victimized in a fraud scheme that involves the U.S. mail, submit a Mail Fraud Complaint form to the U.S. Postal Inspection Service; and/or

   - Alert your state's attorney general. You can find contact information at naag.org or check the blue pages of the phone book under State Government.

Recommendation summary:

- Establish a process for receiving and checking goods delivered;

- Store the goods as close to the user site as possible;
- Have the order received and checked by someone other than the individual who placed the order;
- Always double-check the quantity received; and
- Beware of and report inventory-related scams that target small businesses.

8. Approve the Invoice

Once the delivery, quantity, and quality of an order is verified, the vendor's invoice must be approved. This process can vary according to the practice.

Sometimes the invoice is sent to the department where the original purchase was made. When this happens, that department will match the invoice with the receiving documents to make sure the goods billed have been received and accepted. Then the department manager will approve the invoice and forward the complete set of paperwork to the practice's accounting department.

In other cases, the invoices are mailed to the accounting department, where they are matched with the receiving documents and then approved for payment.

Whichever method is implemented, it is important that invoices be paid only after approving that the paperwork documenting the goods or services was received in good condition.

If there are discrepancies between the invoice and receiving documentation, it is often best to have the accounting department, who is independent of the ordering and receiving function, follow up on the discrepancy.

Recommendation summary:

- Approve invoices in the ordering department or the accounting department; and
- Have the accounting department follow up on any discrepancies.

9. Pay the Supplier

When a vendor invoice is approved, it should be paid promptly and as promised. Normally vendors request payment within 30 days of the invoice (referred to as net 10, net 15, net 30, etc., where the number indicates how many days you have to pay in full). These requests for payment should be honored if the vendors or distributors have provided goods or services as ordered.

Vendors sometimes provide discounts for early and/or cash payment of their invoices. This is often indicated in a note on the invoice itself or as a percentage in the terms (e.g., 1 percent/10, net 30 means you must pay within 30 days, but the vendor offers a 1 percent discount if the invoice is paid in full within 10 days). If vendors offer these discounts to your practice, it is usually cost effective to take advantage of them as long as it doesn't cause a cash-flow problem.

Some practices try to conserve their cash or maximize their investment earnings by delaying vendor payments for 60 or even 90 days. Unless there is a good reason to delay such payments, such as a new piece of equipment not functioning properly, it is best to pay vendors promptly. If a practice needs special treatment from a vendor, then that vendor is much more likely to grant the practice's request if the practice has paid the vendor on time.

Vendor payments should be entered into the practice's accounts payable system in such a way to prevent the inadvertent duplicate payment of invoices. Once paid, the invoices should be clearly marked as paid.

Recommendation summary:

- Pay vendors promptly unless there is a problem with the goods or services;

- Cancel invoices or mark them clearly as paid to prevent duplicate payments; and

- Implement accounting system safeguards to prevent the same invoice from being paid a second time.

10. Use Goods or Services

The final step in the purchasing process is removing goods from inventory and using them in the practice's clinical or business process. When inventory is depleted to a certain level, it triggers a new purchasing cycle. For recurring purchases, the cycle begins at step 5, which is reordering. If new items are needed, the practice will follow steps 1 through 4. Periodically, a practice should solicit new vendor bids for goods and services, as noted in step 4.

::: Increasing Purchasing Power with Group Purchasing Organizations

GPOs negotiate for the purchase of medical goods and services on behalf of their members, which include hospitals, nursing homes, medical practices, and other health providers. Hospitals have used GPOs for several years, and increasing numbers of smaller medical practices are taking advantage of the buying power and economies of scale that GPOs can provide. Vaccines and medical supplies are often available at discounts unavailable to smaller volume purchasers.

Some GPOs have staff who can assist practices in developing and refining their purchasing process.

If a practice is not part of a GPO, it should consider joining one. GPO membership is often available at no cost through many trade associations (including MGMA) or through the medical staff affiliation of a group's physicians.

::: Creating an Inventory Control Plan

Procurement is just one aspect of the purchasing process. Practices must also implement an inventory control plan to keep supplies organized, accessible, and easily inventoried. A good plan will also maximize storage space and track perishable items so they can be disposed of as they expire. Many practices have created par levels for exam rooms and the major supply closet, which determine proper levels of supplies from exam table paper to cotton swabs. Par levels normally will have three to four days' worth of supplies in each room and ensure that the supply closet has enough backup.

Consider consolidating the number of brands and volume according to your space requirements to help avoid product backlogs and preserve precious stockroom space. This will also allow those who place orders to quickly identify approved items and maximize workflow.

Consolidating orders reduces overall costs. Adjust your order frequency to balance how often you order, receive, and pay for your supplies. This also reduces the number of times that boxes are opened and supplies are put away in a given week.

Label items properly to make navigating supply closets easy for those using and stocking items and to ensure that items stay organized. Move newer items behind older ones to rotate stock, and note expiration dates on perishables.

Tablets, particularly iPads, are becoming more popular in the office and can help optimize efficiencies with ordering and inventory management. Practices should consider wireless bar code scanning, which incorporates tablets into electronic supply management. Bar code scanning can also help to capture charges for items to be billed to insurance or the patient.

Technology is also useful for automating supply-chain management processes and can offer suggested orders based on utilization history. It can reduce ordering time, maintain inventory minimum and maximum levels, streamline ordering processes, and track inventory and expiring products to reduce obsolescence and avoid excess inventory.

⣿ Establishing Inventory Purchasing and Usage Guidelines

Unless properly controlled, the purchase, storage, and usage of both billable and nonbillable supplies can become a significant drain on the financial status of the practice. Therefore, guidelines and operating procedures for the ordering, use, and monitoring of supplies should be initiated and maintained. Some examples of these guidelines and procedures are:

- Determination of a schedule for ordering specific groupings of supplies (e.g., clinical, office, pharmaceutical);

- Use of standardized order forms that spell out the specific items that may be ordered;

- Determination of minimum and maximum reorder points to ensure that the organization neither runs out of critical supplies nor stockpiles supplies in quantities that would be categorized as wasteful (these reorder points should be set so that inventory turns over or is completely replaced 8 to 10 times per year); and

- Periodic checking of the purchase of billable supplies against the amounts that are actually billed to patients. The amounts billed to patients when added to the inventory on hand should equal the amount purchased by the practice. If the amount purchased is higher than the total of the amount billed plus inventory, then the reasons for the inventory shrinkage should be investigated and corrected.

Consumables

The larger the organization, the greater the importance of developing and implementing standards for the various consumable products to ensure that the practice does not begin to maintain stocks of multiple brands of the same product based on the desires of individual members of the organization. By standardizing the consumable products purchased and maintaining specific minimum and maximum reorder points, a practice can maximize savings and reduce costs. You can also reduce consumables expenses by periodically comparing prices among various suppliers and negotiating longer-term contracts whereby the practice is committing to purchase specified products from a supplier for fixed prices.

Equipment

When purchasing equipment, other issues should be addressed to ensure that the practice receives the greatest value for the dollar expended. The purchaser must evaluate various models and types of equipment to ensure it meets clinical and/or administrative demands. Equipment purchases must also meet the operational needs of the organization, and all costs must be considered including:

- The acquisition cost of the equipment (whether purchased or leased);
- The cost of supplies and consumables needed to use and maintain the equipment;
- Training costs for staff who will use the equipment;
- Costs of disposal for waste products generated by the equipment;
- Maintenance contract costs;
- Any construction renovations needed to install, maintain, and operate the equipment; and
- Return on investment for the equipment purchased.

Once the final decision is made on the specific make and model of equipment to be purchased, it is the responsibility of the designated administrative officer to negotiate the best purchase price and terms for the equipment. He or she is also responsible for periodically evaluating the equipment to ensure that it continues to meet the organization's needs in an efficient and cost-effective manner.

Buying vs. Leasing

Deciding whether to lease or purchase equipment is one of the major decisions faced by a medical group. There are myriad factors that must be considered when determining if buying or leasing is best for the medical group.

The advantages of leasing property include:

- A leasing arrangement eliminates a large down payment, thereby maximizing the amount of funds available to the medical group (equipment loans usually entail a 10 to 20 percent down payment while leasing requires no initial payment);

- Since the lessor retains ownership of the item being leased, it is often easier to obtain a lease than other types of financing;

- Leasing limits the risk of obsolescence for the lessee (especially important for computer equipment);

- Lease payments, which are generally larger than depreciation charges for a capital item, are 100 percent deductible for income tax purposes;

- Leases often stipulate that the lessor is responsible for servicing the leased equipment, thereby eliminating technical, financial, and administrative worries related to the equipment; and

- Operating leases do not have to be reflected on the balance sheet as liabilities.

Disadvantages to leasing include:

- For lessees that can obtain other financing easily, leasing equipment is generally more costly than borrowing;

- The lessee cannot claim the tax benefits arising from depreciating the asset under the accelerated provisions of income tax laws; and

- Lease vs. buy decisions are important and deserve careful analysis. In many cases, when initially considered, leasing may not be as good as it sounds but is more prevalent today than ever before.

Operating vs. Capital Leases

Regardless of what you decide, it is important to understand the differences between the two major types of leases, operating and capital. In an operating lease, the owner of the equipment (lessor) allows a lessee to use the property for a fee and, at the end of the lease term, the property is returned. The right-of-use is transferred from the lessor to the lessee and recorded as an operating expense in the lessee's statement of operations, and not on a practice's balance sheet.

Although ownership risk lies solely with the lessor in an operating lease, the opposite is true for a capital lease. Here, the item being leased is recognized as an asset to the lessee as well as a liability (the present value of future, scheduled lease payments). Although the amortized principal payments are not recorded as operating expenses as in operating leases, the lessee is able to claim depreciation expense deductions on the leased item as well as any interest expense added onto lease payments.

Waste Disposal

Arrangements should be made to properly dispose of biohazardous waste products, including syringes, sharps (e.g., needles and scalpels), and any products that have been contaminated with bodily fluids and blood. Failure to properly dispose of these items can result in an exposure risk to other patients and staff members. Normally, this type of disposal is handled through contracts with licensed companies.

A second significant waste product issue involves the disposal of documentation that may contain a patient's name and other private information. These waste documents may include daily appointment schedules and duplicate telephone messages. To ensure compliance with the Health Insurance Portability and Accountability Act guidelines, all of these documents should be properly shredded, which involves either obtaining the equipment necessary to internally shred the documents in question or contracting with an independent, bonded shredding company to perform this task and provide receptacles to secure the documents until they are properly destroyed.

⠿ Pharmaceuticals

A final category of supplies, which touches on all of the previous areas of discussion and has several additional issues, is pharmaceuticals. Within a practice, this category may have several distinct subgroupings, based on the practice's specialty and including:

- Vaccines;

- Injectable medications (e.g., Solu-Medrol, Depo-Medrol, vitamin B12);

- Narcotics, and;

- Samples of prescription medications.

With the exception of samples, all of these items would be considered billable consumable supplies.

The maintenance of pharmaceutical supplies within a practice is subject to various federal, state, and local regulations and laws. Narcotics and other controlled substances must be kept in secured locations (e.g., double-locked safes or metal boxes) that are not accessible to unauthorized staff members or others. Utilization logs for these drugs must be kept, and periodic inventories must be conducted. The logs for each pharmaceutical should document the final disposition of all narcotics and controlled substances purchased or received by the practice. All of these documents must be available to designated government investigators charged with the responsibility to ensure compliance with regulatory safeguards.

The practice needs to ensure that all other pharmaceuticals are appropriately secured and dispensed in a clinically correct and safe manner. Many pharmaceuticals and vaccines have significant costs and short shelf lives that may require the need for specific and special storage areas. Because of this, the practice should implement and maintain strong inventory systems, including rotation of stock to ensure that inventory does not reach its expiration date, utilization tracking to ensure that all usage has been properly billed, and proper disposal of out-of-date items. Many out-of-date pharmaceuticals can be returned to the manufacturer or supplier for credit toward new inventory. This inventory should be kept in centralized locked cabinets to ensure that it will be properly maintained and distributed.

Samples

The use of pharmaceutical samples within practices poses significant issues regarding control, storage, and maintenance. Practices are swarmed by pharmaceutical sales representatives who provide information on why their particular pharmaceutical is the best and offer samples for patient use. The practice needs to implement inventory controls when accepting these samples to avoid accumulating significant excess quantities of specific drugs. Once the practice accepts samples for distribution to patients, it accepts responsibility for the proper storage, control, and ultimate disposal of the samples.

The same inventory problems and issues posed by pharmaceuticals that are purchased by the practice also apply to pharmaceutical samples. Most practices secure the samples in cabinets or closets that are locked when the practice is closed. Because of the volume involved, a major issue for a practice is the disposal of samples that have passed their expiration date. These samples cannot be returned to the manufacturer, and the responsibility falls on the practice to properly dispose of them. This disposal process can become extremely time-consuming and expensive for the practice, so keep this in mind when accepting samples. Another common option rather than storing pharma samples on-site is to start asking for and using sample vouchers. These vouchers can be given to patients to get either a free prescription sample or a discounted sample of a particular drug. The patients take these vouchers to a pharmacy to get the pharmaceutical instead of the practice dispensing them.

::: Conclusion

The purchasing cycle ensures that a practice obtains the right goods and services at the right time to meet the needs of its patients, providers, and staff members. It also ensures that these goods and services are obtained at the best price. Keys to effective management of the purchasing process include using tools such as competitive bidding, imposing internal controls to minimize opportunities for fraud and abuse, implementing inventory control methods, and involving external advisors such as accountants or bankers when making significant asset purchases. Managing the procurement and utilization of supplies to support the delivery of patient care is a crucial competency for any medical practice administrator.

Notes

1. Medical Group Management Association, *MGMA Cost Survey for Multispecialty Practices: 2014 Report Based on 2013 Data; MGMA Cost Survey for Single-Specialty Practices: 2014 Report Based on 2013 Data.*

2. Medical Group Management Association, *MGMA Cost Survey for Multispecialty Practices; MGMA Cost Survey for Single-Specialty Practices.*

3. Health Industry Distributors Association, *Strategic Analysis of Physician Office Spending Behavior* (Alexandria, VA, 2005), 15.

4. Health Industry Distributors Association, *Strategic Analysis.*

5. *Small Business Scams*, Federal Trade Commission (FTC), 2014, www.ftc.gov/system/files/documents/plain-language/pdf-0189-small-bus-scams.pdf.

Chapter 4

Designing Facilities to Ensure Quality and Safety

THE DESIGN, construction, maintenance, and appearance of a practice's offices are critical to the delivery of quality patient care as well as the efficiency of the practice. As with any business, the outward appearance of a facility establishes a foundation for patients' expectations of the level and quality of service they will receive. Key competencies required to effectively manage practice facilities include complying with safety regulations, planning facilities for effective work flows, overseeing facility management and preventive maintenance, facilitating maintenance inspections, and managing proper disposal of biohazardous waste products.

The design or layout of a facility, although normally transparent to the patient, will have far-reaching effects on the efficiency of the physicians and staff members. Clinical areas designed to allow easy access to the supplies and support services required during the course of the day enable physicians and staff members to be more productive and effective. Colleen Sweeney, MS, RN, conducted a three-year project called the Patient Empathy Project that identified the major fears patients have regarding their visits to medical facilities.[1] She discovered that patients form a strong opinion of a medical practice within the first three seconds of walking in the door. She also discussed eight fears patients have that are specific to group practices:

1. Diagnosis and/or prognosis;

2. Wait times;

3. Communication issues;

4. Cancer;

5. Rude doctors;

6. The location of the scale for measuring weight;

7. Cost; and

8. Sanitation ("germs").

There may be nothing you can do about a patient's cancer or a bad diagnosis, but good facility design that creates an efficient, safe, and welcoming environment for staff members and patients can go a long way toward addressing all of those other fears.

⠿ Where Should You Locate?

If you are starting a new practice or relocating an established one, always keep your patients and staff members in mind when selecting a location. The optimal location is:

- In the approximate center of your market area;

- Close to your primary hospital;

- In a high-traffic, high-visibility area;

- In a location with easy access to major feeder streets and highways; and

- With adequate parking that fits your patient's needs (wheelchairs, walkers, pregnancy, parents and caregivers transporting children, etc.)

The best location has all of these advantages but is usually unobtainable.

Locating near your primary hospital may have the best combination of features, but may also have the highest cost, and the offices that are available may be unsuitable (e.g., have poor layout, difficult access, or inconvenient parking). A practice serving multiple hospitals has different issues (e.g., travel times for physicians, access for patients), and a practice aligned with a surgery center may seek proximity to the ambulatory surgery center. Locating the practice near a hospital has drawbacks, especially if the hospital is a large medical center with numerous buildings and multiple parking lots in which patients may get lost.

Patient and Referral Base

If a medical practice relocates, owners may lose a portion of the practice's patient and referral base. Most practices establish a referral base from different specialists, hospitals, and referring patients in any given location, which is why it is imperative to identify space that is accessible to existing patients.

In general, patients remain loyal to a certain location out of convenience and rely on accessibility. It's preferable to walk, take public transportation, or have access to public parking. According to experts, it is for this reason that many medical practitioners start their careers and retire in the same location.

⋮⋮ How Big Should the Office Be?

The best size for the office depends on a variety of factors, including:

- The type of practice (medicine or surgery);
- The number of practitioners;
- Ancillaries (especially space-intensive areas for lab, X-ray, and bone densitometry facilities);
- Anticipated growth;
- Support space (for records, staff breaks, etc.); and
- A confidential area to discuss patient finances.

Why is a surgical practice different? Assuming a typical surgeon spends 2.5 days in the office and 2.5 days in surgery, exam room pods can be shared, requiring less square footage per physician. In contrast, family practice physicians should be in the office 4.5 days per week, requiring more exam rooms and probably more waiting room area.

Active ancillary areas, such as a three-unit X-ray module or a laboratory drawing area, will likely require sub-waiting space.

Although it is necessary, office space is considered "unproductive" because it is not used for direct patient care. A group with in-house billing needs sufficient space for billing department personnel, file storage, and computer workstations. Space previously allotted to medical charts can be converted to clinical or office use following conversion to electronic charting.

⠿ How Much Should Real Estate Cost?

Competitive bidding is not often an effective tactic when negotiating leases, rent, and other costs related to the practice's real estate. Most practices cannot regularly move to a different location and are forced to negotiate with existing landlords or landlord brokers to get a better deal. As with supply negotiations, this often puts medical staff members in a position where they are engaging in something they are not skilled at with an expert in negotiation.

In these situations it is important to know that several things which have a direct effect on the practice's overhead can be negotiated into a lease. For example, professionals can negotiate rent reductions and lease length and options to terminate, expand, contract, and renew improvement allowance credits and rental abatement. Improvement allowance credits can include items such as additional space build-out, reconfiguration of space, or other office upgrades. Rental abatements, or free rental, can be negotiated for long-term agreements. Rates for items such as common-area maintenance, security, and janitorial services can often be negotiated.

With an advocate, such as a tenant representative, practices can gain valuable assistance in the renegotiation and/or relocation of their practice to ensure that they get the best deal possible. Tenant representatives do not receive their compensation from the client. Instead, they receive a commission fee from the owner of a building in which their client elects to become a tenant. To ensure a smooth process, consider the options explained in the following sections when weighing real-estate decisions.

Proper Due Diligence

Depending on geographic area, the cost of financing a new medical practice is significant, and many banks have tightened their lending requirements because of the volatile economic environment. In addition, landlords require some type of security such as a letter of credit from the individual practice owners assuring personal liability to cover the costs of facility improvements.

Prior to viewing new space, confer with your financial adviser to ensure that you have the financial reserves and creditworthiness to relocate. Also, during this time, determine what amount you want to spend on the lease or purchase of new space. It may also be helpful to speak with an attorney who specializes in medical lease negotiations.

Medical practitioners need to be prepared to cover relocation costs, which run from $150 to $250 a square foot, plus the cost of specialized medical equipment.

⸬ Technical Requirements

Building or leasing an office demands careful planning for technical resources, especially network cabling, telephone cabling, and electrical outlets. Without careful planning, your office might not have enough outlets for computers or fuses might be blown during office hours. Installing cable after your office opens is expensive, time-consuming, and disruptive.

Practices should have schematics prepared and review them exhaustively for computer connectivity, telephone jacks, and electric outlets. Growth should be factored into the plan, preparing for increased technology and connectivity, such as the next level of wiring capability from CTS to CT6 connecting hardware.

Do not sign a lease until the technology plan is set and you have reviewed it with the agent for the landlord. Be sure that the lease (or an addendum) specifies the party responsible for each component and the right of the tenant group to change, add to, or alter technology features.

Facility Management and Preventive Maintenance

No matter how well a facility is designed and decorated, without proper preventive maintenance, the significant investment that is made in creating the facility will go to waste. Preventive maintenance includes such day-to-day issues as trash removal, vacuuming, dusting, and mopping. In addition, other maintenance items need to be scheduled on a regular basis, including window washing, touch-up painting, replacement of dim or burned-out bulbs, and minor cosmetic repairs of furniture and equipment. Mechanical, electrical, and plumbing elements should be inspected regularly to ensure that major problems are not imminent, as things like electrical fires and burst water pipes could have disastrous consequences. Make sure you understand who is taking responsibility for these items. Are they part of general building maintenance and included in your lease or are you responsible for them as the tenant?

Patients are very quick to identify housekeeping issues and equate them to the quality of the medical services provided. Although patients may not comment when facilities are clean and well maintained, they do notice (and comment) when their expectations are not met, and they apply their observations to determining the professionalism and quality of the physicians of the practice.

The concept of facility design and maintenance goes beyond the confines of the four walls of the practice's office; attention should also be paid to ensuring that adequate, safe parking is available during and after business hours and that the grounds surrounding the building are properly maintained and landscaped. The building should appear inviting, without dark corridors or foreboding entranceways. Patients have choices of where to obtain their medical services, and it is incumbent upon the practice to provide a safe and welcoming environment.

Efficient Workflows and Storage

Failure to be attentive to proper office design results in a variety of problems that often compound one another. For example, an office layout that causes physicians and staff members to become fatigued because of excessive walking may lead to the duplication of expensive supply inventories within examination rooms in an effort to reduce walking demands.

When designing or renovating a facility, attentiveness to small details that enable a facility to be both efficient and attractive is important. Patients and visitors coming to the facility require appropriate signage to help them navigate from the time they enter the parking lot until they reach their final destination within the building and the exit. Adequate signage is also important to assist new employees who are unfamiliar with the office and building layout. Appropriate color schemes for walls, flooring, and furniture are helpful in maintaining a relaxing and inviting environment for patients who might otherwise be stressed and anxious.

Attention should also be paid to the business areas of the practice that patients never see, including billing, scheduling, medical records, accounting, human resources, and storage. Failure to design these areas properly and to provide for sufficient storage space hinders the support staff's ability to do their jobs.

Patients will appreciate the practice providing an area where they can discuss their personal finances, schedule follow-up procedures or surgery, arrange for payment plans, and conduct a confidential conversation about their accounts. No one wants to have others overhear their personal situations about money or medical treatments or procedures discussed in the reception area.

Many practices include quiet areas for older adults or separate play areas for children. Family medicine and pediatric offices often incorporate well vs. sick child areas to minimize exposing healthy children from patients who are ill.

::: Workplace Safety

Employers realize how important occupational health and safety programs are to maintaining a productive and highly efficient workforce. The cost of unsafe and unhealthy conditions in the workplace is substantial considering the lost productivity due to accidents and illness. In addition, the cost of providing workers' compensation coverage and healthcare benefits to the employer continues to rise. The cost of providing safety and training programs is low when compared to the expense of employee accidents, injuries and illnesses, and workers' compensation claims.

More importantly, employees have a right to work in an environment that does not pose a health hazard or an unreasonable risk of injury. No employer wishes to see anyone harmed during the group's everyday operations, but failure to establish and enforce strict health and safety policies invites bad outcomes.

The rise of worldwide disasters and the possible risks to healthcare workers and patients make such policies even more critical. For example, pregnant employees or those attempting to become pregnant should not provide care to patients with a known diagnosis of cytomegalovirus, acquired immunodeficiency syndrome (AIDS), AIDS-related complex, or human immunodeficiency virus. Issues related to significant exposure to blood, bodily fluids, and tissues must be addressed, as well as exposure to contaminated needles, lancets, surgical instruments, incisions, and wounds. Another growing concern is exposure to hepatitis B and the need to administer the hepatitis B and influenza vaccines to those employees involved with direct patient care and supply handling.

Musculoskeletal injuries are common in the healthcare industry. For cases that involve patient handling, almost all are a result of overexertion resulting in sprains, strains, and tears. Nurses, medical assistants, radiology technicians, and support workers are the most likely to be injured, and all employees will benefit from training on moving and assisting patients within the office environment.

Finally, employers have become aware of the importance of protecting the environment, community, and society in which they work. Employers realize that they are a part of the community and must take a role in protecting and enhancing that community. A record of occupational health and safety problems is a detriment to the employer's image and place within the community.

Who Is in Charge of Safety?

Management should develop a comprehensive safety program suited to the group's particular needs. Most small medical groups choose to select an individual to be responsible for safety in the workplace. Larger medical practices may appoint a safety officer for this role. Another option is to establish a safety committee responsible for all safety and health programs.

Safety plans rely on employee compliance for effectiveness, so be sure to budget for adequate education and training. Safety incentive programs are another way to ensure compliance with regulations. Employees who do not follow the safety policies should be properly disciplined because their disregard for the rules could negatively affect the entire practice.

Finally, safety has become an overriding concern in healthcare institutions because they may have patients who are incapable of helping themselves in emergencies. Fire is one of the most dangerous emergencies. Therefore, a fire plan should be included in the policy manual, and fire safety training should be provided for all employees. Other areas to consider in the safety policy are:

- On-the-job injuries;
- Accident and injury reports;
- Medical emergencies;
- Posting of emergency information;
- Evacuation plan;
- First aid equipment;
- Weather-related alerts;
- Care and use of equipment;
- Terrorism threats;
- Bomb threats;
- Protective clothing;
- Safety inspections;
- Reporting of unsafe conditions;
- Firearms;
- Safety designated areas;
- Safety suggestions; and
- Incentive award programs.

Security

Because of vandalism, pilferage, thefts, bomb scares, terrorism, and major incidences of workplace violence, securing your facility is important. For example, the theft of business equipment, especially small items, has greatly increased in recent years and is very costly to employers. The threat of computer hacking and viruses requires technological security precautions.

Security programs involve taking precautionary measures to ensure adequate protection of the group practice's property and assets, as well as that of its employees and patients. A group practice's security needs vary depending on its location, the nature of its operations, and number of employees. Some large groups hire security consultants to develop, administer, and audit their security programs, but even the smallest practice needs to create, implement, and enforce written security policies.

A typical security program requires all employees to wear identification (ID) badges while at work, which helps prevent unauthorized entry and access. Secured doors to authorized-only areas may involve coded or card locks. More sophisticated security techniques include motion sensors, video surveillance, spot inspections, fingerprint scans, retina scans, or on-site security guards.

Managers should take terrorism seriously. The possibility of using everyday substances as biochemical weapons is a threat to both individuals and healthcare providers. Controlled substances should be kept in a secure place and monitored carefully, with only authorized individuals having access.

Workplace Violence

Workplace violence is a very real threat in our daily working lives. The U.S. Bureau of Labor Statistics reports that workplace violence is increasing. Most attackers and harassers are people the victims deal with on a daily basis. Coworkers and supervisors account for most of the harassers at work; customers, clients, and patients account for the largest group of attackers at work. Typical perpetrators of workplace violence are bitter, dissatisfied people who make threats of violence. Other types include:

- Frustrated employees who are shuffled from low-level tasks to even lower-level tasks;
- Those who refuse to accept blame for their own problems;
- Those with pent-up rage;
- Those experiencing substance abuse;
- Those experiencing extreme stress in their personal lives or with their jobs; and
- Those with little or no support systems such as families or friends.

Characteristics of at-risk work environments include group practices with:

- A strict authoritarian management style;
- Numerous grievances filed;
- Many disciplinary actions and/or terminations;
- Inconsistent, inequitable, or insensitive management;

- Chronic labor-management disputes;

- Multiple injury claims;

- Frequent layoffs and downsizing;

- Disgruntled employees;

- Interpersonal conflicts on the job; and

- Failure to recognize and intervene early in the cycle of violence.

Although this list is not exhaustive, it does illustrate typical factors associated with workplace violence. Experts warn that in most cases where violence has occurred there were indicators of potential or impending violence, so watch for them carefully to help prevent violence.

Ineffective or incompetent management contributes to workplace violence by not:

- Promptly responding to preemployment warning signs or clues of future violence;

- Admitting that a potentially violent situation has occurred;

- Following up after warning behaviors;

- Communicating an expectation of self-control to the involved employee; and

- Communicating that the employee will be held responsible for his or her inappropriate and unacceptable behavior.

The emotional and psychological toll on employees subjected to workplace violence can be devastating. Three out of four workers who have experienced workplace violence report having suffered psychological and emotional distress. As a result, an employer's work effectiveness and productivity may be severely damaged.

Workplace Violence Prevention

Employees want to like their work, their peers, and their supervisors, but their work environment is critical to fostering high morale. A consistently positive, supportive atmosphere coupled with transparency and open communication help with employee retention and the prevention of workplace violence. On the whole, average pay combined with excellent working conditions are much preferred to high pay coupled with horrible working conditions.

Federal and state occupational safety and health agencies have taken a more aggressive stance in enforcing an employer's statutory duty to provide employees with a working environment free of harm, including violence. In addition, state legislatures have begun to implement statutory mandates that ensure employers take precautions to minimize workplace violence. Consider implementing the following prevention strategies:

- Training managers and supervisors to recognize early clues and warning signs of potential violence;
- Training workers in the techniques of conflict management and resolution;
- Striving to reduce or eliminate workplace stress;
- Recognizing and rewarding outstanding work and unique contributions;
- Establishing procedures for handling grievances, including listening and responding with empathy and sensitivity to employee concerns and grievances;
- Assisting employees in problem-solving, and referring employees to other resources when appropriate;
- Providing personal counseling for staff;
- Administering discipline consistently;
- Providing employees with written documentation and being clear about what behavior is expected to correct a problem;
- Administering termination, if warranted, with empathy and compassion, and backing it up with documentation;
- Implementing security programs that protect employees from internal and external risks;
- Providing employer-sponsored counseling through employee assistance programs; and
- Setting up a crisis plan.

Detecting Signs of Potential Violence

Supervisors and department heads should be specially trained to recognize the signs of potential violence. Management should be alerted to an employee who becomes romantically obsessed with a coworker, visitor, or patient; engages in stalking or other harassing behavior; threatens or intimidates another employee with expressed or implied threats of violence; or engages in excessive discussion of weapons.

Workplace violence is rarely an isolated incident. It often emerges from a pattern of behaviors. An employee who exhibits paranoid or other outrageous behavior or exhibits extreme job-related or personal stress should raise concern. Any employee who brings a weapon to the workplace should be immediately reprimanded in accordance with the employer's disciplinary policies.

Employee investigations often become necessary when an employee has committed misconduct, exhibited poor work performance, engaged in violent or threatening behavior, or otherwise raised suspicions that they are potentially dangerous. The practice executive has a legal obligation to investigate all credible information indicating that the employee poses a potential threat of violence. This obligation might include conducting employee searches and using surveillance of electronic communications.

Implementing Workplace Safety Policies

Workplace violence can best be prevented by developing and enforcing strong workplace safety policies and procedures for anticipating, handling, and investigating potentially violent situations. Such policies and procedures should provide proper guidance and communication channels for both supervisors and employees.

Appropriate workplace safety policies should include the following:

- Designating an interdisciplinary management task force that is responsible for creating, evaluating, and ensuring implementation of the employer's workplace safety policies, conducting security and safety assessments, developing security plans, improving lighting in parking lots (the greatest areas of liability for workplace violence), and providing training for specially designated individuals to enforce security;

- Training supervisors and department heads to anticipate and analyze potential problems, recognize signs of potential conflict, and respond to potential volatile situations in ways that minimize their escalation;

- Educating employees about the potential danger of workplace violence and the proper response procedures for voicing concerns or complaints;

- Adding mechanical and electronic security devices to enhance employee protection;

- Creating procedures for investigating complaints of employee indiscretions and work incidents that indicate a potential for violence;

- Training designated people or contract professionals to provide emergency aid to victims of violence;

- Establishing procedures for preemployment screening by conducting background checks and security evaluations of job applicants;

- Creating procedures for ensuring adequate training and supervision of employees;

- Establishing a confidential reporting phone number or Website to report threats or fears of violence; and

- Establishing procedures for alerting community law enforcement agencies when appropriate.

Conducting Employee Searches

Managerial guidelines and written policies should clearly define when, where, and how the practice may conduct searches of the employee's person or personal property. Employees should be notified that their person and personal property may be subject to search by the employer at any time. The employer should retain the right to search all computer files, e-mail messages, lockers, offices, filing cabinets, and desks used by staff.

A "reasonable" search is one that balances the employee's expectation of privacy against the employer's legitimate business needs. The practice executive can lower an employee's "expectation of privacy" and take more discretion in conducting employee searches by simply informing employees that their person and property may be subject to search by the employer at any time.

Searching an employee's person should not be taken lightly, as violating their civil rights could cause serious problems for the entire practice. Even if you have probable cause and have informed employees they may be subject to such searches, involve law enforcement if possible. Beyond the potential privacy invasion, employees could claim you coerced or abused (physically or emotionally) into consenting to the search, setting the practice up for a potentially costly lawsuit.

Surveillance of Electronic Communications

Employees also have a reasonable expectation of privacy when engaging in telephone conversations and other electronic communications. State and federal privacy laws may impose liability on an employer for attempting to monitor such communications without the permission of the employee and other relevant parties. An employer should not attempt to monitor electronic communications without legal advice.

In developing and enforcing any workplace safety policy, a practice must balance workplace safety concerns against employee privacy rights. A practice may expose itself to liability from an accused employee for claims of defamation, wrongful discharge, invasion of privacy, fraud and misrepresentation, intentional and negligent infliction of emotional distress, breach of an implied employment contract or an implied covenant of good faith and fair dealing, assault, battery, false imprisonment, or discrimination in violation of equal opportunity and antidiscrimination laws. It is, therefore, very important for the group practice to consider its legal rights and obligations before implementing any workplace safety program.

The increasing acts of violence in the workplace should make us aware of violence and the vulnerabilities everyone may face as we enter our working environments. Having appropriate policies and procedures for limiting violence can enable the practice to control the workplace and limit exposure.

An excellent resource for learning more about workplace violence is the National Organization for Victim Assistance (www.trynova.org).

Monitoring and Updating Safety Policies

Risk exposure monitoring must happen on a regular and ongoing basis. It is essential that the medical practice executive understand the limitations and demands of both federal and state laws that apply to employees, premises liability, and visitors. Furthermore, to protect the organization, the medical practice executive should understand state-permitted use of property surveillance, permissible drug testing of employees, and permitted use of preemployment physicals and reference checks.

Recipients of federal funds are mandated to comply with the Drug-Free Workplace Act of 1988, which requires employers to have a drug-free awareness program and drug-free policies. Employees must be aware that drug use, manufacture, or distribution is not permitted in the workplace. Furthermore, any convictions related to drugs must be reported to the employer. The act, however, does not mandate drug testing.[2] Drug testing and surveillance are guided primarily through state laws. Employers have the right to conduct random drug screening and "for cause" testing. Employee manuals should be up to date with the policy for the practice and comply with local and state regulations.

The Americans with Disabilities Act (ADA) and the Civil Rights Act address reference checks and preemployment physicals. Employee policies should be reviewed by an employment attorney prior to implementation. Employees have certain rights to privacy of their information, so there should be limited access to employee personnel files.[3] Medical files, drug testing (where applicable), and information related to medical conditions and/or bloodborne pathogen exposure should be kept secured and away from regular personnel files. Furthermore, any records related to attorney communication about an employee or involving litigation should be retained separately with limited access.[4] Employees should be apprised of the organization policies regarding employee confidentiality at orientation, and these policies should be reinforced with all staff during orientation and annual training.

Why Have a Security Policy?

To ensure the security of the group practice's property and safety of its employees, employers should develop and maintain a security policy. The best security program cannot function effectively without the support of top management and cooperation of all employees. At the very least, group practices should require employees to wear ID badges to prevent unauthorized entry and possible theft. This allows group practices to identify its employees quickly. The security policy should also note that a member of management is assigned the responsibility of coordinating the group practice's security program.

Issuing keys to employees should be subject to tight security controls. Keys should be issued only with management's approval to employees who need them. Employees should be reminded that keys are medical group property and that they are responsible for safeguarding them. Keys should be returned when an employee is terminated, and before a final paycheck is issued.

When developing policies, the medical practice executive should ensure that security policies are comprehensive. These policies should address violence or potential danger from a variety of sources, including disruptive physicians, visitors, staff, patients, family or friends of staff, and intruders. Systems should be in place to address a variety of situations, and, wherever possible, alliances with local law enforcement should be made in advance of an actual emergency. Although it is important for all practices to have a security plan, practices with known risks should regularly perform drills to test proposed policies and procedures. Obvious risk exposures that generate the need for simulation drills include on-site medications, in-office procedures or surgeries, high-risk locations, known substance-abusing or emotionally disturbed patients, and evenings or weekend hours of operation.

It is essential not only to have a plan and policies, but also a staff that is regularly trained in their use. Emergencies should be rehearsed regularly. Documentation of planning, training, and rehearsal should be maintained and reviewed at least quarterly.

⠿ Regulatory Compliance

There are so many rules and regulations imposed on practices that when the opportunity exists to design a new facilities plan, or to significantly renovate an existing space, it is best to use the expertise of an architect who is well versed and experienced in the design and construction of medical office space. In designing or renovating facilities, applicable building codes and regulations must be integrated. These issues, which span local, state, and federal agencies, create a range of structural requirements that require compliance to ensure a safe environment. In most instances, local building codes will provide the requirements for construction issues, including wiring and plumbing standards; width of corridors; and heating, ventilation, and air conditioning minimums. Sufficient insulation between rooms and noise-dampening materials should also be used in construction to help ensure patient privacy.

⠿ The Major Regulating Agencies: ADA and OSHA

Most facility-related federal regulations a medical practice deals with stem from the ADA of 1990 and the Occupational Safety and Health Administration (OSHA).

Americans with Disabilities Act

The primary goal of the ADA, as it applies to facilities, is to ensure that individuals with disabilities have safe and easy access to and can maneuver within a place of public accommodation. To comply within the parameters of the ADA, a practice must address a host of physical design features. These include ensuring that doors are wide enough to allow for the passage of a wheelchair, providing restroom facilities that can be easily used by the disabled, and providing adequate designated handicapped parking. In cases where the physical space is not owned by the practice, meeting these expectations is the responsibility of building management. If you are designing or planning modifications to a facility, be sure to work with architects and other planners who understand you must operate under full ADA compliance.

Occupational Safety and Health Administration

The safety of staff, patients, and visitors is addressed through adherence to the regulations set forth by OSHA. These safety issues include the proper maintenance, use, and storage of equipment. They also apply to hazardous situations, such as loose extension cords, blocked hallways, and boxes that are stacked too high. Other safety issues concern access to proper fire prevention equipment and the installation of security alarms and/or cameras, where appropriate. In addition to setting forth guidelines and regulations to ensure the safety of patients, visitors, and staff, OSHA regulations require the organization to maintain logs and information on all accidents and injuries that occur on the premises.

OSHA Bloodborne Pathogens Standard

On Dec. 2, 1991, OSHA issued its "Occupational Exposure to Bloodborne Pathogens Standards." This regulation requires employees to identify tasks, procedures, and job classifications where occupational exposure to blood or other bodily fluid occurs and requires "universal precautions" to be taken in regard to treatment of all bodily fluids. The standard requires employers to require, provide, and replace personal protective equipment and to provide postexposure follow-up evaluations for any exposure incident at no cost to employees.

Numerous state and local regulations also affect health and safety in the workplace. The medical group should know and conform to them.

OSHA Tuberculosis Enforcement Guidelines

On May 7, 1992, OSHA issued its "OSHA Enforcement Guidelines for Occupational Exposure to Tuberculosis." The guidelines covered employee training, skin testing, isolation procedures, patient transport requirements, and record-keeping. The guidelines also proposed standards for respirator use in contaminated areas. The guidelines were effective only in New York, New Jersey, Puerto Rico, and the Virgin Islands. However, OSHA considered issuing national standards for the control of tuberculosis (TB) contamination.

On Sept. 14, 1992, the National Institute for Occupational Safety and Health (NIOSH) issued its own "Recommended Guidelines for Personal Respiratory Protection of Workers in Healthcare Facilities Potentially Exposed to Tuberculosis." The NIOSH standard requires use of high-efficiency particulate filters in suspected contaminated areas.

Finally, on Oct. 18, 1994, the national Centers for Disease Control and Prevention issued final guidelines for preventing TB transmission. The final guidelines recommend that a healthcare provider implement and enforce a TB infection control plan program. The guidelines also suggest the use of personal respiratory protective equipment in areas of potential TB exposure. As a result, medical practices should have a tuberculin skin test policy and appropriate follow-up.

OSHA Inspection Case Studies

A small medical practice in Michigan — ABC Clinic (names changed for privacy reasons) — sustained hefty fines when a disgruntled employee complained to OSHA that her employer had not switched to safety needles. Although OSHA found the practice was out of compliance in several areas, the staff's handling of the inspection actually racked up the fines. Why? When an OSHA inspector arrived unannounced at ABC Clinic, he was greeted warmly by the receptionist. After showing his credentials, he asked to be escorted to the clinical area. The staff allowed him to wander freely around the practice! Three hours later, the inspector left with a briefcase full of citations amounting to several thousand dollars. The physicians and staff were shocked two weeks later when they received a 15-page list of penalties. The group wrote a large check to OSHA that week.

In another case initially related to safety needles, a practice employee at DEF Group in California who had been accidentally pricked with a contaminated needle called the local OSHA office and lodged a formal complaint against her employer, which had previously refused to offer safety needles to employees. OSHA soon visited the office and discovered more than $40,000 worth of violations. The employer negotiated to get the fines reduced by $20,000.

In a different type of case, a disgruntled employee in Idaho called OSHA, reporting that his employer, GHI Family Practice, didn't have an OSHA manual and that patient areas weren't disinfected often enough. The surprised administrator received a three-page letter from OSHA containing the employee's allegations and demanding a written response and copies of all applicable OSHA policies.

OSHA has inspected thousands of physicians' offices in the last few years. The most common citations were for violations of the Bloodborne Pathogens Standard and the Hazard Communication Standard (HCS).

What would happen if an OSHA inspector visited your medical practice today? Practice administrators must continually assess their offices' potential risks to prevent malpractice suits, loss control issues, and government claims of abuse and noncompliance.

Creating an OSHA Compliance Program

Every practice needs to create, implement, and document an OSHA compliance plan that encompasses:

- Exit routes, emergency action plans, and fire prevention plans;
- Hazardous materials;
- Personal protective equipment;
- Medical and first aid;
- Fire protection;
- Compressed gases;
- Electrical systems;
- Toxic and hazardous substances;

- Safety data sheets (SDSs; formerly called material safety data sheets) records; and

- Needlestick safety.

The practice administrator must recognize that OSHA can levy citations and fines for noncompliance with its standards. The best way to avoid trouble with OSHA is to take their requirements seriously and integrate them into every level of the practice.

Designate an OSHA Safety Officer

The administrator will need to designate an employee as the OSHA safety officer. In smaller groups, the administrator may assume this role. An employee with a clinical background can also be appropriate. The safety officer is responsible for:

- Developing and maintaining the OSHA safety program and procedure manual for the facility;

- Training all new employees about the safety standards;

- Reviewing the OSHA safety program annually for all employees;

- Meeting record-keeping requirements;

- Conducting annual reviews of the safety standards adopted by the facility; and

- Representing the facility in the event of an inspection by an OSHA compliance safety and health officer.

The safety officer will evaluate and recommend the adoption of standards and procedures for the medical group. It is imperative that the organization provides strong support to the safety officer and that group leaders recognize the importance of the OSHA safety program. The program should be adopted as a component of the group's compliance efforts, and the OSHA safety officer should do the following:

- **Add OSHA managerial duties to your job description.** As your practice's OSHA safety officer, you need time to accomplish your duties, so it's important that your job description include OSHA functions.

- **Make sure everyone understands that you are the safety officer.** Encourage staff to bring safety concerns to your attention. Be the go-to person for safety advice and leadership.

- **Take all complaints seriously.** Keep an open door and open mind to all safety concerns, even if you don't think they're justified. Employees often call OSHA when they believe management isn't listening. Handle minor issues before they escalate into major problems.

- **Document everything associated with an incident or violation.** At inspection time, if it wasn't written down, it didn't happen.

- **Consider safety a value rather than a priority.** Business priorities change over time, but values endure. Since the needs of the moment determine business priorities, safety might not always hold a place at the top of the list.

- **Make safety compliance a requirement in each employee's job description.** Discipline employees who purposely don't comply. First, document the problem. Then speak with the employee. If the problem persists, document the incident and inform the supervisor. For serious cases, approach senior management and consider termination.

- **Manage by walking around.** This well-known approach lets you learn if employees merely give "lip service" to OSHA regulations.

- **Customize annual OSHA training to be applicable to your practice.** Preview videos and identify areas where you can use examples from your practice to reinforce the material. Keep employees involved; have them voice opinions or demonstrate techniques.

- **Keep your cool.** Manage OSHA tasks using monthly and annual checklists to organize your duties. Listen to employee concerns, but don't take safety-related criticisms personally.

- **Remind organizational leaders of the benefits of OSHA compliance.** Part of managing your practice's OSHA safety program is quantifying its contribution: fewer injuries, less downtime, reduced workers' compensation claims, and improved employee morale.

Consider the Physical Environment

Medical practice administrators should consider the overall physical environment when evaluating compliance issues under OSHA's general duty clause. Obvious elements of a compliance program that address this clause include:

- Review of the facility's physical space, including air quality, floor and wall openings, exiting or egress (including evacuation), exit doors and signs, adequate lighting, storage areas, stairs and stairways, and elevated surfaces;

- Evaluation of fire safety, including sprinkler systems, fire alarms, carbon monoxide detectors, fire and evacuation procedures, fire drills, and the availability and use of fire extinguishers;

- Review of electrical safety procedures, including annual inspection of electrical devices, cords, grounding of electrical circuits, and lockout-tagout of machinery, equipment, and circuits as appropriate; and

- Determination of proper installation, training, and use of automated external defibrillators as appropriate.

In addition, a medical practice must comply with OSHA standards for emergency action, personal protective equipment, fire protection, bloodborne pathogens, hazard communications, and tuberculosis control.

Ensure Staff-Wide Commitment

The commitment to creating and complying with standards for workplace safety should begin with physicians but requires buy-in from all members of the staff. To demonstrate management's commitment and to achieve facility-wide involvement, OSHA recommends:[5]

- Posting a statement of policy on worker safety and health next to the OSHA workplace poster;

- Holding meetings to communicate the group's commitment to safety and to discuss objectives for safety and health;

- Involving the administrator in facility assessments and reviews of incident reports to ensure that appropriate follow-up occurs;

- Following facility policy at all times;

- Involving employees in setting safety procedures, conducting training, and investigating accidents to make use of their specialized knowledge and increasing their buy-in;

- Including assignments of safety responsibility as part of the employees' job descriptions;
- Including compliance with safety policies and procedures in employee evaluations;
- Annually reviewing safety objectives and reevaluating the need for compliance program revisions or new objectives;
- Discussing with and training employees which steps to take following the occurrence of a safety violation or an employee or patient adverse event; and
- Training all employees how to report an incident and file possible workers' compensation claims following an injury or incident.

OSHA-Provided Assessment Services

OSHA maintains a consultation service that will provide information about potential hazards and methods to improve workplace safety. The program is targeted to smaller businesses and is separate from the OSHA inspection program. In evaluating potential deficiencies in meeting OSHA standards, the consultation does not issue citations or penalties. Its confidential findings are not routinely reported to OSHA inspection staff. Every state and U.S. territory has an OSHA consultation office, so consider contacting them when developing a compliance plan and after implementing it to make sure nothing important is overlooked. OSHA offices will conduct safety audits for your practice if you want to ensure compliance and a safe workplace.

Mitigating Workplace Hazards

To mitigate hazards in the workplace, OSHA suggests that medical practices:

- Establish safe work procedures and ensure that employees follow them;
- Be prepared to enforce rules with an appropriate disciplinary system;
- Provide personal protective equipment, where appropriate, and train employees in its use and proper maintenance;
- Plan for emergencies, including regular drills;

- Make appropriate arrangements for employees to have access to medical personnel for advice and response to illness or injuries; and

- If required by your state, inform employees of the designated occupational health clinic where injury care will be provided.

OSHA Compliance Training for Employees

Employee training should create knowledge of materials and equipment, the known and potential hazards that may exist in the workplace, and how to control or minimize those hazards. No employee should undertake a job until he or she has been properly trained to perform it, nor undertake a job that appears unsafe or in which potential hazards have not been minimized. Training should include both instruction and demonstration by qualified personnel, such as laboratory or phlebotomy supervisors on the use of sharps, fire department personnel on the use of fire extinguishing equipment, and radiation safety officers on the use of dosimetry badges and lead gowns. Practices can also use Web-based broadcasts on safety-related topics.

All new employees need to receive training on the general standards of the facility (e.g., fire and evacuation procedures) and job-specific hazards. Staff should have additional training when changes in the work environment alter potential or actual safety hazards. A medical practice should provide annual training on all aspects of the safety compliance program. Documentation of this training should include a listing and signatures of the employees present, the date, the type of training, the subjects covered in the training, the person performing the training and his or her credentials.

These points are the basis for the creation and implementation of the OSHA compliance plan for a medical group practice. The OSHA *Small Business Handbook* provides a thorough primer (see "OSHA Online Resources").

OSHA Medical Waste Compliance

Properly identifying, collecting, and disposing of regulated medical waste (RMW) is a fact of life for a medical practice. OSHA strictly regulates and monitors the handling of hazardous medical waste, requiring proper labeling of hazardous waste containers, availability of those containers, and proper disposal of the waste contained in them. The rules surrounding RMW are complex and often imposed by several state agencies. Practices should consider streamlining RMW management by contracting with a reputable medical waste removal company, which provides all of the containers your practice needs, disposes of the waste in them, and keeps up to speed on all OSHA, state, and other regulations regarding that waste.

Developing a Hazard Communication Program

OSHA requires businesses to inform employees about hazardous chemicals, in compliance with the requirements collected in its HCS document. You can communicate the information through a comprehensive hazard communication program, which should include container labeling and other forms of warning, SDSs, and employee training.

Information and training are the core elements of a hazard communication program, which is intended to prevent illness or injury from chemical exposure. Training should include education about HCS, hazardous properties of all chemicals in the workplace, and methods of protection to ensure a safe work environment. Each employee should comprehend and understand the risks associated with any potential exposure.

The hazard communication program is a written plan that describes how an employer will implement and comply with HCS. This plan will be the initial focus of an investigation if an OSHA compliance officer conducts an inspection and should include a complete list of all potentially hazardous chemicals in the workplace, corresponding SDSs, how the SDSs will be maintained and accessed, and documentation of training and education on labeling use and SDSs.

Each employer must have a designated OSHA compliance officer who is responsible for maintaining an up-to-date list of all hazardous chemicals in the workplace and current SDSs on each of the chemicals in the office. The employee should also determine if the chemical containers are properly labeled and updated.

Employees should know where to access SDSs in the workplace. Detailed procedures for purchasing, receiving, storing, and handling chemicals should be readily available. When a new chemical is introduced in the workplace, employees should be educated about the chemical before it is used. Training can be performed on individual chemicals if only a few chemicals are used in the workplace or by hazard categories if there are several chemicals.

In March 2012, OSHA revised HCS to align with the hazardous chemical labeling and classification practices of most international community members. Employee training on the United Nations Globally Harmonized System of Classification and Labelling of Chemicals was held Dec. 1, 2013, and included education on the label elements and requirements as well as training on the new 16-section SDS format. Transition to the new system will occur in stages and be fully operational by Dec. 1, 2016.

Practices can learn more about HCS in *Hazard Communication: Small Entity Compliance Guide for Employers That Use Hazardous Chemicals*, a guide recently published by OSHA. You can also use this compliance checklist to look for problem areas:

- ☐ Obtain a copy of the rule.
- ☐ Read and understand the requirements.
- ☐ Assign responsibility for tasks.
- ☐ Prepare an inventory of chemicals.
- ☐ Ensure containers are labeled.
- ☐ Obtain an SDS for each chemical or have this information readily available online.
- ☐ Prepare a written program.
- ☐ Make SDSs available to workers.
- ☐ Conduct employee training.
- ☐ Establish procedures to maintain current program.
- ☐ Establish procedures to evaluate effectiveness.

State and Local OSHA Compliance

The Occupational Safety and Health Act encourages states and territorial jurisdictions to develop and operate their own safety enforcement programs. These programs are approved and monitored by OSHA, which provides up to 50 percent of the operating costs. States must set safety standards that are at least as effective as the comparable federal standards. Typically, state-level programs adopt standards that are identical to OSHA, although states have the option to establish standards not addressed by federal rules.

OSHA has also created Local Emphasis Programs (LEPs), which are enforcement strategies designed and implemented by OSHA regional or area offices. LEPs address hazards that pose a risk to employees in the given jurisdiction. They typically include increasing awareness of specific hazards and programs to reduce or eliminate them. The group practice administrator should be aware of local LEPs that focus on standards applicable to the practice.

The creation of an effective OSHA compliance program is a substantial responsibility for the medical practice administrator. The complexity and diversity of OSHA standards are significant, and developing an effective program requires more than a cut-and-paste approach. Keys to success are organizational buy-in at all levels, employee involvement in identifying potential workplace hazards and solutions, training and documentation, and constant review of the work environment and evolving OSHA standards.

OSHA eTools

OSHA has developed a series of stand-alone, interactive, Web-based training tools on safety and health topics. They provide information and advice on how OSHA standards apply to a work site. The medical practice administrator will find the following tools invaluable in understanding the applicability of OSHA regulations to the development of an OSHA compliance plan: the Hospital eTool (www.osha.gov/SLTC/etools/hospital/) and the Evacuation Plans and Procedures eTool (www.osha.gov/SLTC/etools/evacuation/).

OSHA Online Resources

The following OSHA resources are available online, with many available as a print-ready PDF:

- *Workers' Rights*: www.osha.gov/Publications/osha3021.pdf (English) or www.osha.gov/Publications/3473workers-rights -spanish.pdf (Spanish);

- Record-keeping forms: www.osha.gov/recordkeeping/RKforms .html;

- *OSHA Recordkeeping Handbook*: www.osha.gov/Publications /recordkeeping/OSHA_3245_REVISED.pdf;

- *Small Business Handbook*, an excellent overview of OSHA requirements and resources: www.osha.gov/Publications/small business/small-business.html;

- *Personal Protective Equipment*: www.osha.gov/Publications/ osha3151.pdf;

- *Model Plans and Programs for the OSHA Bloodborne Pathogens and Hazard Communications Standards*: www.osha.gov/Publications /osha3186.pdf;

- "Bloodborne Infectious Diseases: HIV/AIDS, Hepatitis B, Hepatitis C," information regarding needlestick safety programs: www.cdc.gov/niosh/topics/bbp/safer/; and

- *Workbook for Designing, Implementing, and Evaluating a Sharps Injury Prevention Program*: www.cdc.gov/sharpssafety/pdf/sharps workbook_2008.pdf.

::: Other Federal, State, and Local Laws and Regulations

Not only is it incumbent on employers to be fair and nondiscriminatory in hiring and terminating employees, employers also have a responsibility to provide a safe work environment. A number of laws and regulations apply to protecting personnel.

Title VII of the Civil Rights Act of 1964, which includes actions of sexual harassment, applies not only to the actions of employees and their supervisors, but also to patient interactions with staff members or staff-to-staff interactions. According to the Civil Rights Act, "sexual advances, requests for sexual favors, and other verbal or physical conduct of a sexual nature constitute sexual harassment when this conduct explicitly or implicitly affects an individual's employment, unreasonably interferes with an individual's work performance, or creates an intimidating, hostile, or offensive work environment."[6] This act implies that the employer has a duty to provide protection from psychological harassment or unwanted sexual advances in the workplace.

Through the 1990 ADA, the employer is charged with protecting the employee from discrimination because of life impairment that otherwise does not interfere with the ability to perform the job.[7]

Patient Privacy Protection

Policies must include employee responsibility to maintain the confidentiality of patients. Training on the privacy rules of the Health Insurance Portability and Accountability Act (HIPAA) of 1996 should be part of each employee's orientation and repeated regularly. Risk management has revealed that the most frequent violation of patient privacy occurs when the patient is a fellow employee. Because employees have access to medical information through computerized systems, it is tempting for a caring colleague to check up on a friend, which violates HIPAA regulations.

Another potential abuse of patient privacy by staff involves the use of computerized information to gather personal information. For example, in one hospital, an employee with an otherwise immaculate record used the computer to locate her estranged husband, who was living with a new partner. In the process, the employee became intrigued with the health status of the husband's new partner and discovered she was pregnant. The employee lost perspective on the nature of her actions, and when the new partner learned that the employee knew of her condition, she lodged a complaint about breach of privacy. Disciplinary action was taken against the employee, who did not deny the action and was jolted back into recognizing her wrongful activity. Employees must be told and reminded that their right to access information about another person, whether a colleague, family member, or acquaintance, is based on a job-related need to know, and that any other use is a violation of patient privacy.

HIPAA is only one part of patient privacy protection. In many states, the physical presence of a patient on the premises of a healthcare organization is not, of itself, considered confidential or protected information. This is not true, however, for patients in designated substance abuse treatment programs, who are protected by federal statute,[8] and this is also not true for mental health programs in many states.

Regardless of state protection, it is an unwise practice to acknowledge patient presence in the healthcare office. Unlike an inpatient facility, where the patient has the opportunity to opt out of the patient directory at admission, outpatients are generally not asked their preferences for acknowledgment of their presence. Consequently, it would not be difficult for disgruntled partners, angry acquaintances, estranged spouses, and noncustodial parents to track a potential victim of verbal or physical violence to the physician's office.

Staff should be trained to cautiously handle calls from and the physical arrival of such persons. Scripts that do not validate the presence or absence of the patient should be developed and rehearsed. Messages should be taken from the visitor and delivered by a staff member to the patient, who can then decide whether to allow the person to know of his or her presence in the office. The unanticipated arrival of a spouse or parent bearing a concealed weapon cannot be underestimated. Staff should be trained that patient safety is a priority and that careless management of patient information is grounds for disciplinary action.

::: Conclusion

Facility management is a core part of a practice administrator's job. The physical design and maintenance of the medical practice directly affects the quality of patient care and requires ongoing attention from the administrator with particular focus on safety as well as operational efficiency.

Notes

1. Heather Grimshaw, "A Matter of Perspective: How Patients' Fears Affect Care" *MGMA Connexion* (March 2013).
2. Community Health Assessment Clearinghouse, "New York State Community Health Assessment Guidance Documents," New York State Department of Health, www.health.ny.gov/statistics/chac/.
3. "New York State Community Health Assessment Guidance Documents."
4. Courtney Price, *HR Policies & Procedures: Manual for Medical Practices*, 5th ed. (Englewood, CO: MGMA, 2014), 165.
5. Occupational Safety and Health Administration (OSHA), *Small Business Handbook*, Small Business Safety and Health Management Series 2209-02R (Washington, DC: U.S. Government Printing Office, 2005), 10–13.
6. Title VII of the Civil Rights Act of 1964, 29 C.F.R. pt. 1604.11.
7. Americans with Disabilities Act of 1990, U.S.C. 42 §12101 et seq.
8. Drug Abuse Prevention, Treatment, and Rehabilitation Act, 42 C.F.R. pt. 2.

Chapter 5

Outsourced Services and Alliances

IT IS DIFFICULT to find and retain staff members who are skilled in executing all of the tasks a practice must perform to operate efficiently. Outsourcing work and forming alliances with other groups are helpful tools for reducing administrative and staff workloads, handling the group's legal matters, and letting the entire practice focus on high-quality patient care. The key skills required to effectively manage outsourced business expertise include determining the need for outsourced expertise, establishing the criteria for selecting business partners, pursuing and establishing partnerships and strategic alliances, and monitoring partnership performance.

::: Outsourced Services

Medical professionals must keep pace with rapid advances, manage complex reimbursement policies, understand technology, and comply with ever-changing government regulations. One way to meet these challenges, maintain and improve on high-quality patient experiences, and maximize financial performance is to outsource nonclinical functions.

Dictation

Doctors have outsourced medical transcription since the 1970s. Industry experts say that in solo and two-person practices, where the need was limited and hiring full-time employees was cost prohibitive, dictation services and freelance transcriptionists made sense. Although many specialties out-source this activity, voice-to-text software is reducing the necessity for transcription.

Billing

Billing can be outsourced for smaller practices that cannot afford in-house data encryption, electronic submission, and related technol-ogy. As billing has evolved into revenue cycle management, providers have expanded services to include real-time control over the process, round-the-clock access, and the ability to run reports and schedule appointments.

Miscellaneous Office Administration Tasks

Consider outsourcing other administrative and professional functions to:

- Ensure continuity when key personnel are on vacation or leave;

- Implement new software for practice management, electronic health records (EHRs), or other applications to minimize the effect on patient care;

- Maintain and/or support technology;

- Get a fresh perspective from an outside consultant on workflow issues, technology problems, or administrative concerns; and

- Fill a specific, one-time need for a highly trained professional.

Professional technicians and consultants who specialize in soft-ware functionality, integration requirements, and effect on workflow can drive software selection and implementation processes, help define physician practice–hospital integration, and configure applications.

In many cases, outsourced professionals function as administra-tive advisors and information technology (IT) experts to help practices recover from difficulties with cash flow and accounts receivable after implementing a new practice management or EHR system or to clean up past-due accounts after the loss of a key internal billing person.

⸬ Administrative Checkups

Group practices can benefit from administrative checkups to identify areas for improvement before a crisis strikes. Often, working with an expert will allow the practice to assess workflow to see whether administrative tasks and nonclinical operations can be performed more effectively and at less cost without compromising patient care.

Most practices need accountants, architects, and/or financial planning experts on an ad hoc basis. Having these professionals on your full-time payroll would entail significant fixed costs in terms of salaries and other resources. By outsourcing these services on an as-needed basis, you lower overall costs while receiving the same expertise when you need it. Be sure to interview any candidates to make sure they have experience with medical practices. Request a bid for services based on hourly or flat rates for a specific project to ensure a "not to exceed" price.

Building a Relationship with Legal Counsel

All relationships with outside contractors are important, but finding a lawyer you can trust and who understands the laws pertaining to your practice is crucial. Every medical group practice needs legal advice at some time. Your practice may seek a lawyer for a discrete project, such as assessing or drafting a contract or establishing your group as a business entity. The practice may also need technical legal advice about Medicare reimbursement, human resource issues, or to defend against or pursue a lawsuit.

How do you find a good firm? How do you maintain a positive working relationship? How do you manage certain types of legal services that are commonly viewed as almost unmanageable? The following subsections offer some tips.

Narrow Down the Candidates

Not every lawyer is the same, and many do not specialize in the highly complex world of healthcare law. Just as your patients don't go to a family practitioner for brain surgery, you should avoid lawyers who do not have a background, scope of practice, and experience with physician practices and healthcare-related legal matters.

Look for attorneys with experience in the type of issues your practice faces or that you anticipate it will face. Some, but not all, business lawyers have experience with internal practice legal documents. Some, but not all, have expertise regarding healthcare regulations and compliance (e.g., Stark law, anti-kickback, and Medicare reimbursement). And some issues, such as real estate transactions, require subject-matter expertise that doesn't overlap with healthcare law. Finding an attorney who specializes in the particular legal issue you face is essential for avoiding misunderstandings, improving outcomes, and developing a productive relationship. Asking other professionals you work with, such as your banker or accountant, for a recommendation can be very helpful. You can also reach out to other practices in your community for recommendations or request referrals and references from local colleagues.

Provide All of the Details

Once a lawyer or legal firm is chosen, identify the specifics of your group's situation. For example, if you need legal advice negotiating a property lease for your office, write down all applicable facts, including:

- The location;
- The identities of all of the owners in the new business entity;
- Your underlying business objectives and goals; and
- All concerns and deal breakers.

Similarly, if you are assessing physician relationships with a hospital, outline the nature of the relationship, the services provided, and the terms involved. In every case, begin your acquisition of legal assistance with a clear outline of key facts and assemble pertinent documents to help your legal team spend most of its time assessing the issue at hand instead of chasing paperwork and facts.

Define Your Business Terms

Despite beliefs to the contrary, "standard form" contracts produced at the press of a button rarely meet a medical group's specific needs. However, lawyers who have specialized expertise regarding practices are likely to have dealt with contractual issues common to the group practice world. As a result, they will also be more likely to have drafted legal documents that can be tailored to meet your practice's needs.

When possible, reach closure on business terms and key deal points before laying pen to paper and preparing a draft. Recognize the complexity of the deal and the fact that multiple revisions of the contract could end up costing a lot of money.

Communicate

Managing the attorney–client relationship involves effective communication, and it is important to provide your legal counsel with clear expectations and time frames. Part of the value in establishing an ongo-ing relationship with a lawyer is to ensure that the attorney understands your business, can get to the point in discussions, and can draw on an understanding of your needs and preferences to serve as a technician, counselor, and trusted advisor.

Managing and maintaining your group's legal relationships builds on many of the same skills you rely on as a practice leader. Defined expectations, clarity of communication, and acceptance that there will be some give-and-take go a long way toward ensuring that your practice's legal needs are met in an efficient and cost-effective man-ner. Before contracting services obtain a written estimate of expected charges and identify whether fees are hourly, cost-plus basis, flat fee, or paid by retainer.

Selecting Other Contractors

Once you have pinpointed a need, whether it is IT strategic planning, revenue cycle management, or systems management, check vendor lists vetted by the Medical Group Management Association® and other cred-ible national, regional, and local professional societies. Identify possible vendors based on services offered, then evaluate them and check ref-erences. Talk with existing clients in comparable situations. Ask about consultant continuity:

- Was the same consultant present for the entire engagement or was it a series of consultants?

- If there was more than one, was the transition smooth?

- Were there billing or communication issues?

The answers will tell you as much about the integrity of the company as it will about the quality of services it provides.

After you check references, schedule a meeting. Look for a partner who will listen attentively, learn your situation, collaborate, understand your business objectives, and empathize with your challenges. A consul-tant who appears to offer an "off-the-shelf" response or solution is not listening to the unique needs of your practice.

During your preliminary meetings, establish specific deliverables, deadlines, and expectations. Technical competence, business experi-ence, and a deep understanding of healthcare are important. Sometimes this experience will be reflected in the number of years a company has been in existence, but consider the backgrounds of the owner, key managers, and consultants (particularly the consultant who is assigned to your practice). As with an attorney, ask for recommendations and client references from local colleagues and others within the community.

Consider the Costs

Practice managers have fiduciary responsibilities to control practice costs and make the best decision with the information available. Once the relationship is in place, continue to monitor and evaluate it from a financial, professional, administrative, and informational perspective. For example, if you have outsourced billing, what was the effect on the bottom line? If collections have increased but the net cost of outsourcing exceeds that extra revenue, you are losing money. But also consider patient care and physician and staff lifestyle improvements. For example, if you were previously spending time after hours reviewing denials and no longer have to do it, your increased quality of life might outweigh the additional expense.

Other Outsourcing Options

Today's complex, automated practices have more options than ever when it comes to outsourcing and more reason to leverage them. As your practice evolves, consider the following outsourcing options:

- **EHR services** help practices plan, select, and implement EHR applications.

- **Financial planning services** allow physicians to effectively protect their assets, maximize allowable income tax deductions, and design effective retirement plans.

- **IT strategic planning** can help practice professionals understand the clinical, operational, financial, and technical aspects of IT planning and how it factors into the patient experience and bottom line. Typically vendors also offer core vendor planning and selection, systems integration, and security and disaster planning.

- **Practice management** geared mostly toward healthcare organizations spans executive leadership, practice management, department administration, revenue cycle management, and IT management. Consultants can temporarily fill leadership roles.

- **Remote and on-site systems management expertise**, including system configuration, performance assessments, maintenance programs, and disaster recovery planning and implementation, can optimize overall IT investment, maximize system performance, minimize downtime, and reduce maintenance costs.

- **Revenue cycle management** can accelerate cash flow and optimize business office performance. Services can include interim billing management, revenue cycle assessment, coding and compliance management, performance metrics, and benchmarking.

- **Web-based human resource management** can automate human resource tasks such as accruals, benefits, and payroll management, and the Consolidated Omnibus Budget Reconciliation Act of 1985 (COBRA) administration. These services are often offered free or at reduced rates when the companies offer these services as part of brokering insurance or other benefit programs.

Creating Alliances

An alliance is a cooperative arrangement between two or more physician groups that allows these organizations to combine in a common effort to gain or maintain competitive advantage. The mere formation of an alliance does not guarantee success, but rather requires mutual participation of all parties, a viable business concept, and a realistic strategy for implementing that idea.[1]

Alliances should be strategic in nature rather than a short-term solution to an immediate problem. Medical practice executives need to look past short-term gains and focus on building long-term goals for alliances and partnerships. Because of the potential antitrust concerns, all alliances and partnerships should be reviewed by attorneys prior to execution.

Key Issues in Alliances

There are a number of key questions to answer when partnering with outsiders for knowledge, services, and other mission-critical purposes, including:

- What is the purpose of the alliance?
- Which partner should be selected?
- What is the structure of the alliance?
- What are the roles and responsibilities of each party?
- What risks are involved?
- How long will the alliance last?
- Has the proposed arrangement been reviewed by attorneys for both parties?

Determining the Purpose of the Alliance

Without a clear vision, organizations will waste time, money, and energy entering into alliances and partnerships that do not meet their needs.

Many healthcare organizations engage in alliances and partnerships because of the conflicting demands of cost containment, delivering high-quality care, and expanding access to services. Alliances and partnerships let medical group practices that do not possess the necessary resources individually combine resources with other organizations and gain competitive advantages in the healthcare marketplace.[2] Competitive advantages typically reduce dependencies and improve organizational capacity.

Reduced dependencies can be achieved through vertical integration, where individual practices provide complementary services. This lets the allied groups offer additional services to patients while saving on the overhead and other costs all of the groups would incur if they duplicated those services.

Alliances give each member organization access to the technology, expertise, labor, and possibly even capital of the combined group members, expanding organizational capacity for all members. Organizational capacity is also increased by spreading financial risk across all members, letting individual organizations enter new markets without having to bear all of the financial risk of uncertain conditions inherent in new ventures.

Alliances may also help individual organizations overcome regulatory barriers, increase organizational flexibility, improve access to technological innovations, and achieve efficiency through economies of scale.[3]

Partner Selection

Alliances, like personal relationships, unite unique parties to work together for a common cause, and it is critical to select alliance partners that leverage one another's strengths. Alliances are not a quick fix for all of an organization's deficiencies. As with all relationships, each member has a distinct identity and personality. Alliances bring organizations' employees together, with any cultural differences they may have. For example, one organization may possess formal, clear management structures, while the other operates informally and forms only ad hoc arrangements. To be successful, alliance partners must share compatible, but not necessarily identical, cultures and missions or the alliance will fail.

Self-Assessment

The first step in screening and selecting potential partners is to understand your practice's own objectives, capabilities, and resources or lack thereof. Without a full understanding and accounting for all alliance strategy issues internally, decisions about whom to partner with will be uninformed.[4]

Ideal candidates for alliances will have compatible objectives, complementary resources and skills, compatible cultures and processes, and a willingness to ally with each other. Although collecting this information can be difficult and time-consuming, the payoff for finding a good match is priceless.[5] It is also important to consult with each potential practice's legal counsel to understand the ramifications of aligning with a particular organization.

Conflict Resolution

Differences can be a source of conflict, and alliance partners should use their common interests to help resolve those conflicts. The following steps can help resolve most conflicts that arise in alliances:

1. Clarify the issue;
2. Have each organization present its point of view;
3. Seek to understand each partner's point of view;
4. Discuss differences that arise; and
5. Always agree to solve the problem collaboratively.[6]

It is the medical practice executive's role to watch for warning signs of conflict and proactively resolve problems before they cause conflicts. Warning signs that conflict is imminent include:

- An issue repeatedly arises;
- Individuals choose not to listen during meetings and discussions, and;
- Individuals seem to avoid one another.

Choosing the Appropriate Structure

When considering alliances, many models are available to strengthen a practice's competitive position. Depending on the level of integration or degree of cooperation required, organizations can pick from any of the following types of affiliations, listed loosely in order from least to most integrated.

Network Affiliations

Network affiliations are the least-integrated type of alliance and function as a club with a general purpose. They provide a useful avenue for supportive dialogue, communication, and commiseration; however, they are not functional for contracting or for implementation activities.[7]

Joint Ventures

Joint ventures are typically formed to achieve a well-defined goal that is often focused on capital projects. According to Ginter, Swayne, and Duncan, "a joint venture is the combination of the resources of two or more separate organizations to accomplish a designated task. ...When projects get too large, technology too expensive, or the costs of failure too high for a single organization, joint ventures are often used."[8] The term *joint venture* applies to a wide range of interorganizational arrangements and frequently concerns physician-related ventures.

Joint ventures can provide medical practices with a competitive strategy, typically in an undeveloped or underdeveloped market, moving more directly from existing providers to a more convenient alternative for a targeted population. One advantage of joint ventures is that they can be quickly formed to take advantage of fast-moving opportunities. They also let organizations otherwise constrained by resources and capabilities pursue opportunities together.[9]

Joint ventures can be challenging if there are corporate culture clashes or organizational incompatibilities. Explicit mechanisms need to be developed to identify and manage these potential challenges.[10]

Independent Provider Associations and Provider Organizations

Independent provider associations (IPAs) and provider organizations (POs) are typically formed to organize independent medical group practices for the purpose of contracting with health maintenance organizations and purchasing supplies or other services. The main difference between IPAs and POs is that IPAs are typically affiliated with a hospital.[11]

The primary advantage of IPAs is that they offer a variety of physician choices to their members. They also tend to be more acceptable to managed care organizations (MCOs) than other, less traditional integrated delivery system models. Another reason IPAs are attractive is that they require much less capital to start and maintain relative to other models.[12]

IPAs are not without disadvantages, though. For example, because IPAs are one of the least-integrated forms of alliances, they do not offer the opportunity to leverage resources and achieve economies of scale that more integrated forms offer. Management of this loose type of alliance structure can be challenging because individual physician practices maintain their independence in an IPA. This issue grows as more practices enter the IPA.[13]

Physician Hospital Organizations

Physician hospital organizations (PHOs) involve physicians and hospitals that become partners in the delivery of healthcare. Exclusivity is an issue because most PHOs implement a selection process to qualify the doctors involved. The ownership arrangements of PHOs vary widely, but most strive to provide physicians and hospitals an equal voice and ownership. In most PHOs, the hospital organization may supply the most capital, but board composition does not typically reflect this equity position.[14]

PHOs have the advantage of being inexpensive to form and maintain. They are also desirable to many group practices because they are allowed to maintain group autonomy.

One of the biggest advantages that PHOs provide is the ability to negotiate on behalf of their membership. Additionally, they provide an opportunity for greater integration between a hospital and its medical staff.[15]

Along with these advantages come several disadvantages, stemming from the unpredictable nature of the independent groups that make up the alliance. Because their affiliations with one another are loose, PHOs often do not provide partners with economies of scale or improvements in contracting ability. In fact, MCOs often view PHOs as a barrier to effective communication with individual practitioners, decreasing the effectiveness of utilization of management activities.[16] MCOs often choose to deal directly with individual physicians because they want to exercise their right to select providers themselves.

Management Services Organizations

Management services organizations (MSOs) are typically formed to provide management services and administrative systems to one or more medical group practices. MSOs are normally based on one or more healthcare organizations. For example, MSOs may conduct billing, marketing, and/or human resource functions for their members. Each medical practice remains a separate entity and chooses whether to use the services that the MSO offers. In addition to providing the preceding services, many MSOs purchase the assets of the physicians' practices.[17]

MSOs are more closely aligned with hospitals relative to PHOs. MSOs provide their members economies of scale and the advantage of sharing data regarding practice behavior, which can help to increase the efficiency and effectiveness of individual practices.[18]

Similar to the PHO, physicians in an MSO remain independent contractors and thus maintain the ability to change allegiances, a downside to this type of affiliation. This point may also be considered an advantage, however, especially from the physician's viewpoint. Another disadvantage is the hospital mind-set, where physician practices are viewed as another hospital department, negatively affecting the practice's performance.[19]

Group Practice without Walls

A group practice without walls (GPWW) is not a true alliance because individual groups or sites can continue to manage themselves. GPWWs offer a high degree of integration of physician services and do not require the participation of a hospital organization. Most GPWWs are formed to address antitrust or hazards of the Stark self-referral law. In fact, a GPWW is a legal merging of all assets of the physician's practice, which is different than the acquisition of tangible assets, as in the MSO.[20]

An advantage of this type of affiliation is that each site maintains its independence, and thus is easy to manage and does not have to sacrifice much autonomy. Despite this, GPWWs help to present a united front to MCOs because they have the legal ability to negotiate and commit resources on behalf of their members. Because of the increased level of integration, GPWWs are able to achieve a moderate level of economies of scale. Examples may include shared billing, group purchasing, contracting for human resources, and payroll. Because the financial performances of its members are dependent on one another, GPWWs are able to exert pressure to influence the practice behavior of their members.[21]

The independence of individual medical practices within a GPWW can also be a drawback. It is sometimes a managerial challenge to align incentives, even though fiscal performance in a GPWW is interdependent. The independence of the physician practices in a GPWW can also lead to ineffectual leadership of the alliance as a whole.[22]

Single-Specialty Group Practices

Single-specialty group practices include only physicians of the same specialty and provide a significant level of integration. Single-specialty groups share a common billing number, fee schedule, benefits package, and a formal governance structure.

Multispecialty Group Practices

Multispecialty group practices are those that include multiple specialties and disciplines. Multispecialty group practices must be formed to ensure that the group includes the right mix of specialties and the appropriate proportions to allow for a mutually beneficial existence.[23]

Multispecialty group practices are advantageous because they can accept capitation, are able to leverage economies of scale, offer an environment conducive for the exchange of ideas between physicians, and are attractive to MCOs. Despite these advantages, they have the potential to threaten the existing autonomy of individual specialties and consequently can be functionally challenging to manage. Additionally, specialties that receive higher compensation relative to others are often forced to subsidize lower-paying specialties, giving them an incentive to leave and form their own single-specialty group practice.[24]

Due Diligence Process

Due diligence entails collecting information and data to assess the feasibility of a particular venture so that a decision is reached only after considering all prudent viewpoints. To minimize exposure to risk when embarking on a strategic alliance or partnership, it is critical to conduct due diligence to ensure that the proposed venture is a prudent decision.

Due diligence should take place on numerous fronts, including recruiting, membership in a strategic alliance, considering managed care contracts, adopting new technology, initiating marketing campaigns, and determining the compensation of employees. Due diligence is a complex activity, and a knowledgeable healthcare attorney and a qualified CPA or financial advisor should be consulted when considering opportunities and drafting essential legal documents.[25]

Recruiting

Ensuring the effective and successful recruitment of personnel, including physicians, is a critical responsibility of the medical practice executive. Due diligence should be conducted to ensure that personnel are qualified and that they fit the culture of the organization. Medical practice executives should understand the marketplace prior to conducting a search process so they can respond to candidates' questions, know the most effective sources for personnel, set clear expectations about the time frame needed for the search process, and understand the financial implications of attracting and hiring staff.[26]

Medical practices must present an appealing practice environment to attract quality personnel. Prospective employees are not only interested in pleasant surroundings, they are also concerned with financial stability, up-to-date technology, and considerate schedules and policies. By addressing these concerns, medical practice executives will be more successful in selling the organization to prospective employees, setting up new employees for success, and mitigating future employee turnover.[27]

Due diligence is especially critical when recruiting physicians. Failure to attract the right candidate for that key position could put the entire practice in jeopardy, especially in a small practice where incoming physicians often work on a salary subsidized by their partners until they build a big enough patient base to switch to production-based pay.

Practices often employ recruiters to present qualified candidates to the practice. Recruiters assist with negotiating the salary and benefits package and can suggest parameters for relocation and start dates.

Due Diligence for Strategic Alliances

In a perfect world, a comprehensive due diligence investigation would be undertaken when considering whether to partner with a particular organization. The process is so costly and time-consuming, however, that it is not always feasible to investigate every detail of a potential strategic alliance. This becomes an even bigger problem when considering smaller alliances and transactions, as too much due diligence can kill the transaction.[28]

Key questions to assist in the due diligence of a potential strategic alliance include the following:

- What in the alliance is important to your medical group practice? What isn't?

- Which problems will be costly? Which problems will be minor and/or worth the expense of fixing them?

- Where are you likely to find problems? Where are you unlikely to find problems?

- What type of transaction are you expecting? How large or small is the transaction? How complex is it? What will the due diligence investigation cost in both time and money?

- What is the risk to your medical group practice if the transaction goes bad?

- How much time do you have? What do you have to lose by delaying? What does the potential partner have to lose? How important to your medical practice is the alliance? How important is your practice to the potential partners?[29]

Additionally, more specific questions can be asked to further clarify whether a potential merger is a prudent move; for example:

- What is the organization's public image? Have there been any tensions between the community and the organization?

- Are there any pending lawsuits against the organization?
- Does the organization have a good reputation?
- How long has the organization been in business?
- Is the organization financially stable?[30]

Managed Care Contracts

When considering partnerships and strategic alliances, it is critical to review all managed care contracts — both old and new. Frequently, new alliances may change the structure of current contracts, particularly the reimbursement mechanisms for physicians. Thus it is important to review and decide whether to continue the contracts in the present form or make changes. Another important consideration regarding managed care contracting is that the structure of the proposed partnership or alliance may actually make renegotiating contracts more favorable for reimbursement levels.[31]

Technology Concerns for Alliances

The technological know-how of each partner involved in a potential alliance must also be considered because of the costly nature of technology. For example, if the medical practice is currently using a paper-based medical records system, it may be inordinately expensive to convert to EHRs to facilitate the alliance. Often, the expense of adopting new technology may outweigh the benefits of the potential partnership.

Marketing of Alliances

The power of marketing cannot be overlooked. A carefully constructed marketing campaign can assist a new partnership or alliance to rapidly succeed, especially in generating cash flow. Thus medical practice executives need to carefully align marketing activity to showcase their new organizational form and make the practice's current patients, future patients, and the medical community aware of its existence.[32]

Physician Compensation

Physician compensation must be carefully evaluated prior to considering potential partnerships and alliances. Conflict can arise when a medical practice whose physicians are dependent on a salary compensation structure attempt to partner or align with a practice whose physicians have a production-based ownership approach to compensation. Another area to consider is that of benefits packages, as physicians in integrated organizations typically receive more generous packages than a new group can offer, thus potentially contributing to discord.[33]

Roles and Responsibilities

Successful alliances require well-defined processes to address key issues in alliance formation, implementation, and operation. Negotiation among partners is necessary. The strategic objectives of the alliance should be evaluated and aligned to increase the probability of success. It is at this stage that staffing decisions should be considered, with all partners striving for a reasonable share of control that facilitates equitable involvement from all sides.

Because an alliance is a long-term venture, it is advisable to commit the best personnel who are striving for long-term placement; otherwise, high turnover can doom the alliance before it gets started. Alliance relationships take time to build and gain trust; thus frequently changing alliance personnel can disrupt the process.[34] Knowledge about the practice's capabilities is particularly important for defining work roles and supporting the requirements of current and future partners.[35]

At the outset of the partnership, alliance partners should collaboratively set goals and measure performance parameters that are quantifiable. These goals and measures should be congruent with the alliance's primary objectives. Additionally, alliance partners should address governance issues and develop an operating framework built around the clearly defined roles and expectations of each partner. Without resolving these critical issues, the success of the alliance may be in jeopardy.

Risks

Risk can be defined as unanticipated or negative variation, typically associated with negative outcomes. Risk sharing or risk controlling is a key justification for joining strategic alliances.[36]

Risk is a significant factor in the formation of alliances because strategic decision making is ultimately concerned with assessing odds for success.[37] Two types of risks are generally associated with alliances: (1) relational risk, or the probability that one or more partners does not comply with the rules governing the alliance; and (2) performance risk, which refers to the probability that the intended strategic goals of the alliance may not be achieved despite diligent cooperation among the partners.[38]

Duration

As with strategic plans, alliances should be reviewed and evaluated on an annual basis to estimate their effectiveness and worth, which is similar to how a portfolio of investments should be managed. Using this approach allows organizations to manage, review, and evaluate alliances as an aggregate business, and it permits organizations to evaluate current resource allocations with a focus on identifying how alliance concentrations contribute to possible duplication or gaps.[39]

While conducting an ongoing evaluation, it is important for the organization to develop an effective working environment with all partners to facilitate the completion of the actual work. It is critical to include performance measures combined with feedback from alliance partners to assess the progress of the alliance.

If an alliance is not functioning as intended and is not salvageable, dissolving it is appropriate. This situation is often due to a change in market conditions, with no one partner to blame. Regardless of the reason for the termination of the alliance, it is important for the practice to maintain a positive relationship with the former partners, as new opportunities for collaboration may present themselves in the future.[40]

Managing Partnerships and Strategic Alliances

Alliances should be managed similarly to how you manage your practice. Medical practice executives should continually acknowledge and actively monitor the concerns of all legitimate stakeholders and shareholders and should take their interests into consideration when making operational decisions. A stakeholder is anyone who has an investment in the success of the organization, including physicians, administrators, staff members, patients, vendors, and the community. Shareowners have a special status among stakeholders in that the potential gain or loss from their involvement with the corporation is determined by the organization's profit margin.[41]

Practice executives should maintain open lines of communication with stakeholders about their respective concerns and contributions, and about the risks that they assume because of their involvement with the corporation.[42] The more open managers can be about critical decisions and their consequences, and the more clearly managers understand and appreciate the perspectives and concerns of affected parties, the more likely it is that problematic situations can be satisfactorily resolved. Open communication and dialogue are, in themselves, stakeholder benefits, quite apart from their content or conclusions.[43]

By joining an alliance, organizations lose some freedom to make decisions without concern for alliance partners. Medical practice executives should be sensitive to the concerns and capabilities of the other alliance stakeholders. To maintain the survival of the alliance, the interdependence of efforts among the alliance partners must be recognized. All attempts should be made to achieve a fair distribution of rewards and burdens in the alliance, and at the same time to account for each organization's vulnerabilities.[44]

A commitment to engage in dialogue, however, does not constitute a commitment to practice collective decision-making. There are obvious limits to the amount and content of information (particularly information about strategic options under consideration) that can be appropriately shared with particular stakeholder groups.

Practice executives should acknowledge that conflict is an inevitable part of alliances, as it is with all interactions with people. In the interests of all parties involved, any conflicts should be handled openly and fairly, and, where necessary, adjudicated by third-party review. Maintaining fairness and openness will guarantee that all parties will act responsibly and not threaten the existence of the alliance.[45]

::: Conclusion

Developing and exercising the capacity to identify, establish, and implement key strategic alliances with external entities is necessary to effectively lead a medical practice. Skill in negotiation, recognition of potential strategic opportunities, and the ability to monitor the ongoing effectiveness of business relationships will serve practice administrators well throughout their careers.

Notes

1. Timothy Rotarius and Dawn Oetjen, "Dialysis Center Alliances," *Dialysis & Transplantation* 31, no. 3 (2002): 151–154.
2. Rotarius and Oetjen, "Dialysis Center Alliances."

3. Peter R. Kongstvedt, David W. Plocher, and Jean C. Stanford, "Integrated Health Care Delivery Systems," in *Essentials of Managed Health Care*, 4th ed., ed. Peter R. Kongstvedt (Gaithersburg, MD: Aspen, 2001), 31–62.

4. Michael K. Rich, "Requirements for Successful Marketing Alliances," *The Journal of Business and Industrial Marketing* 18, no. 4/5 (2003): 447–457.

5. Salvatore Parise and Lisa Sasson, "Leveraging Knowledge Management Across Strategic Alliances," *Ivey Business Journal* 66, no. 4 (March/April 2002): 41–47.

6. Rich, "Requirements for Successful Marketing Alliances."

7. Kongstvedt et al., "Integrated Health Care Delivery Systems."

8. Peter M. Ginter, Linda E. Swayne, and W. Jack Duncan, *Strategic Management of Health Care Organizations*, 4th ed. (Malden, MA: Blackwell, 2002), 240.

9. Alan M. Zuckerman, "Strategic Alliances and Joint Ventures: Why Make When You Can Buy?" *Healthcare Financial Management* 59, no. 8 (2005): 122–124.

10. Zuckerman, "Strategic Alliances and Joint Ventures."

11. Kongstvedt et al., "Integrated Health Care Delivery Systems."

12. Kongstvedt et al., "Integrated Health Care Delivery Systems."

13. Kongstvedt et al., "Integrated Health Care Delivery Systems."

14. Kongstvedt et al., "Integrated Health Care Delivery Systems."

15. Kongstvedt et al., "Integrated Health Care Delivery Systems."

16. Kongstvedt et al., "Integrated Health Care Delivery Systems."

17. Kongstvedt et al., "Integrated Health Care Delivery Systems."

18. Kongstvedt et al., "Integrated Health Care Delivery Systems."

19. Kongstvedt et al., "Integrated Health Care Delivery Systems."

20. Kongstvedt et al., "Integrated Health Care Delivery Systems."

21. Kongstvedt et al., "Integrated Health Care Delivery Systems."

22. Kongstvedt et al., "Integrated Health Care Delivery Systems."

23. Kongstvedt et al., "Integrated Health Care Delivery Systems."

24. Kongstvedt et al., "Integrated Health Care Delivery Systems."

25. Rod Aymond and Theodore Hariton, "Regrouping after Disintegration," *Family Practice Management* 7, no. 3 (2000): 37–40.

26. Kriss Barlow and Allison McCarthy, "Due Diligence on the Internal Front Enhances Recruiting Success," *New England Journal of Medicine* (January/February 2004).

27. Barlow and McCarthy, "Due Diligence on the Internal Front."

28. "Due Diligence Step-by-Step Guide," United States Agency for International Development (USAID), www.usaid.gov/sites/default/files/documents/1880/Section_5_Due_Diligence_Step_by_Step_updated.pdf.

29. "Due Diligence Step-by-Step Guide."

30. "Due Diligence Step-by-Step Guide."

31. Aymond and Hariton, "Regrouping after Disintegration."

32. Aymond and Hariton, "Regrouping after Disintegration."

33. Aymond and Hariton, "Regrouping after Disintegration."

34. Parise and Sasson, "Leveraging Knowledge Management."

35. Rich, "Requirements for Successful Marketing Alliances."

36. John Hagedoorn, "Understanding the Rationale of Strategic Technology Partnering: Interorganizational Modes of Cooperation and Sectoral Differences," *Strategic Management Journal* 14 (1993): 371–385; B. Kogut, "Joint Ventures: Theoretical and Empirical Perspectives," *Strategic Management Journal* 9 (1988): 319–332.

37. James G. March and Zur Shapira, "Managerial Perspectives on Risk and Risk Taking," *Management Science* 33 (1987): 1404–1418.

38. Oliver E. Williamson, "Credible Commitments: Using Hostages to Support Exchange," *American Economic Review* 73 (1983): 519–540; Oliver E. Williamson, *The Economic Institutions of Capitalism* (New York: Free Press, 1985).

39. S. Anderson, "In Today's Economy (and Tomorrow's), Strategic Alliances Open Doors to Opportunities," *Orange County Business Journal*, 25, no. 4 (2002): 4.

40. Anderson, "In Today's Economy (and Tomorrow's)."

41. Clarkson Centre for Business Ethics, *Principles of Stakeholder Management* (Toronto: University of Toronto, Rotman School of Management, 1999), 4. www.rotman.utoronto.ca/-/media/Files/Programs-and-Areas/Institutes/Clarkson/Principles%20of%20Stakeholder%20Management.pdf.

42. Clarkson Centre for Business Ethics, *Principles of Stakeholder Management*.

43. Clarkson Centre for Business Ethics, *Principles of Stakeholder Management*.

44. Clarkson Centre for Business Ethics, *Principles of Stakeholder Management*.

45. Clarkson Centre for Business Ethics, *Principles of Stakeholder Management*.

Chapter 6

Information Technology

::: Developing a Technology Plan

EFFECTIVE PRACTICE MANAGEMENT is only possible when information technology (IT) provides useful information for good decision making and assists in performing business and clinical processes. Information management technology is no longer an adjunct, separate program that supports the practice. It is a vital, integrated component that underlies ongoing success. A successful IT plan helps improve efficiency and ensure outstanding service and clinical quality. Technology can assist in standardizing processes, identifying potential problems, speeding up processes for better outcomes, and improving communication. Key competencies required to effectively manage information systems include determining business needs and identifying goals; developing a technology plan, policies, and budget; selecting appropriate technological solutions; overseeing technology implementation; maintaining equipment; safeguarding information; and developing a technology disaster plan.

Assessing Technology Needs

The approach to assessing IT needs and then establishing a plan to address those needs is similar to the approach to strategic planning, and in fact should be part of the overall strategy-making process for the organization. This process includes evaluation of existing conditions and systems, consideration of alternatives relative to potential systems, selection of appropriate alternatives, and then implementation of those decisions.[1]

Purchasing the right IT equipment for your group requires understanding the processes used in practice operation and knowing what technology is available that can be integrated into those processes. This analysis is usually undertaken by a team that includes both clinical and business staff, headed by the medical practice executive. Be sure to solicit both physician and nonphysician provider input.[2] A clear understanding of the organization's mission, vision, strategy, goals, and objectives is critical to ensuring that the team's efforts will result in successful implementation.

Evaluating Business Processes

Historically, IT applications to improve medical practice operations were first applied to business processes. For example, most practices handle claims and billing through some type of computerized system. These systems, however, account for only a few of the business processes that can be streamlined, expedited, and standardized to improve the overall quality of the business operations. Every business aspect — from the management of supplies to the disposition of medical waste, from environmental services to utilities and energy management — must be considered to identify potential improvement through the use of available technology.

One of the best methods for identifying and addressing business process needs is to examine the practice's financial statements. Consider each line item as a potential location for using technology to improve the bottom line.

Improving Existing Business Processes

Technology can certainly make your life easier; electronic health records (EHRs) and practice management systems have been widely adopted partly because they can be more efficient than handling reams of paper every day. However, as many vendors can attest, sometimes practice managers attempt to fix problems (such as scheduling or verifying insurance eligibility) with technology, even though adding a software program could just make the problem worse.

For example, you could have an unwieldy process for something as simple as verifying insurance eligibility. Collecting this information several days before an appointment gives your office time to check eligibility and address other potential problems before the patient walks in the door. Waiting until the patient shows up to collect the information wastes time as it is verified and any problems related to it are resolved, and it can reduce the efficiency of the entire practice. Whether or not you are using technology to collect the information is irrelevant because the process is time dependent instead of technology dependent. Thus, even the most sophisticated EHR isn't helpful if you can't verify insurance eligibility up front.

Scheduling is another area that often benefits from a process tweak instead of a technology fix. Scheduling patients based on generic categories such as "new" and "acute" doesn't provide enough context to accurately gauge the time those patients will require. A new patient could be there for a simple annual checkup or show up with a long list of ailments, for example. Once again, there is no technology fix for problems like this, and the solution lies in hiring staff members who are good at assessing patient needs during appointment scheduling and can assign more accurate time slots.

There are some key performance indicators that will help you ascertain whether your processes need streamlining. For example, you can benchmark performance indicators against better performers in the *MGMA Performance and Practices of Successful Medical Groups: 2014 Report Based on 2013 Data* to see how your practice measures up against common metrics such as percentage of total accounts receivable over 120 days and adjusted fee-for-service collection percentage.

You can also analyze:

- **Claims denied at first pass** to pinpoint billing process pitfalls;

- **Percentage of copayments collected at time of service** to look at your front-desk reception performance; and

- **Date of the third-next-available appointment** to identify patient-access issues. (Looking at the first- and second-next-available appointments could be misleading because of last-minute cancellations.)

Cataloging Existing Applications and Tools

Any assessment should start with an inventory of all existing applications. The software may be integrated or may consist of several stand-alone systems. The final inventory prepared by an individual practice should include documentation on each particular software's standard capabilities, the age and costs of existing applications, and once the applications have been reviewed by the team, their strengths and weaknesses. This information can be entered into a spreadsheet for convenient storage and access for analysis.

Business Applications

Business applications support the operational aspects of the practice, including scheduling, communications, test and data management, and financial transactions. Common applications include the following.

Practice management. The heart of an effective system manages the patient flow and the demographic, financial, and clinical information that is important for moving the patient through the care process. An excellent system will automatically prompt staff members as to when and what they need to do, prepare and present the proper information the caregivers need to accurately evaluate and treat their patients, and assist in documenting what was done and accurately bill for the work. Systems can also assist with reminding patients of appointments through automated phone calls and e-mails, reducing the number of no-shows.

Services (e.g., e-mail, groupware). Most providers communicate with their patients through e-mail and Internet communications. IT is also used to coordinate care among caregivers in the practice, practice clinicians, and those who provide referral and specialty care.

Claims processing. Many insurers require claims to be filed electronically. The elimination of the human element in this process reduces errors and speeds the reimbursement in addition to reducing costs.

Document processing, spreadsheets, and databases. Practice management requires various reports and information to adequately understand the business and to report necessary information to stakeholders.

Transcription. Modern transcription systems link the physician's thoughts and comments to the EHR system; provide key prompts to ensure comprehensive, standard documentation; and allow accurate billing for the services provided. Voice-recognition systems have been slow to develop, but newer systems will include direct dictation.

Personnel management. Staffing is a major cost factor for any practice. Accurate records ensure reliable compensation systems and provide management with information to make staffing decisions. For example, with IT, time clocks and manual systems can be replaced by radio frequency identification technology that will detect when employees enter and leave the facility.[3]

Inventory management. Eliminating human error in inventory management reduces carrying costs and eliminates stocking problems and shortages.

Waste management. Waste management programs are often elementary in design but have become increasingly crucial to regulatory compliance. Accurate tracking ensures that medical waste is handled properly and helps to document the practice's compliance with all regulations.

Energy management. Recent energy cost increases dictate that facilities control and wisely handle all energy requirements, including electricity, gas, and water usage.

Clinical Applications

Clinical applications support patient care activities. EHRs are the most widely discussed, but other clinical applications, such as those that follow, may help a particular practice.

Electronic health records. The drive for EHRs originated with the need for easier handling and storage of documentation. Now EHRs are critical support tools for ensuring quality care and for enabling accurate billing for services.

Prescription management. Newer prescription systems allow good documentation for care, guard against conflicting medications, and allow proper oversight for detecting misuse and abuse.

Disease management. Good disease management programs allow the provider to assist the patient in proactive interventions rather than waiting until reactionary efforts are required. They can reduce the overall costs of care for chronic diseases and improve the patient's quality of life.

Patient Applications

Patient applications are crucial marketing and service delivery methods for medical practices. Following are some common examples.

Electronic communication (Website, e-mail). Patients increasingly research their health problems and actively participate in their own care, and physicians must be able to provide accurate and timely information. Many medical practices establish Websites and other online tools so patients can communicate with the provider electronically. Done properly and with adequate security, these programs can speed care delivery and recovery. For example, such applications can facilitate speedy prescription refills, help make appointments, and report follow-up information to the provider without the effort and cost of an office visit.

Electronic monitoring. Telephone lines and the Internet allow many patients with chronic conditions to regularly track and report their physical conditions. This is especially beneficial to those who are unable to drive or travel. Continuous monitoring of body temperature, blood pressure, and heart rates can allow the provider to be alerted instantly when the patient experiences a problem. Implanted defibrillators, a common health maintenance item, can now be monitored through wireless Internet connections for faster response by caregivers and clinical providers.

Online education. In addition to providing information that can help patients manage their own health problems, the Internet offers opportunities for encouraging the patients to participate in health and wellness promotion activities.

Telehealth. Internet and telehealth programs let clinicians conduct patient examinations without needing to travel. Two-way links between the provider's offices and the patient's home or business allow for quick and effective consultations that reduce travel costs and time away from the home or office.

Inventory of Existing Hardware

Once the software and applications have been determined, the hardware that supports the systems should be identified. The connectivity of the equipment also needs to be specified. Some equipment may be capable of supporting or connecting with other systems, whereas some may be strictly independent. Overall strengths and weaknesses of the equipment should be identified. The evaluation of the hardware and its flexibility will provide a basis for the long-term planning of system support, training, and maintenance. Types of hardware are discussed in the following subsections.

Workstations

Workstations are the interface points between humans (e.g., care providers and support personnel) and the IT systems that assist in providing quality care to the patients. These data entry and retrieval points have evolved from simple hardware components, formerly placed in the back rooms of the office area, to mobile information centers that connect with real-time information at the point of care. Today, the workstation is more likely a tablet PC or a personal digital assistant (PDA) that the provider uses in place of paper documents. These innovations have decreased data access and documentation time, giving providers more time to spend directly with the patient. Direct data entry improves the quality of documentation, provides more accurate billing, and increases patient satisfaction.

Servers

Servers are collections of hardware components, similar to those in normal PCs, which provide the "brains" of the information systems. Servers have replaced large mainframe computer hardware because of their flexibility and robust capabilities. The equipment is usually designed for 24-hour, 7-days-per-week operation. Therefore, servers are more durable than regular PCs and actually may contain redundant components providing backup to ensure continuous stability of service. For example, a server might contain multiple hard drives containing the same information so that if one drive fails, no data is lost. These drives are also often hot-swappable, meaning dead drives can be pulled and replacement drives can be installed without shutting down the server and disrupting service to the office.

Multiple servers can also be connected to enhance capacity and service. Servers have recently been constructed in high-density modules known as blades that can provide powerful systems in small spaces. Blade servers are intended for use with single dedicated applications, such as Web pages, and computing capacity can be expanded by adding more blades to a system instead of purchasing all-new server hardware.

Tablets and PDAs

As mentioned, many new practice management systems have replaced large stationary workstations with handheld devices that allow point-of-service entry of information. Most of these come in the form of tablet PCs or PDAs. These devices are small enough to be carried into the exam room and used by the provider while interacting with the patient. Often, the device is wirelessly connected to the main information system so data are captured in real time.

Records and files maintained on servers and in central storage devices are automatically updated. These systems usually provide boilerplate information templates and touch-pad entry for faster data capture. A template can capture and store a larger volume of information than a free-text format. Ideally, data input at the time care is given will result in improved quality of information and better subsequent care.[4]

⠿ Patient Portals

Patient portals let authorized users gain entry to information systems. Access can be granted to patients so they can easily find pertinent information about their health and the care provided by the medical practice in a one-stop environment. Patients can access health record information, health educational materials, care instructions, clinical data, pharmacy and drug information, and billing information. Portals can also provide access to providers via secure e-mail and facilitate online appointment making.

Captured data may be stored on in-house PCs or on a centralized server, either on site in the facility or in an off-site data bank. Outsourcing data storage is often used to ensure data security. As the cost of electronic storage (e.g., CDs and DVDs) has decreased, it has become the preferred medium compared to hard-copy systems because of its speed and ease of access.

Data Security

The importance of data security applies to all aspects of the software and hardware components of information management systems. A review of the systems with respect to the security of the information they contain, whether financial, clinical, demographic, or personal, should be made while inventorying the resources of the systems. The threefold approach established by the Health Insurance Portability and Accountability Act (HIPAA) is an excellent method for reviewing the systems.[5]

The first review in the HIPAA approach should be of administrative systems, including the backup systems, disaster recovery systems, and emergency-mode operational capabilities. The second level of review should be of physical resources. This includes hardware and software for workstations and storage media, as well as the overall physical facility. Finally, the technical aspects of the systems should be reviewed, including the authentication and transmission of data programs, data integrity systems, and other control systems.[6]

Mobile Data Security

Mobile devices, such as smartphones, tablets, laptops, and PDAs, provide group practices with unprecedented flexibility, but the use of these devices comes at the price of increased security risks. A series of recent HIPAA settlements, including the largest to date ($4.8 million)[7], highlights the increased risk that mobile and portable devices containing electronic protected health information (ePHI) present to physician practices.

Mobile devices are extremely vulnerable to loss and theft, which can result in significant breach reporting costs and, in some cases, can automatically initiate an Office for Civil Rights investigation. Practice professionals will need to develop and implement mobile device procedures and policies that will protect the protected health information (PHI) used by their staff.

Here are nine important steps you can take to identify appropriate technology, safeguard your mobile devices, and protect your practice.

1. Choose Devices Wisely

Work with your clinical team to decide whether mobile devices will be used to access, receive, transmit, or store PHI or be used as part of the organization's internal network or systems, such as an EHR. Many clinicians already use mobile technology outside the practice and are eager to leverage the compact size, versatility, and computing power of these devices in the workplace.

Consider using mobile devices that access ePHI but do not store the data. This reduces the danger that ePHI will be disclosed if a device is lost or stolen.

2. Review Your Technology Options

For practices that use EHRs, there are several device options for accessing ePHI, including large and small laptops, tablets, and smartphones. Each device has benefits and liabilities. Typically, the smaller the device, the easier it is to transport and the more vulnerable it is to loss.

Clinician usability should be a determining factor for whichever device is purchased. A small keyboard that is difficult to type on might frustrate a clinician and result in decreased productivity and satisfaction. Test various options with your clinical staff members and consider using different technology for different staff members. The goal is maximum performance and satisfaction with minimum risk of loss.

3. Conduct a Risk Analysis

Every practice is required by law to conduct a thorough risk analysis that identifies threats and vulnerabilities to ePHI from internal and external sources. While the most common threat to mobile devices is loss or theft, practice professionals must also review the risks associated with flooding, fire, and other environmental issues.

4. Create a Risk Management Strategy

Develop and implement mobile device safeguards to reduce risks identified in the risk analysis, including an evaluation and regular maintenance of the mobile device safeguards you establish. Security or configuration settings for mobile devices will be part of this. Your risk management strategy should include the physical safeguards of a mobile device (e.g., Is it locked up at night?), administrative safeguards (Who has the right to look at the ePHI on the device?), and technical safeguards (Is there an automatic logout?).

5. Document Your Actions

Documenting the results of a risk analysis and the policies and procedures that resulted from it allows the practice to continually review and revise them, and it helps protect the practice if there is a compliance audit. This documentation is required if the practice is participating in the meaningful use (MU) EHR incentive program. Lack of this documentation is the leading cause of failing an MU audit.

6. Restrict Usage Outside the Practice

Mobile devices can be helpful for clinicians to use while making rounds at a hospital or for home use to access ePHI remotely. However, once a device has left the premises, it is more vulnerable to loss and theft. Develop stringent policies and procedures to address critical issues such as the use of strong passwords ("Ab12#%@" instead of "password"), physical security of a device (Is it locked up at a clinician's home when not in use?), and sharing of the device with nonauthorized individuals.

Mobile devices should be encrypted. If an encrypted device is lost or stolen, it is not considered a legal breach and the practice would not be required to go through the onerous and costly breach notification process that includes notifying the affected patients, the government, and, for larger breaches, local media.

7. Consider Outside Assistance

Consider contracting with an EHR and/or security vendor that can help identify the most appropriate mobile technology for your organization, help conduct a risk analysis, and help develop mobile security policies and procedures. Networking with your MGMA colleagues provides an excellent opportunity to discuss mobile device use and security with those who have gone through the implementation process. Visit the online MGMA Member Community for more information.

8. Establish Contingency Plans

Contingency plans help protect organizations in the event of a loss or inoperable mobile device. They should address these questions:

- What data access redundancies has the practice established?
- Are there spare devices if one does not work?
- How quickly can a vendor replace a device?
- Is there a securely protected master list of all passwords if one is forgotten?
- Can the device be remotely locked, or can content be remotely deleted?

Practice professionals are also encouraged to engage in regular breach drills to ensure that staff knows the answers to the following questions:

- What do we do if a device is lost or stolen?
- How do we notify patients that their information has been disclosed, and who is responsible for making those notifications?
- Which staff members will be charged with determining how the breach happened?
- Who is responsible for finding the breach and fixing the problem so it doesn't happen again?

9. Train and Retrain Staff

Mobile device privacy and security training for administrative and clinical staff should be an integral part of your regular and ongoing compliance awareness efforts. Volunteer staff members must also be trained. Always document all staff training efforts.

Practice professionals should consider incorporating mobile device security awareness into staff meetings, e-mail bulletins, educational lunches, and other staff communications. Building a culture of security takes time, but it can lead to a greater focus on mobile device security issues and fewer problems.

::: Strategic Information Partners

The information needs of the medical practice are not the only reasons for performing an IT assessment. The needs of organizations and entities with which the practice interacts should be considered as well. For example, organizations that process payment for healthcare and those that provide adjunct support services, such as reference laboratories, diagnostic facilities, and hospitals to which patients are referred, all have information needs. Planning for providing the information these entities require in an efficient, seamless process strengthens working relationships and reduces costs for all parties involved.

Payers collect increasingly more data on their customers. Through data analysis, they hope to provide interventions that improve their beneficiaries' health, and thus lower costs of care overall. Information from medical practice records is useful to track patients' compliance with interventions. Data-mining programs can provide better information regarding the efficacy of treatments.

Regulatory agencies monitor activities and treatments more aggressively because policy interest is placed on the quality of outcomes, the costs of specific treatment programs, and disease management. The monitors search for better outcomes associated with a given approach and watch for abuses and misuses that may occur.

Reference labs and diagnostic centers used by medical practices require clinical and financial information that practices typically collect. Shared information can yield cost and quality improvements for both the medical practice and the diagnostic service, but is important to find ways to share this information in a confidential manner.

Inpatient programs need to know the treatments and drugs a medical practice provided to a patient prior to admission. The availability of current clinical information prevents duplication or omission of needed care and facilitates timely response to patient needs. The patient's financial information is also required to facilitate the reimbursement process.

Gap Analysis

A gap analysis identifies areas of dissatisfaction with existing systems, needs for planned business process changes, needs for planned clinical service changes, and any desired patient applications. Staff is often frustrated with existing systems that may not fit the current workflow. Stopping the clinical thought process or interrupting it while making entries into an information system may result in lost time, mental fatigue, and at times create a situation in which quality is compromised. The existing system may not provide the appropriate information for the practice or its strategic partners. Finding a solution requires not only an understanding of the problem, but also knowledge of the technologies and systems available to fix the problem.

A survey of the clinicians and staff will determine whether existing systems satisfy their job needs to their levels of satisfaction. Clinicians may not be immediately cognizant of problems or opportunities for improvement because of their experience and comfort with the existing system, which may have led to their acceptance of an existing, inefficient process.

Changes in reimbursement filing requirements or additional regulatory reporting may dictate necessary modifications in processes. Any new or modified services should be documented, and a special note should be made of the required information and processes resulting from these changes.

Communications with patients traditionally have been person to person, but many patients prefer (and sometimes insist) that their contact with a clinician be through electronic media. The practice must assess whether its patient base is sophisticated enough to take advantage of the Internet, e-mails, online education, and Websites as standard communication modes.

In addition to the dissemination of information, both private and communal, the practice may also need to consider telehealth programs that allow the patient to provide the practice with ongoing data such as blood pressure, glucose levels, and other metrics that can be transmitted over telephone lines or the Internet.

Gap Analysis: Step by Step

The following example of goal assessment questions can be used for a gap analysis:[8]

- Where are you compared to where you wanted to be?
- What was your vision for an EHR before you implemented it?
- If you're not using the EHR as originally planned, what do you need to do to realize the goals?

During the post-implementation review, ask the following additional questions:

- Are physicians and staff using the EHR as envisioned, or is more training needed?
- Are they following the new workflow or stuck in the old ways?
- Are physicians doing what they should be doing, or are they doing clerical work or using work-arounds?
- Is the workflow reaching the ideal as it was mapped, or do changes need to be made?
- Are employees still writing down or printing information unnecessarily?
- Is after-hours time needed to catch up on work? What efficiencies are needed to accomplish work during the day?
- Do policies and procedures reflect the changes brought about by EHR implementation? Are they updated as needed?
- How are the interfaces with pharmacies, laboratories, and billing or insurance companies working? Measure this by the percentage of prescriptions and test orders sent and received electronically.
- Do you have appropriate staff for achieving optimization?

- Do you need a consultant or additional employee with skills that are currently lacking in your practice?
- Are charges captured and posted correctly? How is the interface with the practice management software working? (Review charges on a daily basis to ensure accurate charge capture.)
- Are coding functions providing accurate coding?
- Is the EHR system producing the reports you want containing the data you need?

Addressing Workflow Issues Using Lean

The gap analysis and system evaluation will identify problems related to workflow related to technology in the office, but it is not always easy to envision the best workflow process with a major shift, such as implementing an EHR system. The Lean method is one technique for redesigning workflow. The following steps are for conducting a Lean process analysis:

1. Develop a statement specifying the goals and expected outcomes of the process.

2. Identify a team that includes involved staff and stakeholders.

3. Diagram the current process with the known start and end points, needed inputs and desired results, people involved in the process, and steps during the process.

4. Identify steps where work piles up, people are waiting, information is missing, or there are other slowdowns.

5. Identify any unnecessary steps. Were tasks maintained because they were needed in the paper-based system that can now be modified or removed?

6. Compare the mapped process with the desired process and results. Are there any deviations, shortcuts, or inconsistencies because of personnel preferences?

7. Identify who is completing the tasks. Is the task appropriate for his or her level of license, or should another staffer handle it?

8. Discuss the technology capabilities related to the process.

9. Diagram the ideal process based on the previous steps and known functionalities of the technology. Can steps be eliminated or combined?

10. Test the workflow redesign first with a walkthrough and then with the actual technology. Implement changes or modify as necessary.

11. Develop measures to track improvement and celebrate when goals are attained.[9,10]

Practice operations, employees, and EHR functions thrive with standardization. The workflow analysis should identify variations caused by personal preferences or attempts to accommodate various work styles. Also look for opportunities to standardize templates, forms, data input, and so on to simplify the process. Accept that you may go through several transitional workflows or procedures as users adapt practice styles to the system and learn new and improved ways of using it.

::: Planning Future Information Technology Architecture

One of the most difficult aspects of technology planning is predicting the future. Technology changes quickly and seldom in a linear fashion. Tremendous amounts of time can be expended attempting to monitor and assess the state of the art within the industry. Often this is an area for which the practice may wish to employ outside assistance. If the practice is considering growing or changing services, or becoming part of a larger or different organization, its future IT requirements may be dramatically different from those for the current clinical practice.

For the medical practice executive, monitoring trends is a time-consuming but necessary requirement for determining the proper direction for moving the IT program. Outside assistance from an expert consultant may be valuable. Reliable IT vendors are a key source of information, not only about their own systems but about industry trends as well. MGMA also offers seminars, books, and other materials that can help.

Hardware Considerations

Although new information systems require less space than earlier systems because of their more compact design, the physical space requirements should still be considered. Proper ventilation, security, and utility support may dictate limits to hardware selections. Off-site or outsourced services may be required.

Staff Issues

The lack of existing staff with the necessary IT support skills, or an inability to recruit such staff, may result in a decision to outsource IT services. A clear understanding of the system requirements for maintenance and upkeep of the system should be made before selecting the equipment. If the practice staff is not capable of supporting the new systems, serious problems could result. The costs for providing long-term internal support vs. the costs for outsourcing should be carefully compared.

Costs Considerations

Initial capital investment cost is often the least-expensive component of an IT decision. Typically, the first year of operational support is built into the purchase agreement, but subsequent costs for upkeep may negate any initial benefits. Ongoing costs for staffing and consultation, support, updates, and hardware maintenance can overwhelm a medical practice, particularly a smaller one. Serious consideration must be made of the overall costs for the IT investment over an extended time. A five-year projection of costs and return on investment (ROI) will provide insight into the true value of the system.

Government and Payer Compliance

Meaningful use and the penalties associated with not complying with MU requirements should also factor into any IT infrastructure plan. There are often four main challenges associated with this:

1. **Compliance.** The vendor or product will not be able to meet government requirements for MU certification.

2. **Usability.** This often is a case where the technology seemed user friendly during the vendor's demonstration but turned out to be anything but friendly once it was implemented or now that new demands are placed on it.

3. **Customization.** This involves buying an EHR that is purportedly ideal for a specialty practice — orthopedics, for example — only to discover that it needs to be customized based on each

physician's specific needs. For example, doctors who specialize in knees require different functions than doctors who work on shoulders or those who work on feet.

4. **Customer support.** What kind of support are you able to get from the vendor? Sometimes this can be more specifically described as a lack of customer support.

Compliance is a particular challenge, as you are at the mercy of the vendor for keeping their products certified and recertified for the different stages of MU. If you choose a vendor who refuses to obtain certification or takes too long to do it, you may need to scrap everything you purchased and buy an entirely new system that is compliant.

Other pressure can come from payment programs that impose detailed reporting requirements on practices. A system that meets MU requirements may need further tweaking to comply with the payer's standards, adding more cost and staff training time. And the compliant EHR system you purchase may not interface properly with your compliant practice management system, causing additional inefficiency and costs. Some practices hire staff programmers to keep up with the ever-changing compliance demands.

⠿ Updating Existing Information Technology Architecture

Sometimes it is difficult to tell if an all-new IT infrastructure is needed or the existing one can be revamped. There are no simple answers, but the following case study provides valuable guidance.

Buy New or Revamp the Old IT System: A Case Study

As a multispecialty group practice of 27 providers approached its five-year initial implementation of an electronic medical record (EMR) system, the practice administrator realized the initial IT equipment and software investment was nearly paid off, and decisions needed to be made so updates could accommodate the patient care and billing documentation needs.

The outsourced IT management services vendor had become increasingly more expensive despite offering less support, decreased availability, poor service, and slow response time. Server support was declining, hardware needs were increasing as upgrades became necessary, and the outsourced IT manager could not provide software application support. The physician group agreed to begin a search for new IT services and possibly an in-house IT manager.

The board of directors created an EMR-IT committee consisting of three champion or superuser physicians, the IT manager, a medical records staff member, the software trainer/application specialist, and the practice administrator. The committee was charged to create a project proposal for the following:

- Improvements for optimal software stability and performance with the current EMR environment;

- Improved IT management and support services;

- A detailed plan for modernization, including virtualization (creating a virtual version of the server platform and operations system in which servers would be consolidated to a smaller environment with redundancy built in);

- Confirmed security of the current network infrastructure; and

- A comprehensive ROI analysis including a forecast of long-term budget adjustments.

The committee actions included:

- Conducting committee meetings and extensive research for IT management;

- Interviewing and selecting an outsourced IT senior engineering consultant firm;

- Reviewing of EMR vendor options;

- Conducting site visits for alternative considerations of local data centers for hosting the computer system and servers and managing telecom vendor services; and

- Interviewing other providers using software as a service (SaaS) models in which the software application is hosted centrally and is accessed by users with a "thin client" in which data is shared with a common server.

The committee decided that a critical review and analysis of the current network infrastructure was warranted, with the stability and high-performance needs of the software application servers having equal importance. The current servers were approaching obsolescence and needed upgrades, maintenance, and license renewals.

The committee started with a review of the current data center and the consideration of a location change. A review of the expenses associated with the current lease was completed and demonstrated that by moving to an off-site data center, as well as the virtualization of the current server environment, significant cost savings would be achieved. This would also decrease the need for the numerous hours of IT support and maintenance. After meetings were held with the building landlord, a loss would be realized if a move was made because of the sunk costs of a recently purchased, expensive high-end gas generator and an upgraded air conditioning unit.

In revealing that the current outsourced IT management vendor had failed to provide service, support, and adequate security precautions, the committee recommended that the board of directors consider other contracted IT vendors as an option for ongoing management needs.

The committee requested IT management for references confirming the vendors' previous experience with server migrations. The board of directors approved recommendation of a six-month retainer that included 20 IT consulting hours per week with a senior technician.

The contract also included a complete analysis and presentation of a remediation plan. During the initial work phase with the consulting firm, the committee agreed to move forward with the search for and selection of an in-house IT manager. This manager would be a technician who could troubleshoot hardware, servers, and software applications. The consultant provided guidance to administration for bringing the new manager on board and training. After a three-month interview process, a candidate was approved by the board of directors. The new IT manager began with a three-week orientation.

Together, the consultant and new IT manager:

- Completed a full analysis of the current infrastructure;

- Developed a schematic drawing illustrating the current network functionality; and

- Developed a security and privacy gap analysis including system passwords and security updates.

A complete analysis and remediation plan clearly identified the current data communications connectivity as the primary source of performance and stability issues with the EMR application. The recommendation to the committee was moving to a SaaS hosted server environment, specifically hosted by the EMR vendor.

The board of directors asked the committee to research other cost-effective EMR vendors that might be adaptable to the current hardware infrastructure and eliminate increased expenses of creating a new server environment. However, the group was not in favor of changing EMR vendors and refused to consider this alternative. The board did vote to move the EMR application to an alternative hosting solution.

After research and contractual discussions with the EMR vendor, the SaaS model proved the best opportunity for significant performance and stability improvements, such as increased speed, interface functionality, and smooth daily workflow for review of patient documents. A pro forma was developed and illustrated not only cost savings from a server standpoint but also for support and maintenance expenses. The vendor SaaS model was also found to provide better customer service to the physicians and, more importantly, better end-user acceptance.

The committee and board of directors agreed that the expected project outcomes produced positive results including:

- EMR server performance and stability;

- Security and privacy compliance developed and implemented through new documentation, ongoing updates, and training modules for staff; and

- Better forecasting of IT needs and department budget savings through new cost-saving procedures, required approval of new expenditures, and adopting company financial awareness where possible.

Positive effects were also reported from personnel regarding workloads and process workflow as the new IT manager took on the responsibility for the department. Additionally, significant financial improvements were reported because of the close monitoring and new cost-saving protocols. Physicians and staff began to have a sense of relief knowing there was an internal IT staff member to troubleshoot daily issues that normally would have gone through a tedious ticketing system with an external IT vendor that incurred more expense each time an issue, big or small, was reported.

EXHIBIT 6.1

Categories and Examples of Tools for IT Projects

Initial Planning	Business Analysis	Project Management
■ Idea generation techniques (i.e., brainstorming)	■ Cost-benefit analysis	■ Budgets
■ Team design	■ Prioritization matrices	■ Time lines
■ Communication structure	■ Critical-path analysis	■ Variance analysis
■ Evaluation criteria	■ Feasibility analysis	■ Training programs
	■ Process-capability analysis	■ Evaluation criteria

⣿ Planning for Implementation and Process Changes

Standard planning, decision making, and project management tools can be used to evaluate and determine the proper components of the new IT program. These tools can be broken down into three areas, as summarized in Exhibit 6.1.

The first group, initial planning tools, assists in organizing and initiating the process. Team design and development methods taken from standard total quality management systems will jumpstart the process. Basic communications systems for the team should be established. A strategic management review should be undertaken early in the process, examining the practice's mission, vision, goals, and objectives.

The second group, business analysis tools, should be employed once fundamental information is collected. These tools include cost-benefit analysis, systems prioritization, and critical-path analysis for implementation time frames.

Finally, project management systems will help with the actual implementation once the key systems decisions are made. The team should agree on metrics that will assess the success of the implementation and the ultimate success of the IT programs.

Assessing Readiness for Change

Resistance to change is an ever-present problem when planning modifications to IT systems. Staff and clinicians alike are often comfortable with existing systems. They may worry about the time and energy required to learn new systems and processes, despite their awareness of the potential for improved efficiency and outcomes.

Informal discussions with staff can provide insight into the existence or extent of their anxiety about changes in technology. Resistance should be met with open, clear communications about the planned changes. The level and intensity of these communications should be determined by the level of resistance encountered.

Before the process is started, everyone should understand the personnel requirements necessary to plan and implement the changes. The staff and clinicians affected by the changes should understand the required efforts and tasks and should be comfortable about their capabilities to perform those requirements. If there is a deficiency in the capabilities of the existing staff, outside consultants or support may be necessary.

Facilitating Information System Procurement and Installation

Purchasing and installing an IT system is not a simple matter of calling up a vendor and placing an order. It requires research, involvement from outsiders and staff members, and extensive planning to be successful.

Selecting an Information Technology Solution

Because selecting and purchasing an IT solution is a major decision, it should unquestionably be based on careful planning and evaluation. The first step is to identify a relatively large group of potential vendors who offer the applications or services the practice is seeking to acquire. Information is typically gathered from a variety of sources, including print and online media, direct sales marketing, and personal recommendations.

Establishing a Selection Committee

The selection and final purchasing decision for an IT solution should not be made by an individual, not even if that person is the medical practice executive. Instead, the selection should be made by a committee comprised of end users of various aspects of the proposed system, the medical practice executive, physician leaders, and representative staff. This selection committee will assist with the following aspects of the selection process:

- Identifying vendors;
- Categorizing vendors;
- Developing the request for information (RFI);
- Assessing RFI responses;
- Developing the comparison matrix;
- Developing the request for proposal (RFP);
- Assessing RFP responses;
- Collecting information from references;
- Making site visits to vendor clients; and
- Selecting the finalist.

Most RFPs are similar and you can use the template shown in Exhibit 6.2 to develop yours.

Evaluating Vendor Proposals

Vendors are not in business to tell you the truth or save you money. They are in business to sell you products and services by making theirs look superior to those of their competitors. Even if you have established good relationships with one or more IT vendors, it pays to comparison shop when planning every IT-related purchase for your group. Even small purchases can have negative ramifications down the road if they do not work as advertised or do not integrate well with the group's future IT infrastructure.

Trade shows are a terrific way to compare a large number of vendors in a short period of time, making quick comparisons of major product attributes. Other useful sources of information are trade publications (printed or on the Web), promotional materials received through direct marketing, and resources provided through MGMA forums.

Once an acceptable number of prospective vendors is identified, the list must be refined into a useful tool to guide the investigation. Categorizing the vendors in a logical framework facilitates comparison on key variables. Categories may include portal type, market niche served, specific functionality requirements, or some other grouping that

EXHIBIT 6.2
Example Request for Proposal (RFP) for EHR

1. Purpose of RFP
2. Timeline for key steps in the selection process
   a. Issue RFP
   b. Dates for site visit, interview, demonstrations at your location
   c. Proposal due date
   d. Target selection completion date
3. Contact information
4. Number of copies and delivery location, plus information on whether submissions should be paper or electronic
5. Format and guidelines for the proposal to be addressed by the vendor
   a. Vendor capabilities for your specific functional requirements
   b. Company (vendor's) information
      i. Financial information
      ii. Background
      iii. Commitment to the proposed application
      iv. Customer references
   c. Technical and cost information instructions
   d. Your terms and conditions

is meaningful to the practice. Sorting the vendors into categories helps target those offering key products and services under consideration and shows where more information about their products and services is needed. Focus on eliminating as many vendors as possible from consideration at this point, as it will reduce your workload going forward.

The vendors remaining on this initial list should be sent an RFI. The RFI collects a standard set of information on each vendor to enable comparison on similar products. Amatayakul recommends a two- to three-page set of questions in the following areas:[11]

- **Company background.** Information on the vendor's size and financial stability;

- **Product information.** Product name, primary market, technical platform, and overview of product capabilities (later, this will be matched with key functionality criteria);

- **Market information.** Vendor identification of its major competitors and explanation of how it differs from the competitors;

- **Installed base and clients.** Number of product sales, number of projects in implementation, and number of full installations; and

- **Special criteria.** Unique features or functions desired by the practice.

As responses to the RFI are received, an information base helps to analyze the vendors on important company characteristics and product functionality. A commonly employed method is to create a comparison matrix, which can be easily constructed in a spreadsheet. This allows easy visual comparison of the data obtained, and the spreadsheet works well to apply a ranking scheme. The Better Business Bureau can also supply information on any complaints filed concerning particular vendors. Thorough review of the data supplied in response to the RFI and analysis of the extracted data in the comparison matrix helps to narrow the number of vendors to a short list.

The committee now seriously investigates the vendors on the short list. Additional, and more-detailed, information is required to make a final choice.

The next step is to submit an RFP to the short-list vendors. The RFP specifies all the system requirements defined by the practice and solicits a detailed, official proposal from each vendor. The format and content of an RFP varies across organizations, but most RFPs and vendor proposals include the information categories shown in Exhibit 6.3.

As responses arrive, the medical practice executive should review the proposals, again using a comparison matrix, and identify the most qualified vendors. The executive should take this opportunity to sell or report back to physician leadership. The physicians are often the owners of a medical practice, and any venture into a new system should be portrayed in a positive light as an investment.

EXHIBIT 6.3

Request for Proposal and Vendor Proposal Content

Category	Request for Proposal	Expected Proposal Content
Selection Criteria	This section should explain to potential vendors the criteria that will be used in the practice's evaluation process.	The vendor should know and acknowledge the most important elements affecting the purchase decision and how the various rating criteria will be weighted.
Practice Profile	The RFP should contain a description of the practice, including its basic demographics, mission, goals, organizational structure, services provided, and current information infrastructure. In addition, activity information, such as number of patients seen per day, number of modalities performed, number of employees, number of physicians, and number of departments expected to use the application, may also be provided.	This information helps the vendor understand the purpose, size, and complexity of the practice as well as the type of activity and volume of transactions the application will be expected to handle. The vendor's response should address these capabilities.
Specific Platform	The RFP must specify the functional and technical requirements for the proposed system. Any specific features or functionality must be described.	The vendor's response should indicate whether its product currently has the listed function/feature or whether the feature is planned for development. The vendor should describe the technical environment (hardware, network, software) required for its application to operate effectively and efficiently.
Price Range	The RFP should request quotes of one-time cost estimates as well as recurring costs for system maintenance.	The vendor's response should provide the cost of implementing its proposed technology solution to meet the specified functional and technical requirements.
Delivery Timeline	The RFP should describe the vendor's expected deliverables and state the practice's desired timeline for various aspects of project implementation and completion.	The vendor should respond with specific, accurate feedback about its ability to comply with the timeline.

continued on next page

EXHIBIT 6.3   (continued)

Request for Proposal and Vendor Proposal Content

Category	Request for Proposal	Expected Proposal Content
Ongoing Service	The RFP should outline the practice's system maintenance expectations.	The vendor's response should describe maintenance plans and options available to the organization.
References/ Portfolio	The RFP should request a list of references from other clients similar to the practice in size and type, and clients that implemented the products under consideration.	The vendor should provide a list of clients that may be contacted for interviews and on-site demonstrations of the implemented product under consideration.
Other Criteria	The practice should require the vendor to outline training and support policies and procedures.	The vendor may have specific training and support plans that apply to its products. All training and support should be mapped out, as well as any additional training and support that may need to be purchased separately.

As qualified vendors are identified, the selection committee should contact the references listed by the vendor. In addition to discussing general pros and cons of the application and the vendor, the following factors should be discussed with reference clients:

- Overall quality and reliability of the product;
- Product performance under operating conditions;
- Quality of after-sale service and support;
- Trustworthiness of vendor and its sales representatives;
- Ease of doing business with the vendor; and
- Openness of future strategies and plans.

The complexity of the RFP responses may make evaluation impossible without a visit to a client site where the application is used. The site visit serves as an opportunity to discuss the pros and cons of the application and the other issues as previously identified and provides a chance to view a live demonstration of the application.

Just as with the RFI, creating a spreadsheet matrix of all items in the RFP as well as information gathered from references can greatly assist with the final evaluation and selection. A rating or ranking scheme should be applied to the selection factors, with system functionality, overall quality of the technology, sale and maintenance price, and customer support services typically given higher weights. After a weight is established for each criterion, the selection committee should rate each vendor on all criteria. When the individual scores are added, the vendor with the highest total points is typically chosen for contract negotiations. Sometimes make-or-break factors are identified early in the process to eliminate vendors that cannot provide an essential service.

Negotiating Vendor Contracts

Contract negotiation begins with incorporating content from the RFP and the vendor's proposal into the vendor's standard contract template. The contract should clearly define performance expectations and include penalties if requirements are not met. The medical practice executive should give special attention to the schedule, budget, responsibility for system support, support response times, and upgrades. The practice manager should ensure that all payments to the vendor are tied to completion of milestones and acceptance of deliverables. The Healthcare Financial Management Association has compiled a guide to IT contract negotiation that identifies the 10 critical components shown in Exhibit 6.4.[12]

::: Developing and Implementing Information System Training and Support Programs

One of the most important factors in creating any type of training or employee development program is determining explicitly what training is required. This premise is as important in designing training programs for information systems applications as it is for other skill-based activities in the medical practice. Early in the planning process, the practice manager should establish the expected learning outcomes, meaning the knowledge and skills that are expected to exist at the conclusion of the training.

EXHIBIT 6.4

Recommended Components of IT Contract Negotiation

1. Product definition and contract structure;
2. Scope of license;
3. Pricing structure;
4. Implementation;
5. Key personnel;
6. Acceptance testing and payment;
7. Performance warranties;
8. Limitations on liability;
9. Change in vendor control and product obsolescence; and
10. Dispute resolution and exit strategies.

As an immediate follow-up, the manager should determine the staff's existing knowledge and skill levels. Simplistically, the gap between what is already known and what should be known determines the content of the training program. Realistically, though, not all individuals are at the same beginning skill level, and not all individuals will achieve the same outcome skill level. Therein lies the challenge, which is how to design (or purchase) effective training programs that meet the diverse needs of the staff and are also efficient and cost effective from a business standpoint.

The key is establishing evaluation criteria based on recognized characteristics of good training and education programs. These criteria can be used to evaluate purchased training services or to serve as guidelines for developing in-house efforts. In general, good training programs are:

- Designed with clearly established and clearly communicated outcome goals;

- Delivered in an efficient manner that draws from and builds on the staff's existing knowledge; and

- Structured to develop knowledge and skills that have immediate utility for the learner.

Assessing Staff Training Needs

The manager should consider several factors in planning training for a new system implementation or system upgrade. Business staff and clinical staff in the practice use different aspects of the information system's functionality, so training needs should be assessed separately for each group.

Surveys are a good way to collect data about the staff's current knowledge and preferences for training programs. Based on staff size and the amount of information needed, the survey may be as formal as a written document to be completed and returned to the medical practice executive or as informal as an e-mail message with a few questions sent to all staff members.

Selecting Training Approaches

Any type of learning is achieved primarily through five generic approaches: reading, hearing, seeing, saying, and doing. Training activities that use more than one of these methods produce better learning and retention than single-method approaches. Most people, however, learn more by doing. Exercises in which staff members practice the new skills and apply what they are learning in different situations are key to effective learning.

Characteristics of Adult Learners

It is important to consider personal characteristics associated with working adults when assessing training preferences. For example, most adults prefer *task-* or *problem-centered training*. This means that the more a learning activity simulates a real problem encountered in a job, the more likely the staff will learn the underlying facts or concepts associated with a correct action or solution. Working adults also tend to be more enthusiastic about training and education that is relevant to their current job tasks.

The learn-by-doing principle is applied in most on-the-job training for staff development by using one of four broad categories of approaches:

1. Lecture and/or demonstration to a group;

2. Self-learning with print materials;

3. Technology-assisted learning; or

4. One-on-one training with a facilitator.

Train All or Train-the-Trainer

The medical practice executive should consider whether all staff members need training and if they require the same training, understanding that training needs often vary by job position.

In some instances it is best to select one or a few individuals who can learn the required skills relatively quickly because of their existing knowledge base or aptitude for information management technology. These individuals may receive broad-based training (from the vendor or through self-instruction) and then provide more personalized instruction to practice staff who need skill only in a specific system functionality.

This train-the-trainer approach can be an efficient and cost-effective way to provide differing levels of instruction to staff members with diverse job requirements related to the information system and its various applications. Some staff members are more comfortable learning from coworkers than from professional trainers. This approach is particularly suitable for those who prefer just-in-time and just-enough training.

On-Site vs. Off-Site Training

A final factor to consider in selecting the training approach is determining whether training should occur on or off site. Although the key points to consider are relatively simple, the answers may not lead to a clear decision. These key points are:

- Whether training on site will disrupt practice operations;
- Whether staff members will have adequate job downtime to concentrate on training as needed;
- Whether staff members can be relieved of job duties to go off site;
- How important it is for staff members to apply the training in the operating environment to maximize its utility; and
- Whether training on the new system can occur concurrently with implementation.

Time Analysis

The medical practice executive should determine the time required to complete training for all affected staff, being as realistic as possible.

Creating a work schedule that maximizes staff productivity is a daunting challenge. Establishing a training schedule that doesn't adversely affect the work schedule is even harder. Nevertheless, it is important that all staff members who are expected to use the information system receive training to use it correctly and efficiently. Inadequate training can result in work process inefficiency and costly (and sometimes dangerous) errors, as well as staff frustration and dissatisfaction. Staff members may perceive the system as too difficult and seek ways to avoid using it.

The medical practice executive should establish a schedule that provides training first to staff members in key positions, that is, those individuals whose use of the information system is critical to business and clinical operations. Allow adequate time for key staff to master the required skills before training the next level of information system users. The schedule should also include makeup options. For example, if training occurs on site during operating hours, the demands of the work environment may require staff members to abort training sessions to deal with pressing business or clinical matters.

Retraining needs should be considered as well. Few people can master difficult skills or change existing procedures in one session. It is usually a good plan to provide instruction, spend some time using the application, and return to the training mode to respond to questions or to verify that learning has been sufficient.

Cost Analysis

The training budget is an important element of the overall cost-benefit analysis for system implementation. The medical practice executive should investigate several cost factors for the analysis. Key factors include trainer costs, personnel costs, equipment and training materials, and various miscellaneous (usually hidden) costs.

Training by vendor personnel may be included in the purchase price of the information system or it may be an add-on option that is priced separately. The medical practice executive, who may be very familiar with the system through the selection process, may underestimate the amount of training required for staff with no previous orientation to the system. In some cases, the training price may seem high relative to the expected amount of training required, and the practice manager may misjudge the cost-benefit of training to the bottom-line value of the system.

The medical practice executive should realistically evaluate the cost of purchasing training against the difficulty staff may have in migrating to the new application(s) without training, as well as the effect a long self-learning curve may have on system implementation. A system that cannot be used efficiently or that requires a long phase-in period while staff members learn its functionality may be more costly than the price of training.

Employees should be compensated directly for the time spent in training. Lost productive time while staff members are in the training sessions, however, is often an unforeseen and sometimes surprisingly large cost. As noted previously, the productivity issue may be a consideration in deciding when and where training will occur. In some cases, such as a limited system upgrade, staff members may be trained effectively while continuing to do their daily jobs. In other cases, staff members should not reasonably be expected to work and train concurrently; one or both of the expected outcomes — production or learning — will be less than satisfactory.

Unless all training equipment is provided by the trainer, those costs should be determined as specifically as possible. Room rentals and projection equipment can add several hundred dollars per day of training to the budget. The medical practice executive must understand how costs are affected by where training occurs and the practice's responsibility for bearing those costs.

Although training materials are generally prepared by the trainer, and the cost of the materials is usually included in the training fee, the medical practice executive should question whether all materials will be provided and in what format. For example, help manuals and other learning resources provided electronically may need reproduction into a hard copy for efficient use, which can add significant hidden costs.

Miscellaneous costs are more difficult to anticipate and quantify. Talking with colleagues who have been burned by unplanned costs may be the most useful source for this type of information. In the final analysis, some costs will remain unknown and perhaps unknowable. Each budgeting process is a learning experience that informs the next process.

Evaluation of Instruction and Learning

Evaluating the effectiveness of training programs is generally the responsibility of the medical practice executive. Unfortunately, this crucial task is not often undertaken; some authors estimate that fewer than 10 percent of staff education programs are evaluated adequately.[13]

The medical practice executive should establish the criteria for evaluating the training programs in the early stages of planning the program. In general, these should include outcome measures for effectiveness, efficiency, and cost. When considered in the aggregate, these measures help in assessing the value of the training program to the practice.

Regarding effectiveness, the primary focus is whether the desired learning occurred; that is, do staff members now have the desired knowledge and skills initially established as outcome goals for the training program?

Efficiency measures determine whether the learning occurred with expenditure of reasonable or acceptable resources, primarily considering resources associated with time and operational impact. Questions to answer include:

- Was the training period within the estimated time line?

- How many worker hours were allocated to training?

- What was the overall effect on productive staff time?

- Was operating revenue lost because of training time?

- Were projections appropriate, or were variances significant?

Although the cost of training certainly is important, focus on assessing actual costs relative to budgeted costs. Your choices of training options were based in part on the expected cost of those options, but would those same choices have been made if the true costs had been known? Investigate each budget variance to determine the underlying cause. Was the variance caused by cost items not anticipated and planned for? Was the variance caused by errors in estimation within cost categories? Cost analysis should be viewed as a learning process rather than a punitive exercise, and knowledge gained through this analytical method informs the choices made in future processes.

Providing Access to Electronic Education and Information Resources and Systems

Today's healthcare workforce has access to more opportunities for professional development and continuing education than can be cataloged.

High-quality programs are available on almost any topic of interest, and many programs are available in electronic formats that are accessible at the worker's convenience. The savvy medical practice executive determines what technology-based training solutions provide the greatest value to clinicians, to operating staff, and, in the long run, to the practice.

Resource Options

Available education resources are numerous, have a wide range of costs (financial increased worker time), and are highly variable in their utility and quality. Managers planning for the education and professional development needs of the practice should draw from a variety of sources, but may rely primarily on a few tried-and-true known sponsors. Representative categories of education sponsors include professional associations, proprietary organizations, and academic institutions. Perhaps most well-known to the medical practice executive is MGMA.

Medical Group Management Association Knowledge Base

MGMA offers a large volume of educational and practice resources of benefit to practice managers, clinicians, and business staff. A very real benefit of offerings from MGMA is that the context and content of its programs and other resource media is relevant to clinical practice and operations.

In addition to face-to-face conferences and seminars, MGMA offerings include technology-based resources such as Webcasts, audio conferences, and online study options. The MGMA menu of training options offers selections to meet most specific requirements for content, access, or cost. The MGMA Website stores an extensive collection of practice-related articles and guidelines available as a member service.

Web-Based Education

The ubiquity, low cost of entry, and data delivery qualities of the Internet set the stage for an explosion of virtual businesses, including many education and training companies. Established businesses and academic institutions exploit the Internet's opportunities as well. Judicious evaluation of these opportunities can yield training to meet specific needs while avoiding travel costs and reducing lost work time.

The key point lies in establishing criteria for evaluating training and education options available. These criteria would typically be some variation on the "cost, access, quality" themes.

Cost comparisons of a given program within an existing training budget are relatively simple. The difficulty here lies in initially setting the training budget.

The convenience of access to online training is frequently a strong selling point. Time or day availability restrictions may be important criteria. The length of the training program and the number of staff members involved are likely relevant factors as well.

By far the most difficult to evaluate prospectively is the quality of an educational offering, online or otherwise. Because the actual content is not available for preview, proxy measures must be used for judgment. The most commonly used proxy criteria include the reputation and credibility of the sponsoring organization, the name recognition of the faculty as experts in the field, and recommendations by colleagues. If information about any of these points is unavailable or insufficient, the fallback approach is to examine the promotional materials for answers to some key questions, such as:

- Are meaningful learning objectives specified?
- Do the objectives fit with the practice's expectations and desires?
- Do the objectives promise the skill level needed, or are they too basic or too advanced?
- Will additional resources, such as print materials or application models, be provided?
- Has the program been approved for continuing education credit by professional societies?
- Is the cost acceptable compared to other training options?

Equipment, Software, and Media Options

Most medical practices have in place at least minimal computer and technology resources that can be used to deliver or access education and professional development opportunities. This section presents a brief overview of the most commonly used technologies for on-the-job training and professional development.

Most office workstations now consist of a PC with various peripheral devices and applications including word processing, spreadsheet, presentation, and database. Workstations may be networked, with some shared applications housed on a server, or stand-alone with all programs resident on the individual processors. Whatever the configuration, PCs used to access online resources must have adequate processing speed and sufficient memory to manage multimedia files in real time.

By far the larger market for audio and video training materials in portable format is that of the CD or DVD. Newer PCs, including notebooks, have CD-DVD drives that read and write as standard features.

Streaming audio and video over the Internet is commonly used in education programs. The caveat for this format is that the speed of the Internet connection is crucial to the quality of the video received. Training via streamed video can take place at the workstation, but productive work cannot be carried out simultaneously.

Interactive media, which require the user to input selections or responses that modify how subsequent information is presented, offer one of the best media choices for learning applications. This technology applies learning principles such as involvement, feedback, and repetition to engage the user in the learning process. Not surprisingly, this approach is also more expensive than most of the other options because of the development cost.

Establishing Practice Priorities and Topics for Training

Building clinical and business skill sets to achieve strategic goals should be the practice's first priority for allocating training and professional development funds. One of the first tasks in the process of establishing professional development plans is reviewing the practice's strategic plan. The medical practice executive should review the strategic objectives established for the next two to three years, paying particular attention to any that require specific key personnel skills to be successful. Training and education funds are generally budgeted for an operating cycle, so the manager should pay particular attention to any skill sets required during or immediately following the budget period.

In addition, the manager should ascertain what expert knowledge or advanced skills personnel must possess to perform their jobs under future conditions as the strategy is implemented. This includes determining the level of knowledge and skills that currently exist and identifying gaps that must be corrected with education and training.

Secondary priorities for education funds for the staff may include training needed to achieve specialty certifications or earn advanced degrees, or other personal education goals that benefit the practice as well as the individual. These choices may be negotiated with individuals as employment benefits during recruitment.

Tertiary funding priorities are those that are of interest to individual staff members but do not have a direct return to the practice. These funds may be allocated as rewards for performance or for other reasons.

Communicating Options to Staff

Clinical and professional staff often have their own professional development agenda, which may or may not coincide with the practice's strategy. Negotiating performance objectives with individual staff members is an ideal context in which to discuss their personal development plans and their future with the practice.

Employees should be involved in decisions about changes to their jobs and any resulting commitments for skills development that will be required, including training options, media, and time allocation. However, the medical practice executive is ultimately responsible for establishing a training plan that will result in the desired learning outcomes without exceeding acceptable cost limits or disrupting business operations.

Providing Support for Education

It is a rare medical practice that can provide full financial and time support for all the educational pursuits of its staff. The direct costs of education can be high, and hidden costs can equal or exceed them. Certainly, the practice should bear the major costs associated with staff development to support strategic goals. Because an enhanced skill set is an asset to the employee as well, sharing education costs may be appropriate in some situations. The extent of support for education should be clearly established and communicated to affected staff.

Some practices allocate financial resources to reimburse staff for tuition, fees, and other expenses associated with earning an academic degree. Although tuition benefits can be an excellent employee recruiting and retention tactic, a formal policy that specifies eligibility guidelines and funding limitations must be in place. Again, these guidelines should be published and communicated to staff.

Scheduling Flexibility

The business and clinical operations of the practice must certainly be protected, but some flexibility in scheduling that allows staff to pursue education and professional development opportunities can generally be accommodated. In some instances when financial support cannot be provided, a time accommodation may be an acceptable, if less desirable, alternative.

Evaluating Results and Providing Feedback

Professional development and education programs follow the same general control model as all management activities: plan, implement, evaluate, and provide feedback of evaluation findings. Use evaluation and feedback to improve future planning and implementation, remembering that it is not a linear activity. Evaluation and feedback should occur continuously at key control points.

The medical practice executive should periodically review the professional development plan to make adjustments required by changes in personnel or learning needs. The training budget should be monitored and variances analyzed routinely with other budget elements. Most important, however, is the need to evaluate the actual learning outcomes achieved.

The manager should meet with employees following training events and ask them to evaluate the experience based on a few key indicators, including:

- The instructor's expertise in the subject;

- How well the program met the stated objectives;

- The knowledge or skill gained as a return on time investment; and

- The knowledge or skill gained as a return on financial investment.

Over time, patterns of responses may emerge that affect the medical practice executive's future choices of training approaches for education vendors.

⠿ Overseeing Database Management and Maintenance

The ultimate purpose of a database management system (DBMS) is to convert large volumes of stored data into actionable information. Medical practice management is full of changes and shifting priorities, so the value of an information management system is tied to the ease with which information can be accessed, manipulated, securely shared, and presented to support decision making.

Most medical practice data, such as patient records, treatment reports, accounting data, schedules, and appointments, are held in some form of database. Some data sets are in relatively simple "flat files," such as spreadsheets, that are easily updated and manipulated and require minimal management. Other databases, such as *relational databases*, comprising multiple tables of data, require more active management. As with most aspects of management, the first step in planning DBMS development is to conduct a needs assessment.

Types of Data

The ultimate purpose of a DBMS in a practice is to transform data into usable information that is translatable into action. Databases allow definition of data types and data formats for the stored information. Each variable in a database is contained in a field. An example of a field is a patient's last name. Databases store entered data in a record. A record is a collection of multiple related data fields, perhaps about a particular patient or inventory item. For example, the fields comprising a patient's complete demographic information or clinical data from an encounter are stored as a record. In the database, records are displayed in an electronic form, where field data may be entered, edited, viewed, and deleted.

Several records with the same related fields of information for entries are referred to as a database table. The data contained in database tables can be presented in a formatted, easy-to-read report. A single report could contain data from many different tables and incorporate a complex set of relationships created by using multiple links within the database.

For example, a table named "patient" will likely contain fields including patient identifiers and encounter information. The best way to form tables is to express relationships between two key variables. A patient may have one or more visits and may be treated by one or more providers during a visit. If the relationships are logical, the next step is to identify attributes associated with patient, provider, and visit. These attributes become fields assigned to the associated table.[14]

Policies and Procedures

The DBMS administrator should work with key clinical and administrative staff to develop policies and procedures ensuring the security and confidentiality of the practice's identifiable health data. Plans, policies, and procedures should be established for the following DBMS issues at a minimum:

- Regular, routine data backup;
- Journal or log for documenting alterations to operational software;
- Formal process for database maintenance by accountable personnel;
- Physical database security;
- User access control and monitoring; and
- Database recovery plan.

⁝⁝ Protecting Patient and Practice Data Systems

Ensuring Network and System Security

The medical practice must ensure that its electronic network and information systems are secure. Any security program in a healthcare organization should have three principal goals:

1. Protecting the informational privacy of patient-related data;
2. Ensuring the integrity of information; and
3. Ensuring the availability of information to the appropriate individuals in a timely manner.

With the adoption of standards for electronic transmission, a HIPAA-specified transaction typically requires the use of an electronic signature, generally defined as the act of attaching an identifying name or code by electronic means. The electronic signature process involves the authentication of the signer's identity, a signature process according to system and software instructions, binding of the signature to the document, and nonalterability after the signature has been affixed to the document. The Department of Health and Human Services (HHS) proposes that a cryptographically based digital signature be adopted as the standard. The same legal weight is associated with a digital signature as with an original signature on a paper document.

Providers who transmit health information electronically in connection with any of the standard transactions just mentioned are required to obtain a National Provider Identifier.

Employers may need to be identified when they transmit information to health plans to enroll or disenroll an employee as a participant. Whenever information about the employer is transmitted electronically, it is beneficial to identify the employer by using a standard identifier. On May 31, 2002, HHS published the Final Rule for Standard Unique Employer Identifiers,[15] which required that the Internal Revenue Service Employer Identification Number be used as the standard identifier of employers in HIPAA-covered transactions.

The HIPAA Privacy Rule established standards for who may have access to PHI and how the information can be used. Key provisions of these standards include:

- Patients' access to their medical records;

- Notification to patients of their providers' privacy practices;

- Limits on how providers may use personal medical information;

- Restrictions and limits on the use of patient information for marketing purposes; and

- Assurance that providers take reasonable steps to make their communications with patients confidential.

The Privacy Rule also requires physicians and their practices to establish policies and procedures to protect the confidentiality of PHI about their patients, including a description of staff members who have access to protected information, how this information will be used, and when it will be disclosed. The rule also requires physician practices to train their employees regarding their privacy procedures and to designate an individual responsible for ensuring that the procedures are followed.

HIPAA requires healthcare employees to use or share only "minimum necessary" information to do their jobs effectively. The minimum necessary requirement does not apply, however, to treatment. Clinical staff can see a patient's entire record and freely share information with other clinicians who care for that patient if necessary.

The HIPAA Security Rule sets the standards for ensuring that only those who should have access to ePHI have access to it. The rule requires a three-pronged strategy: (1) technical safeguards, (2) administrative safeguards, and (3) physical safeguards. Technical safeguards include access controls, audit controls, data integrity controls, authentication, and transmission security. Administrative safeguards include backup plans, disaster recovery plans, an emergency-mode operation plan, and testing and revision procedures. Physical safeguards include facility security, device and media control, and workstation use and security.

Accountability

HIPAA identifies data confidentiality, integrity, availability, and accountability as the primary areas of concern. Access controls are measures to ensure that only authorized personnel have access to a computer or network or to certain applications or data. The most common way to control access is through user identification and strong passwords. Passwords should be at least eight characters in length (longer passphrases are better) and contain a combination of letters (a mix of capital and lowercase), numbers, and special characters (e.g., %, $) . In addition, passwords should be changed routinely every 30 to 60 days. Biometric authentication, such as fingerprint scanning, is increasingly installed in mobile devices but is not widely available and has not been perfected to the point where it is a suitable substitute for strong passwords or passphrases.

To supplement access controls, Johns[16] recommends putting other automatic security functions in place, including:

- Automatically terminating a user's session after a predetermined period of inactivity;
- Routinely logging all transactions automatically, including additions, deletions, or changes to the data;
- Automatically and regularly producing and monitoring audit trails;

- Maintaining current antivirus software on the network and workstation PCs, and routinely scanning for viruses and worms; and

- Immediately revoking access privileges when an employee leaves the organization or is terminated.

Confidentiality of Information

A major purpose of the HIPAA Privacy Rule is to define and limit the circumstances in which an individual's PHI may be used or disclosed. As a rule, the medical practice may not use or disclose PHI except as the Privacy Rule permits or requires or as authorized in writing by the individual who is the subject of the information or the individual's personal representative.

The medical practice must develop and implement policies and procedures for releasing PHI. Procedures must also be established to document the process of restricting access and use of PHI based on employees' specific job roles. These policies and procedures must identify the individuals who need access to PHI to conduct their duties, the categories of PHI to which access is needed, and any conditions under which they need the information to do their jobs.

These policies and procedures should reference state regulations and other federal regulations that govern the disclosure of protected patient information, such as the Confidentiality of Alcohol and Drug Abuse Patient Records Regulation, the Medicare Conditions of Participation, and the Clinical Laboratory Improvement Amendments, if applicable.

System Integrity

System integrity is grounded in protecting the information system and the data it contains against tampering. Unauthorized access is one of the most serious threats to security in any information system. Prevention of unauthorized access relies on a good access control system. Passwords and user identification have been discussed previously as the primary mechanisms for controlling access to the information system and its data by practice staff.

In dealing with unauthorized access to systems over the Internet, the best defense is a firewall, which is special hardware and software that blocks access to computer resources. Firewall software screens the activities of a person who logs on to a Website. The firewall allows retrieval and viewing of certain authorized material but blocks attempts to change the information or to access other resources that reside on the network or computer. The software screens for viruses and for active attempts to invade company resources through open communication lines.

Encryption is another way to limit unauthorized access of confidential information sent over the Web. Encryption scrambles messages at the sending end and descrambles them at the receiving end. Encryption is also used to authenticate the sender or recipient of a message, verifying that the user is indeed the party it claims to be, keeping messages private.

Physician and Staff Responsibilities

Formal confidentiality statements must be signed by all practice staff, including physicians, at least annually. These statements should include language indicating that the signer understands and will adhere to the medical practice's policies and procedures to maintain the security of patient information. Recommendations for content in the confidentiality statement[17] include specifying that practice staff will:

- Not use practice e-mail for personal messages;
- Never open or redistribute attached files from an unknown source;
- Never send confidential patient information in an e-mail unless it is encrypted;
- Always verify the address line of an e-mail before it is sent;
- Never share passwords;
- Never log in to the information system with someone else's password;
- Always keep computer screens pointed away from public view; and
- Never remove computer equipment, disks, or software from the facility without the express permission of the practice manager.

Organizations such as MGMA offer policies manuals that cover these and many other protocols:

- Disaster management;
- Stolen or lost computers or access cards; and
- Personal use of practice-owned equipment.

Conduct in-service education and training annually to reinforce privacy and security issues. Assign one person, potentially the medical practice executive, responsibility for monitoring physician and staff confidentiality and security practices.

Consequences for breaching privacy and ignoring security practices should be explicitly stated and communicated to all staff. Consequences established by the practice should be determined by the severity of the infraction and may range from written warnings to immediate termination. Put these policies in writing, distribute them to all employees, and incorporate them into your training (documenting that you did so).

⁞⁞ Data Backup and Recovery

The failure of data storage systems is not a question of if, but when. As medical practices increasingly adopt EHRs, their leaders must not overlook the protection of valuable data. EHR vendors do not always address data backup and recovery, so it is up to the administrator to explore options. If your group has recently installed an EHR or business office system and you lack a process for data retention and recovery, you risk a crippling blow to your practice.

Backup Tool Features

Evaluate business recovery plans that include the recovery time objective (RTO) and recovery point objective (RPO).

RTO is the acceptable or contracted downtime for a computer system. The cost of EHR systems varies greatly. While some systems may only cost a few hundred dollars per full-time equivalent (FTE) physician, they deliver little more than a medical word processing program compared to full-featured, robust, and integrated front-and-back office systems that cost thousands of dollars per FTE physician. Even these costs vary depending on whether new hardware is required and how software is deployed (as a stand-alone system or licensed as an online application).

Equally important is RPO, the amount of data that can be lost. Essentially, RPO represents the time between the last data backup and a disaster. When setting the backup frequency, physicians and staff members should consider how far back they could remember if they were forced to recreate an EMR. Specialists who see few patients in a day, for example, can make backups less frequently than a specialist who sees dozens of patients a day.

Ideally, practice professionals reach a balance between RTO and RPO. Systems that offer short RTOs and minimal RPOs (including ones that support continual backup) are available, but they cost more.

Weigh different solutions against your group's risk tolerance and budget. When assessing the true cost of EHR, consider data recovery. A system priced at a few thousand dollars might sound like a bargain until it fails and data cannot be restored for weeks.

Data Backup Options

Several options exist for protecting and recovering data, as discussed in the following paragraphs.

Tape backup. External or internal tape drives and magnetic tapes store duplicate disk files. Removable disk drives accomplish the same task. You remove the old tape or drive and install a new one daily. For data storage, experts advise using a secure, off-site location. Depending on the amount of data, daily backups can take anywhere from 25 minutes to four hours. At the same time, RPO can take a full day. A word of caution: If a system fails at the end of your business day, all of the data entered could be lost because backups are usually done after hours.

Image capture. Although more expensive than tapes, this option can have an effective RPO because images are captured more frequently. Like physical tape storage, image archives should be maintained off site for disaster recovery. Images are likely tied to capturing hardware (a device used to create the image), so recovery is easiest when you use the same hardware. To mitigate this issue, use software that allows hardware-independent recovery. However, flexibility and hardware independence usually come at a higher price.

Outsourcing. If your group is small and has few internal IT resources, consider outsourcing data backup and recovery. Vendors usually do backups on a guaranteed schedule that does not interfere with practice operations, and recovery times can be customized. Some companies install hardware at secure locations to ensure maintenance and full backup capability, redundant power sources, and equipment. You can maintain a server and do backups online, or vendors can establish a base at their locations. These vendors often insist on using their equipment. For a list of companies, search "Remote or Managed Backup online" on the Internet.

The downside to outsourcing is increasing costs for data storage (based on the amount of data) and the considerable cost of recovery. While many vendors say you can recover data online, this is not practical beyond a few small files. And to recover an entire system, some companies charge thousands of dollars in fees to ship a hard drive containing your recovered data.

Virtualization. This approach entails operating duplicate servers on a virtual device that includes all system information. This device monitors servers throughout the day and captures images every 15 minutes. As a result, practice professionals have an RPO of 15 minutes and an RTO of less than an hour.

In the event of a disaster, virtual machines take over to minimize data loss and downtime. Users switch to a virtual backup within minutes to ensure that systems and data are operational and switch back to the production server when it is repaired or replaced without any data loss.

Application Service Provider (ASP). Many EHR providers offer their products under this model, which allows practices to license the use of the EHR but not install software on their local servers. Instead, professionals install a small "client" program on their computers.

The ASP maintains software, provides updates and support, stores data at a secure location, and provides full backup services. While the practice must purchase and maintain computers (desktops, laptops, or tablets) to enter data and must have a reliable and fast Internet connection to enter and access data, this option, if available, offers several advantages for backup and sustainability of the practice's data in the event of a disaster.

While there is a monthly fee, this option offers a viable option for professionals who are considering EHR adoption or are replacing a server.

Steps to Getting the Right EHR Protection for Your Organization

Computers play a crucial role in medical practice operations. That role will only grow with the expansion of EHR systems, which heighten the importance of data security and integrity. To get the right protection, here are a few suggestions:

- Hold frank discussions with physician users to determine comfort levels with system downtime (RTO) and how much data loss is tolerable;

- Learn how much physician users are willing to pay for data security;

- Decide whether to keep data recovery in-house or contract with a service; and

- Write a plan for disaster prevention and recovery, and test it annually.

Understanding Cloud-Based Storage

Cloud-based technology is becoming a more readily available option for practices deciding where to store their patients' health information. Cloud storage involves storing data (patient, clinical, and financial data in the case of medical practices) in a virtual storage pool, which is typically hosted by a vendor. Some MGMA members report that cloud-based technology can increase application usability and improve data accessibility and flexibility, all while providing seamless integration between multiple practice sites.

Leveraging the cloud can also ensure that all users have the most up-to-date versions of an application and provide notification for different users in a practice, whether they're in the same clinic or scattered across a city.

With growing concern regarding practices maintaining confidentiality, cloud-based systems offer significant privacy and security protections when configured appropriately. Practices, however, must take the proper precautions as cloud-based technologies, like any other, can be susceptible to specific vulnerabilities (including data breaches), which can lead to HIPAA violations.

Should you switch to a cloud-based EHR? Here are some considerations to help you make the best decision for your practice and patients.

Cost. Cloud-based systems can be cheaper than stand-alone software programs. Many cloud-based vendors offer subscription fees to the service, usually on a monthly basis. Paying the fee allows the practice to access the records just with a computer and Internet connection; no other hardware or servers are needed. Unlike a standard equipment purchase or lease, the upfront cost is very low.

Seamless updates. With cloud-based storage there is no downtime from systems having to upload applications and interfaces. Cloud-based systems usually update and back up automatically. This means every user in your practice will have the same software version and will be working with the same information and data.

Disaster recovery. Cloud-based storage plans often offer less expensive disaster recovery solutions compared to other options. If the practice has a fast Internet connection, it can download data from the cloud, and most plans support versioning so you can revert to an earlier version of a file if the newer one becomes corrupted. In the event of a total disaster, most cloud-based storage plans will mail a hard drive containing all of your data for a few hundred dollars.

Ensure maximum performance of your cloud-based system by keeping your hardware and cloud interface up to date and maintaining a robust Internet connection. Some cloud-based systems require you to purchase privacy protections or to provide them yourself, usually through another vendor. If you're not confident in your interface system or network connection, consider upgrading them or using a software-based program instead of a cloud-based program.

Contracts must be crafted and read carefully. As with any vendor agreement, cloud-based storage contracts come with their own set of potential pitfalls. You will want to make sure you are clearly outlining how long you will have access to the data you're uploading, how that data is secured, how often the data is backed up, and how frequently cloud applications are updated.

⁞ Conclusion

Leveraging the power of technology is a cornerstone of effective medical practice management. Key skills in this area include identifying technological opportunities tied to business goals, obtaining and implementing particular technology systems, safeguarding the integrity of systems and data, and mitigating risk to technology in the event of disaster. The medical practice administrator exercises considerable leadership in the realm of technology management for the successful practice.

Notes

1. S. Cohen, "Emerging Benefits of Integrated IT Systems," *Healthcare Executive* 20, no. 5 (2005): 14–18.

2. E.L. May, "The Transformational Power of IT: Experience from Patient Safety Leaders," *Healthcare Executive* 20, no. 5 (2005): 8–13.

3. D. Scalise, "Where the Patient and Technology Meet," *Hospital & Health Networks* 79, no. 8 (2005): 34–42.

4. T. Moore and S. Roberts, "Worlds Collide: A Look at Wireless Systems Convergence in Health Care Facilities," *Health Facilities Management* 18, no. 8 (2005): 31–34.

5. C. Pope, "The Hereafter: Why IT Security Matters to Your Practice Even After the HIPAA Security Rule Deadline," *MGMA Connexion* 5, no. 6 (2005): 36–41.

6. Pope, "The Hereafter."

7. U.S. Department of Health and Human Services, "Data Breach Results in $4.8 Million HIPAA Settlements," press release, www.hhs.gov/news/press/2014pres/05/20140507b.html.

8. Mary Mourar, Derek Kosiorek, Cynthia Dunn, and Rosemarie Neslons, *EHR Optimization and Operations Guide for Medical Practices* (Englewood, CO: Medical Group Management Association, 2012).

9. Donna Daniel and Patricia Lohman, "Think Lean: Redesign Workflow to Adopt EHR," *MGMA Connexion* 7, no. 1 (2007): 17–18.

10. Mary Mourar, *Experts Answer 95 New Practice Management Questions* (Englewood, CO: Medical Group Management Association, 2012).

11. M.K. Amatayakul, *Electronic Health Records: A Practical Guide for Professionals and Organizations*, 2nd ed. (Chicago: American Health Information Management Association, 2004).

12. Healthcare Financial Management Association, *Dotting the i's and Crossing the t's: Ensuring the Best IT Contract* [promotional material] (2004).

13. R.J. Wager and R. Weigand, "Measuring the Organizational Impact of Training Programs," in *Guide to Effective Staff Development in Health Care Organizations: A Systems Approach to Successful Training*, ed. Patrice Spath (San Francisco: Jossey-Bass, 2002), 113–125.

14. D.T. Mon, "Relational Database Management: What You Need to Know," *Journal of AHIMA* 74, no. 10 (2003): 40–45.

15. Department of Health and Human Services, 45 C.F.R. pt. 162, HIPAA Administrative Simplification: Standard Unique Health Identifier for Health Care Providers; Final Rule, *Fed. Reg.* (May 31, 2002), 3433–3469.

16. M.L. Johns, *Information Management for Health Professions*, 2nd ed. (Albany, NY: Delmar/Thomson Learning, 2002).

17. HCPro, *Preserving Privacy and Security: HIPAA Training Handbook for Healthcare Organizations* (Marblehead, MA: Healthcare Compliance Company, 2004).

Chapter 7

Marketing, Communications, and Public Relations

MARKETING FOR A MEDICAL PRACTICE involves activities associated with identifying patient needs and satisfying those needs as well as possible, given the personal health concerns of the individual patient. Typical marketing tasks may include market research, patient needs analysis, strategic decision making about service design, and promotion of the practice. These marketing tasks can be best accomplished when analyzed through the four A's of marketing for medical practices: access, availability, accountability, and accommodation.[1] Keeping patients at the forefront of your marketing plan will ensure that a practice's services best match their needs and expectations.

Key competencies aligned with effective marketing management in a medical practice include: understanding the local market and community resources, developing a marketing plan, applying aspects of the plan to establish a corporate image, using public relations to promote the practice, and collaborating with community organizations to foster patient health.

::: Marketing Basics

The best service is of little value until someone knows it exists and wants to buy it. If you are in an area desperate for physicians, intensive marketing may be unnecessary; if the field is crowded, you may need to do more. In either case, a solid public image and name recognition are an important start.

Naming Your Practice

Your business's name is often the first thing potential patients encounter. Many practices make mistakes in this area, and starting over is difficult and expensive.

Your practice name should be brief, geographically descriptive (if possible), easy to remember, and easy to fit onto a Web page and on signs and stationery. A simple test is whether the receptionist can say the practice name in a pleasant voice so the patients can understand the name. Before you make an announcement and print materials with the letterhead, your lawyer must check to be certain your chosen name is available for use.

Geographical Association

Bear in mind that geographical identification is fine if it is not overused. Avoid geographical names that are too broad to be helpful, such as "Denver Family Practice." Similarly, avoid names that are too specific, such as "Broadway Avenue Family Practice," in case the practice moves in the future.

Using Physician Names

Using names of physicians is acceptable, especially if some of the physicians have excellent reputations or are eminent in their field. Avoid creating a practice name that is too long, however, such as "Drs. Jones, Smith, Brown, Sharpe, Reeves, and Elway, Family Practice, LLC."

When considering using physician names, think about what the plan is. When additional physicians join the practice, will you add their names to the practice name? Also, keep in mind that a physician's retirement will likely require the practice's name to change. Unlike law and accounting firms, retired or deceased physicians generally are not included in practice names.

Logos and Signage

As soon as possible, decide if the practice needs a logo. If so, have it prepared early so you can use it on everything. You should adopt a color scheme, type font, and general graphic design so everything you do has a consistent, professional look.

Signage for medical practices is often insufficient, both outside and sometimes inside the building. Your patients and families should not have to struggle to find your building, yet your lease may contain signage regulations that restrict you from positioning some useful signs. Also, be aware of local sign ordinances, as some are particularly detailed.

If you locate in an out-of-the-way location or in the back of a development, you may need additional directional signage. The bigger your draw area, the better signage you need. If you deal with a significant geriatric population, design your signs for patients with diminished sight.

Branding

When you think of your practice's brand, what do you think of? Do you consider it to be the sign in front of your building or your Website? Those are important, but a brand is more than that.

The Medical Group Management Association® (MGMA®) changed its brand to focus on advancing medical practices to prepare them for the shift toward patient-centered coordinated care, long-term financial stability, increased clinician-administrator teamwork, better patient outcomes, and new payment models. The new brand is what MGMA members want MGMA to be. The goals are to:

- Foster partnerships between practice management professionals and their doctors that result in the highest-quality patient care;

- Equip members with the tools needed to drive excellence in their practices; and

- Drive dialogue in the practice management community to address the most pressing issues that could affect the success of medical group practices.

To fulfill its new brand aspirations, MGMA is focused on creating experiences that live up to its members' needs. Knowing what those experiences entail comes from gathering feedback from members on what their current experience is and what they want from MGMA in the future. Medical practices are encouraged to do the same.

Expectation + Interaction = Experience

A brand is a person's feeling about a product, service, or organization, and it comes from his or her experience with you. Learning about your patients' experiences means understanding whether they feel good, bad, or indifferent about your practice. Many practices might already know about their patients' experiences from patient satisfaction surveys or other forms of feedback, but learning about your patients' current experience and what experience they want to have with your practice is the first step in establishing your practice's brand.

⋮⋮⋮ Public Relations

Some years ago, aggressive advertising and public relations (PR) campaigns were considered unprofessional and undignified. Those days are gone. Dignified, professional advertising and targeted PR are important for three phases of group operation:

1. Start-up;

2. Ongoing practice; and

3. When new practitioners and/or new services are added.

Tips for Start-up Public Relations

At the start-up of a new practice or merger, a careful, organized marketing and PR campaign should be conducted. The campaign should emphasize "who/what/when/where" by identifying the following:

- Name of the entity;

- Formation of the group and the nature of its services;

- Location of the entity, including a map;

- Phone number; and

- Hours of operation.

Your initial campaign should be a mixture of PR (press releases, radio interviews, etc.) and paid advertising. Paid advertising should emphasize the points previously listed. PR should target your referral base as well as your potential patients.

You must establish a connection with your current or potential referral base. If you are affiliated with a hospital, it may help you (within Stark law rules) with initial contacts. Certainly an individualized professional letter is appropriate for the physicians you turn to for referrals.

In the case of a merger, contact the existing patient base in writing with your "who/what/when/where" facts and information about how the merger will improve service for patients.

Open House?

You may wonder if your group should hold an open house. If the answer to any of these questions is yes, an open house may be a good idea:

- Is your group doing something new for the service area?
- Is your new facility special?
- Do you have interesting, new ancillary services?
- Do you have a surgery center or procedure rooms?
- Do you want local employers to see the facility?
- Do you need to "rub elbows" with your referral sources?

Do not have an open house unless you are willing to do it properly. Ask your colleagues from other groups and local hospital personnel what arrangements may be suitable. Keep in mind that your referral-base physicians are busy people; attracting them to an open house may be difficult.

Ongoing Public Relations

Your practice needs an ongoing PR and advertising presence. What kind and how much are the key questions.

PR is not the same as advertising. PR uses other avenues of approach and is hopefully free or inexpensive. Sample PR activities include:

- Issuing press releases about a new physician, a new service, or a new procedure;
- Featuring physicians on radio call-in shows and local cable talk shows;
- Participating in local health fairs, senior citizen events, high school athletics, and so forth;

- Sponsoring health-related events (5K runs, antismoking campaigns, screening sessions); and

- Providing t-shirts to American Cancer Society fundraisers.

PR activities are an inexpensive way to gain attention and build
goodwill because they show your group in a positive light, without any
hard-sell advertising. Do not breeze through the preparation and hard
work involved in making these important events successful.

Expert Advice on Successful Public Relations

With healthcare reform dominating the headlines, there's no better
time for your medical group's good news to be in the news. Smart media
relations are an inexpensive and effective method to raise awareness of
your medical group practice, from adding new physicians or services to
announcing the prestigious award your practice won last week.

Follow these suggestions for creating a successful media outreach
campaign and you'll have your community positively buzzing about
your practice.

Take an appropriate angle. An important early step in evaluating
your approach to the media is to assess the news item or news angle
to report. Ask yourself whether your news is timely, interesting, and
relevant to your desired audience. Stay away from announcements that
are obviously self-serving or product focused. Try to link your organization's news to broader trends in the marketplace or healthcare issues
that affect everyone. Even better, find angles that coincide with information that can improve the health of the people in your community
or answer their healthcare-related questions (e.g., how to find out more
about the insurance you carry or how to avoid getting the flu).

Know your audience. The most common grievance from reporters
is that communicators fail to do their research. Take the time to learn
reporters' beats. Would they cover your news? Would the media outlet's
readers, viewers, or listeners be interested in the proposed news piece?
Research the outlets' preferred delivery methods. Do they want news
ideas by e-mail or are they more receptive to personal phone calls? This
is an easy way to make allies of reporters and to increase the chance of
your news being read.

Create one, two, three messages. Choose one to three key messages or takeaways to communicate to the media. For example:

- **Message one** — "Our medical group is expanding to accommodate the needs of the community and offer more options for
  patients."

- **Message two** — "Our practice is finding ways to grow despite
  tough economic conditions."

- **Message three** — "Our physicians remain dedicated to the community they serve."

Having more than three messages will muddy the communication
and can cause you to lose control of your news item. Write these messages down to help you stay on track throughout your campaign.

Channel surf. Next, look at the possible channels your organization has available to communicate with the media. Can you use your
Website? Can you create HTML e-mails? Do you have resources to conduct one-on-one meetings with media contacts? Can you use social
media such as Twitter and Facebook? Assess the best combination of
media channels for your news.

Choose your communication method wisely. Media relations
professionals use many communications tools depending on the news,
the desired outcome, and the audience. Assess which tool fits best with
your news. You may choose the traditional press release to make an
official announcement. You may prefer personal phone calls for a more
tailored approach. You may opt to conduct a media event if the news
is urgent.

Rinse, repeat. Do you remember the three messages you drafted
earlier? Make these the foundation of all your communications to the
media. Ensure that these messages appear in all of your communications and are consistently repeated by spokespeople and sources. It may
seem redundant, but research shows it may take many reporters several
references to absorb your messages, so stick with it.

Establish effective relationships with reporters. A sure way to fail
with the media is to violate the cardinal rules of media relations. Here
are a few tips to help foster productive relationships with the press.

- **Respect deadlines:** Reporters' lives are deadline-driven; therefore, missing due dates or forcing reporters to scramble to make
  them doesn't help your chances of publicity. Don't contact
  reporters when they are on deadline. The only exception is if
  you have breaking news.

- **Avoid the follow-up phone call:** It's not a good idea to call or e-mail reporters to ask if they received your press release, e-mail, or fax. Unless you had technical difficulties in distribution, assume they received it. If they didn't contact you, assume they are not interested.

- **Avoid the spin cycle:** Reporters appreciate straightforward news that serves the consumers of their news outlet. Over-spinning frustrates reporters and will discourage coverage of your news. Avoid marketing language.

- **Avoid typos, sloppy writing, and other errors:** Errors can ruin your credibility with the media. Good writing is a fundamental element of journalism, and reporters respond to quality writing.

- **Be prepared:** Make sure you can answer reporters' questions before you contact them by phone.

Don't be discouraged. So, you did your research, you followed the rules, you drafted an interesting and relevant press release, you sent it to the right reporters at the right time in the right format, but you received no news coverage. Keep in mind that it may take several positive encounters over many months to establish the kind of relationships that produce frequent coverage. Be mindful of these tips, respectful of the press, do your research, and the media will listen.

Dealing with Negative Press

As Warren Buffett put so well, "It takes 20 years to build a reputation and five minutes to ruin it."[2] A crisis communication plan can help your hospital or medical practice be prepared for negative press. Denver's Rose Medical Center, which has long enjoyed a stellar reputation as one of Denver's premier hospitals, learned that lesson the hard way.

Rose's reputation was badly damaged when the public learned that a drug-addicted surgical scrub technician with hepatitis C had potentially exposed thousands of patients to the disease. For six months, she stole syringes with pain medication, injected herself, refilled the syringes with saline, and returned them for use on patients. Not only did the hospital have to deal with outrage over how this happened and why it took so long to discover the problem, but it faced dozens of lawsuits and a daily stream of negative news stories.

If something similar happens to your practice, keep the following tips in mind.

Don't panic. Unfortunately, when faced with a crisis or negative press, the first instinct of many medical practice leaders is to hide and hope it goes away. Others get defensive. Some request retractions or go to war with a publication. Obviously, none of these responses is very smart. You can't hide and you can rarely intimidate the media into a retraction. Better still, you can plan ahead. A good crisis communications plan anticipates potential problems and develops a response for each scenario. It designates roles and responsibilities for each member of the crisis team, identifies a primary spokesperson, and establishes a command center where accurate information can be managed and delivered at specified times through specific channels, such as your Website, social media, or a media briefing.

Follow the CAP formula. CAP stands for compassion, action, and perspective, and keeping those principles at the forefront during a crisis can help mitigate more problems:

- **Compassion.** The most important part of your response is to show compassion to the public. For example, "Our top priority is the safety of our patients and staff. We've established a 24-hour hotline where patients and family members can get information and we've arranged counseling for our employees." Provide accurate, honest information as quickly as possible. Explain what you know so far by sticking to the facts. Never speculate, and make sure to focus on public benefits instead of the practice's problems. Speak with one consistent voice.

- **Action.** Explain what you are doing to fix the problem and make sure that it does not happen again. For example, "We are reviewing all our safety and hiring procedures to make sure that our security and screening processes are the best they can be."

- **Perspective.** Use your history to your advantage, for example, "We've been a part of this community for 50 years. Nothing like this has ever happened, and we are doing everything we can to make sure this is an isolated incident and that it never happens again."

Of course, bad press doesn't come only from a disaster. It can result from an unhappy employee, an angry patient suing for malpractice, a bad business deal, a crossed ethical boundary, or something as simple as a bruised ego or poor customer service.

That's why it's vital to establish and maintain good relationships with local media and your patients. It can help you mitigate the damage from a negative story by making it more likely that the reporter and the public will give you the benefit of the doubt. Once you get that opportunity, don't waste it. Make sure you adhere to the following guidelines:

- Communicate openly, honestly, factually, and compassionately.

- Keep your cool. Don't get baited into a confrontation.

- Ask the reporter for an opportunity to convey your point of view. Don't demand a retraction; instead, ask for a meeting to tell your side of the story.

- Avoid saying "no comment." It sounds like you have something to hide. If you don't know the answer, tell reporters you will find out and get back to them. If your lawyer recommends not answering, find a way to respond without giving your lawyer a heart attack.

- Stay on message. Create three key messages and stick to them as much as possible. "We are devastated that this happened." "We are doing everything we can to fix the problem." "This is an isolated incident and we are doing everything in our power to make sure it will never happen again." Express your key points and repeat them as often as you can without sounding like a robot.

The reputation you've worked so hard to build can be damaged in the blink of an eye. If you wait until a disaster occurs to start thinking about damage control, it could be too late. If you don't have a crisis communications plan now, get one. Gather your team, brainstorm every possible scenario, assign roles and responsibilities, and create a sample response to every crisis using the CAP formula.

⫶ Creating an Advertising Plan

There is a cliché among advertising experts: Half of all advertising is wasted; we just don't know which half. Advertising is part art and part science, and more than a dollop of guesswork. We know we should do some of it, but we are not certain how much or in what media.

A PR and advertising firm can help with an advertising plan, which includes:

- The overall size and budget of the campaign;
- The message and focus of the ads;
- The design and production of the ads; and
- The placement and price of the ads.

Advertising campaigns can be ongoing, occasional, seasonal, or tied to events such as new providers and new services.

Promoting New Providers, New Services, and Major Events

The group should have a standard protocol for promoting a new provider, touting a new service, and highlighting a major event (e.g., a physician's board certification). A standard checklist minimizes advertising agency fees and lets the staff complete the work with minimal discussion. Promotional tools that cost little to no money are discussed in the following paragraphs.

Press releases. Your ad agency can provide you with a standard outline for preparing press releases; any release not in professional format will be discarded by busy editors. Each new provider should have a professional quality photograph available in both print and digital formats (many newspapers now want digital photos via e-mail).

Not everyone is a good writer. Press releases must be clear and concise, so consult or hire a professional if your press releases are too long or clumsy. To save immense embarrassment, proofread *everything* twice and then one more time for good measure.

Television newscasts. Many local television stations are on the hunt for content. With a professional approach, you may gain some free publicity for your practice.

Electronic media outlets do various remotes telecasts and might consider covering an open house. Let local television stations know that selected physicians are available to be interviewed on major topics of public interest, such as hormone replacement therapy, advances in orthopedics, problems with obesity, breakthrough drugs, and so forth. Choose physicians who can be concise and look and sound good on television.

Radio shows. Radio station producers have a lot of dead air to fill and often look for content or call-in shows. If you have a physician who can fill this role and make a good impression, volunteer for some airtime on medical topics.

Books. An abundance of advertising and media messages has made it difficult for some medical professionals to connect with prospective patients in meaningful ways. Although there are several aspects to authority-based marketing, a credible way to become a recognized subject-matter expert is to publish a book.

Steven Hotze, MD, rose above the clutter by positioning himself as an expert on hormone therapy and general well-being. Hotze, founder and chief executive officer of the Hotze Health & Wellness Center in Houston, employed authority-based marketing, a process of establishing yourself as a subject-matter expert. During his 30 years as a specialist in natural hormone therapy and allergy treatment, Hotze noticed that some of his patients' past experiences were fraught with misdiagnoses and doctor bias. To educate people and elevate his status in the field, Hotze decided to write a book, *Hormones, Health and Happiness*. Hotze says he garnered more than 500 new patient inquiries in a matter of months, and more than a third of them scheduled an appointment. It also generated media coverage for the clinic and allowed Hotze to position himself as an expert source for television shows and publications.

::: Creating a Marketing Plan

A marketing plan similar to the strategic plan discussed in Chapter 2 needs to be developed using the following framework:

- Executive summary;
- Situational analysis;
- Marketing research; and
- Marketing strategy.

Executive Summary

The executive summary of the practice's marketing plan should address the following key elements:

- What are the dominant issues discovered in the practice's situational analysis?

- What are the key objectives — in the shortest possible form — the practice seeks to achieve?

- What, in one or two sentences, is the practice's marketing strategy to achieve those objectives?

- What other concepts unique to the practice should be addressed?

Answers to these questions comprise the body of the marketing plan; therefore, the executive summary cannot be written until the plan has been completed. It will then serve as the "snapshot" of what the practice aims to accomplish with its strategic marketing.

Situational Analysis

The situational analysis investigates the macro- and microenvironment in a manner similar to the strategic plan. In fact, the strengths, weaknesses, opportunities, and threats (SWOT) analysis discussed earlier in this book can be used in this stage of the marketing plan process. The practice should review its strategic plan's SWOT and then consider each of the SWOT's components from a consumer and market viewpoint, including external threats and opportunities, internal strengths and weaknesses, key success factors in the healthcare industry, and the practice's sustainable competitive advantage.

A two-by-two matrix can also be created to identify specific focus areas for the marketing plan: the macroenvironment, the internal practice environment, consumer analyses, and market analyses (see Exhibit 7.1).

External Analysis

Macroenvironmental analysis refers to continuous structured data collection and processing on a broad range of environmental factors, such as the economy, the governmental and legal environments, technology, and social culture. This allows the practice to act quickly, take advantage of opportunities before competitors do, and respond to environmental threats before significant damage is done. Scanning these macroenvironmental variables for threats and opportunities requires that each issue be rated on two dimensions, which are its potential impact on the

EXHIBIT 7.1
Marketing Plan Situational Analysis Two-by-Two Matrix

Macroenvironment	Market Analysis
What does your practice do well? ■ Innovative leadership ■ Good reputation	*Where are the opportunities for your practice?* ■ Untapped market for new procedure ■ Hiring new physician in practice ■ Need for geriatric care in community
Consumer Analysis	**Internal Practice Analysis**
What part of your practice needs improvement? ■ High nurse turnover ■ Location of practice ■ Retiring physician ■ Providing geriatric care	*What is happening in your area that could threaten your practice?* ■ New regulation ■ Growing elderly population

practice and its likelihood of occurrence. Weighing its potential impact by its likelihood of occurrence indicates its importance to the practice.

Internal Analysis

The microenvironmental, or internal, analysis seeks to uncover the resources of the practice that apply or can be applied to marketing efforts. These resources include money, time, people, and skills.

The key question to ask is what internal resources the practice has that are underexploited? Finding these resources internally as opposed to having to seek them externally provides countless benefits to the practice. Along with identification of resources, the practice's vision, mission, and goals (in particular, long-term goals and objectives, marketing goals and objectives, and financial goals and objectives) should be reviewed, and the culture of the practice should be considered. Each of these areas has an effect on the marketing strategy of the practice.

Consumer Analysis

A consumer analysis explores the demographic makeup of the practice's consumer base, but also delves a bit deeper into the consumers' purchasing and decision-making behaviors, their motivations and expectations, and loyalty segments. Key questions here are "who are the practice's current consumers," and "what brought them to the practice in the first place?"

Market Analysis

The final piece of the situational analysis is the market analysis. Here the medical practice defines its market; identifies its market size and industry market trends; evaluates the market segmentation and strategic groups; and studies the competition's strengths, weaknesses, and market share.

Five Forces Analysis

Michael Porter's Five Forces Analysis[3] is a tool that allows for a systematic and structured analysis of the market structure and competitive situation. The five forces consist of those forces close to a company that affect its ability to serve its customers and make a profit.

Four of the forces — the bargaining power of consumers, the bargaining power of suppliers, the threat of new entrants, and the threat of substitute products — combine with other variables to influence a fifth force, the level of competition in an industry. A change in any of the forces normally requires a practice to reassess the marketplace. Exhibit 7.2 illustrates Porter's Five Forces Analysis.

The bargaining power of customers determines how much pressure on margins and volumes customers can impose. For example, customers have high bargaining power when the ability to switch to an alternative product (e.g., a new prescription plan) is relatively simple and is not related to high costs, or when the customers have low margins and are price sensitive (e.g., a small practice with few employees on a plan, but still needing a good price).

The bargaining power of suppliers is similar. The term *suppliers* comprises all sources for inputs that are needed to provide goods or services.

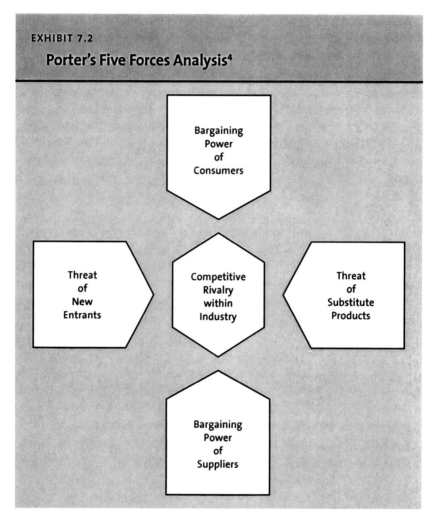

Porter's Five Forces Analysis[4]

Bargaining
Power
of
Consumers

Threat
of
New
Entrants

Competitive
Rivalry
within
Industry

Threat
of
Substitute
Products

Bargaining
Power
of
Suppliers

In such situations, the buying industry often faces high pressure on margins from its suppliers. The relationship to powerful suppliers can potentially reduce strategic options for the practice.

When there is a threat of new entrants in the community that will compete with the practice, changes may occur in the major determinants of the market environment (e.g., market shares, prices, and patient and staff loyalty) at any time. Remember that there is always a latent pressure for reaction and adjustment for existing competitors in the healthcare industry. A threat from substitutes exists if there are alternative products or services or complementary products or services with lower prices and/or higher quality that can be used for the same purpose. These competitors could potentially attract a significant proportion of market volume and consequently reduce the potential sales volume. Competitive rivalry within the industry derives the intensity of competition among existing practices. High competitive pressure results in pressure on prices, margins, and profitability for every single company in the industry.

After the analysis of the current and potential future state of the five forces, the practice can search for options to influence these forces in its favor, thereby reducing the competitive forces' power.

Marketing Research

Marketing research is the next major task undertaken in the marketing plan process. The American Marketing Association defines it as:

> ...the function that links the consumer, customer, and public to the marketer through information — information used to identify and define marketing opportunities and problems; generate, refine, and evaluate marketing actions; monitor marketing performance; and improve understanding of marketing as a process. Market research specifies the information required to address these issues, designs the method for collecting information, manages and implements the data collection process, analyzes the results, and communicates the findings and their implications.[5]

The aim of marketing research is to answer the following questions:

- Who are the customers?
- What services do they want?
- When do they want these services provided?
- Where do they want these services provided?

Answers to these questions can reveal problems with current services and potential trends for the future. Market research should also help the practice determine its market share and the effectiveness of its advertising and promotions.

Three general sources of market data can be gathered:

1. Data already available externally (e.g., from chambers of commerce, business coalitions, state trade organizations, and the U.S. Census Bureau);

2. Data readily available internally (e.g., from employees, current customers, and company records and files); and

3. Data that can be collected by and/or for the practice (e.g., through surveys, interviews, evaluation and response cards, customer feedback, and observations of competition).

The practice executive should determine what form of market research is best based on the value the practice will receive vs. the time and other resources it will need to invest to gain access to that information. No matter what method is chosen, use the following tips to get the most out of it.

Gather information early and often. Regardless of your group's size or specialty, gathering information on the environment in which it operates is critically important to its success. Keep abreast of competing practices and what they're doing. If they're adding new services or making strategic affiliations, your organization may feel the effects.

If you have been practicing in the area or have been a resident nearby, you should have a good idea of several key indicators:

- Patient volume;
- Underserved needs;
- Insurance contract availability;
- Percentage of patients with Medicaid;
- Percentage of uninsured patients;
- General economic climate;
- Business and industrial base (including the major health insurers);
- Supply of physicians in your specialty, including:
  - Physicians approaching retirement;
  - Physicians recently recruited to the area;
  - Physicians within driving distance for your patients; and
  - Specialty centers whose physicians could compete with you.

Constantly appraise your patient population. Is it changing? Are you seeing a more ethnically diverse clientele than previously? Do you have an aging population or more working mothers? Perhaps you need to adjust staffing, physical access, or clinic hours to meet shifting patient needs.

Know what the community wants. If a competing organization has a cardiac catheterization laboratory, determine whether the market can support a second facility run by your group. Maybe patient demand justifies opening your office on evenings and weekends. If a large employer has contracted with a health insurer with which your practice does not affiliate, perhaps it is time to court that payer.

Know your competition. When a practice grows more slowly than the market, it loses market share to competitors. Unless they understand what occurs outside their facilities, physicians and administrators operate with limited insight.

Competition data have been available to the public for some time, but only hospitals have used them to make comparisons to other hospitals. To maintain neutrality with hospital-affiliated physicians, hospital administrators have not provided them with market insight. The time has come for physician leaders and practice administrators to use competitive information to create marketing strategies to promote long-term success.

ZIP code data can show high-demand areas. Conducting market research by geographic region can give medical groups valuable insight on positioning themselves to take advantage of high patient demand. With data showing how the volume trend in your practice compares to the trend across all practices in the service area, you can form a strategy for business development. You may consider recruiting new physicians to handle greater patient demand or establishing satellite facilities in areas of high market growth. Gather market research data to ensure that strategic planning efforts produce successful results.

Obtain market data for your region. In most states, you can obtain medical market data from two sources: a private national firm or each state's hospital and healthcare association. Ambulatory surgery data are available in most states through a hospital data-sharing program.

The strategic plan should guide expansion. Adding new services or making infrastructure changes shouldn't be a knee-jerk reaction to competition. Your practice's strategic plan, based on its mission, vision, and values, should be the guiding force behind any organizational enterprise. Your group may hold a niche position in a specialized area of medicine and want to keep it that way. Or it may seek to offer comprehensive services in its field, making expansion part of its objectives.

The strategic plan and market awareness should guide change. Unfortunately, leaders of small practices often get lost in day-to-day management and fail to formulate strategic plans. They often lack the resources — in personnel and know-how — to conduct market research. Yet your practice's survival depends on an awareness of its environment. Make time to set direction and long-term goals. Learn how to analyze your market. Knowledge is power, and knowledge facilitates adaptability.

Marketing Strategy

With the market research completed, the next step in the marketing plan is to develop a market strategy detailing the broad plan to achieve the practice's marketing goals and objectives. This may include using the information and data collected to determine which consumers' wants and needs are not being met by the practice or by the competition, or determining areas where new services or different services would capture new markets.[6]

Target Markets

To develop a marketing strategy, the practice needs to identify a target market. This is a specific group of consumers who have a want or need for the practice's services or products. For example, a dermatology practice looking to market its new laser therapy to women may determine the target market as women ranging from 24 to 50 years of age. Target marketing allows the practice to reach, create awareness in, and influence the group of consumers (e.g., in this case, women aged 24 to 50) most likely to select its services while conserving resources and generating greater returns.

Market Segmentation

Market segmentation — the method of grouping a market into smaller subgroups — is the process of target marketing. Market segments can be geographic (certain regions or climates), demographic (age or race), psychographic (attitudes, behaviors, lifestyles, or loyalty characteristics), or historical (previous customers).

If the practice's services are confined to a specific geographic area, then the target market can be further defined to reflect the number of users of the service within that geographic segment. For example, an orthopedic practice in Aspen, Colo., might market its products and services at the local hospital; to local employers; and at ski companies, resorts, hotels, and lodges where injured skiers or family members would seek recommendations.

The Marketing Mix

Once target markets are identified, the practice needs to develop a marketing mix that is positioned to be attractive to that segment. The marketing mix enables practices to join together different marketing decision areas, such as products, prices, promotions, and place (also known as E. Jerome McCarthy's 4P's) to develop an overall marketing plan.[7]

Products. In medical group practices, products are typically services. In determining the marketing mix and developing the marketing plan, these services should be used as marketing resources, and a focal point should be differentiation of the practice's services from that of the competition. For example, the orthopedic practice in Aspen may offer a product line that includes orthopedic consultation, radiology services, surgery, and possibly physical therapy or medical massage, in addition to standard medical equipment such as crutches, bandages, or braces.

Prices. Determining and setting prices for a medical practice and the visits or procedures that are offered is not a simple process. It is important to look at insurance contracts, the amount allowed, and if there are procedures or visits that are not covered under insurance that need to have cash or self-pay prices set.

Promotion. Communicating with and selling to potential customers requires promotion, including sales promotions, advertising, and PR (only the latter two are applicable to most group practices). For example, think about orthopedists in Aspen. For promotion they may choose to direct their efforts toward television or radio advertisements, listings in the phone book, announcements about the practice in the local newspaper, public service announcements, and/or community service programs to attract local and visiting patients.

Place. Place, meaning placement or distribution, refers to decisions regarding market coverage, member selection, logistics, levels of service, and convenience to the customer. Distribution decisions are best made by analyzing competitors to determine the channels they use and then deciding whether to use the same type of channel or an alternative that may provide the practice with a strategic advantage. The distribution strategy chosen by the practice will also be based on factors in addition to the channels being used by its competition, including pricing strategy and internal resources.

For example, perhaps an orthopedic practice's administrator finds that the competition runs advertising in the Saturday newspaper. The administrator may choose to run placement of the practice's ad head-to-head on Saturday, or may decide to run the ad on Sunday, or instead use completely different media for advertising, for example, sponsoring the equipment for a local youth group's ski club or providing the prizes for a downhill race.

Positioning. Although not a part of McCarthy's original 4P's of the marketing mix, there is a fifth P — positioning — for practices to consider as well. This is the special niche your practice occupies in a customer's mind. A practice's positioning strategy is affected by a number of variables that are closely tied to the motivations and requirements of target customers as well as the actions of primary competitors.

Before a product can be positioned, several strategic questions need to be addressed, including:

- How are the practice's competitors positioning themselves (e.g., the region's best at shoulders, arms, and hand surgery)?

- What specific attributes do the practice's services have that its competitors do not (e.g., radiology in-house)?

- What customer needs does the practice's service fulfill (e.g., emergency consultation)?

Once these questions are addressed based on market research, the practice executive can develop a positioning strategy illustrating exactly how the practice wants its services perceived by both customers and the competition.

Practice Structure and Culture

The marketing plan in general, as well as specific tasks, such as the development of the marketing mix, should consider the structure and culture of the practice. Structural features of the practice are formal, usually inflexible, created and maintained by documentation, and contingency centered. They set responsibilities, formal rights, and rewards or punishments on which individual behavior or group action is con-tingent.[8] The structure determines how the practice is supposed to oper-ate and for what purpose.

The culture of the practice, in contrast, is informal, flexible, cre-ated and maintained by word of mouth, and ideology centered. It defines good and bad, winning and losing, friends and enemies, and so forth.[9] The cultural characterizations of the practice — people, circum-stances, events, objects, facts, processes, and information — are critical for practice decisions and progress. Structure and culture are unique to each practice and shape the image that the practice presents to the community.

The marketing plan for the practice should align with the practice's structure and culture, its style and image, and what makes the practice unique. "Truth in marketing and advertising" is an adage that applies well here. Marketing materials should accurately depict the practice, and the messages used should be shared by members of the practice. For example, if the practice has a culture of building relationships with patients, the marketing materials should reflect this, rather than focus on maintaining high efficiency and quick turnaround in seeing patients. The style or image of the practice must be evaluated.

Advertising

The final component of the marketing plan is advertising, which, as mentioned earlier, relates to promotion. Gone are the days when a prac-tice could "hang out a shingle" and the phone would begin to ring. Healthcare is an extremely competitive marketplace that requires prac-tices to engage in innovative advertising practices.

Today's practices are, in every sense of the word, "businesses," and they must use advertising concepts that were once shunned by the healthcare industry, including direct-to-consumer marketing through television and radio advertisements, direct mail, public seminars, Websites, e-mail newsletters, and even billboards or other signage.

The choice of advertising method should be guided by the answers to the following questions:

- What is the source of the practice's current patients?

- What method is optimal for conveying the practice's "message"?

- What method will reach the largest concentration of potential customers?

- What is the cost per unit (i.e., new patient) for this type of method? What is the expected return on investment (ROI)?

- Is this method ethical in all possible respects?

Once an advertising method has been selected, the practice needs to ensure that the materials designed are written at an appropriate reading level and are clear, concise, and appealing, and take into consideration the population most likely to be served by the practice. Advertising materials, as with all other components of the marketing plan, also need to accurately and honestly portray the practice.

Using the Internet

Patients increasingly use the Internet to find doctors, and if you don't meet them where they are online, you stand to lose a lot of business. When you do meet them there, you don't get a second chance to make a first impression, so make sure your Website and social media platforms are presented as professionally as possible.

Your Website

Millions of businesses have Websites on the Internet, many of which are ugly and/or dysfunctional. It is tempting to save money by following suit, but this is one area where a little extra investment can yield tremendous dividends. A welcoming Website that loads quickly and is easy to read and navigate gives your group an unparalleled point of contact for educating and interacting with patients.

Buying a Domain Name

Before developing a Website, reserve your practice name (and any close variation), if for no other reason than to prevent another group from using the name someday. On registrar services, these are called domain names, and you can reserve them for a few dollars a year.

No matter what hosting service you use, it is important to never let the domain name lapse; otherwise, an unscrupulous reseller can snap it up and hold it for ransom. If this happens, they can shut down your Website, intercept or block all e-mail sent through your domain name, or simply sell the name to someone else and your business will have no recourse.

Put someone in charge of renewing the domain name and make sure a protocol is in place so ownership can be confirmed regularly. Sign up for multiple years at a time, put the account on auto-renew, and make sure the credit card or other payment account associated with it is checked for expiration and/or insufficient funds at least twice per year.

Building the Website

Once you decide to have a Website, hire a professional to design and maintain the site. Security and maintenance are arguably more important than the Website's design, so make sure you contract with a firm that can handle and be accountable for those ongoing issues.

Interview at least three Website design services and review a dozen or so sample Websites designed by each. Look through other sites used by practices similar to yours, and if you find one you like, contact the practice to see who they contracted. Then choose a firm that can deliver what you want and keep it running.

Before a Website is designed, the group must decide the function they want it to serve, such as:

- A source of information only;
- An information and marketing tool;
- An information, marketing, and educational tool; or
- An interactive appointment-making and referral site.

It may be prudent to start with an expository Website and work up to one that is more sophisticated. Whatever your thoughts, a professional should design the initial site with expansion in mind and so the site reads and functions well. New online services, such as patient portals, appear constantly, and you want to make sure your site can handle the integration of those services without needing an expensive redesign.

Tapping into Social Media

Because growth in the healthcare system is strongly correlated to patient referrals, it is only natural that professionals tap social media outlets to foster relationships with patients. More professionals see that social media channels offer an effective method to communicate ideas, share information, and connect with people across all age and socioeconomic groups, as evidenced by growing popularity.

Healthcare professionals, although somewhat slow to ride the social media wave, are realizing the power these tools offer for developing connections with patients, potential patients, physicians, and healthcare leaders.

Although increasing numbers of large healthcare organizations and health systems are using the power of social media to engage patients, social media experts say smaller private physician groups and individual physician offices are only cautiously dipping their toes in the social media pool. One can understand why healthcare professionals take a strategic approach to interacting with and engaging patients online, given potential Health Insurance Portability and Accountability Act (HIPAA) privacy issues and other challenges. However, with a carefully crafted social media policy governing the use of networking tools for the organization — and an appropriately executed social media strategy — many organizations are realizing the benefits of becoming more accessible in their marketing and reaching out to inform, educate, build rapport, and increase patient trust through open, real-time communication with patients.

Making a Social Media Plan

When using social media, develop a clear and concise plan for online activity. Identify your goals, your audience, and where those patients connect online. Here are some additional questions to ask:

- What resources do you have to allocate to this new marketing initiative?
- Who will manage this strategy once it has been developed?
- What legal implications must be considered as you move forward to protect patient privacy?

Managing various social media channels is more time-consuming than you think. Social media's power lies in its immediate nature and back-and-forth dialogue, especially platforms such as Facebook and Twitter, so be ready to respond to patient complaints and compliments quickly. And think carefully before outsourcing your social media plan; a social media marketing strategy is most effective when the person managing the accounts is skilled at engaging in thoughtful, authentic dialogue with consumers and is already immersed in your company's brand.

Studies show that only a low percentage of consumers trust advertising. Instead of marketing to your patients, use social media to connect with them outside your office and to build relationships that last. When you can make these types of connections, you build loyalty, and your organization will begin to see social media as an effective way to increase the volume of your referrals and recommendations.

How Much Should We Share?

Social media sites can be used to communicate with patients about everything from weather or holiday closings to special events and center donations. You can share staff birthdays, information about new clinics, and biographies of new physicians and staff members. Used to its full potential, social media lets you create a dialogue with patients about important or even lighthearted topics.

Remember that social media can be a minefield when it comes to complying with HIPAA. Train employees so they don't post on the group's behalf or cause problems by posting pictures of patients online.

How Much Does Social Media Cost?

Don't worry about dipping into your marketing budget for social media, because creating and managing an online profile on many sites is free. In a couple of easy steps, you can be up and running. Social media monitoring platform subscriptions keep your social media posts organized and alert you to any online mention. It's an inexpensive and effective way to keep track of the conversation about your organization, industry experts say.

How Much Time Do We Have to Invest?

Although the cost of using social media is minimal, it takes time to build and cultivate a social media presence. It's essential to develop a robust profile on whatever social media channel you choose. It's not enough to just throw your practice's name up on a social media site. Invest some time to create a dynamic presence, which might include staff photos and bios, a virtual tour of your office, and updated contact information. Imagine that this is the first place a patient learns about your practice. Put your best foot forward and spend time on the front end making your profile reflect the work you do to serve patients.

Once you're up and running, continue to devote time to posting and monitoring your social media accounts. It's recommended that you designate about a half-hour a day to share new information and engage with your followers. Designate a few employees to post on the practice's behalf and ensure that they are properly trained and can represent your practice's "voice" effectively and responsibly.

Don't forget to be creative. Develop special promotions, share exclusive information, or run a practice referral contest on your social media platform. Don't be afraid to think outside the box and brainstorm new ways to interact with your fans. Keep in mind, though, that social media platforms are not designed to share or communicate protected health information, and MGMA recommends that members and physicians keep their personal accounts separate and distinct from their professional pages.

What's the Return on Our Investment?

Measuring the true ROI on social media can be complicated. But consider this: MGMA spends less than $10 a month and about 45 minutes of staff time a day to update and monitor its channels and has thousands of followers and fans. Its online presence grows daily, and this allows MGMA to share news and connect with new people. This includes members, consultants, physicians, and others allied with the field. Consider how this same type of situation could ultimately affect your business. These are potential new partners in your community and new patients who will learn about your services.

Although an exact amount may not be simple to calculate, there are many things to consider when you evaluate ROI, including:

- **Reach.** This includes all your followers, your fans and their connections. One of your followers might have 200 followers of their own while another has 4,000 followers. Added together, these connections can help you determine how many people you could potentially connect with on social media.

- **Engagement.** Every time a fan "likes" your message, answers a question you've posted, or re-tweets you, it creates a bond with your organization, and, in the long term, builds loyalty with your follower base.

- **Sentiment.** In addition to commenting and posting on your wall, it's essential to keep track of what fans are saying about you. Do you have a steady stream of posts about great service and short wait times? That's fantastic! Or do you have post after post about difficulty scheduling an appointment? Respond to your followers and handle the issue just as you would if a patient were at the front desk giving you feedback. Be aware that positive and negative comments on your social media channels can have a major effect on your business and how it is perceived on these channels.

Social media also lets you monitor what others are saying about you, share resources and information, and correct any misinformation directly. Consider how using social media and investing a little bit of time and money might affect your practice in the long run. It can expose your business to brand-new audiences and help establish your group as the go-to practice in your community, both locally and online.

Responding to Negative Posts

Social media is designed to be interactive, and sometimes it becomes a venue to share negative experiences or criticisms. Experts suggest viewing these posts as opportunities for service recovery. If someone posts about having to wait 45 minutes to see a physician, respond to the comment just as you would if the patient were in the office. Here is one suggested response: "We're sorry for your inconvenience and appreciate your feedback. We will make every effort to ensure that you never wait more than 10 minutes to see our physicians."

If you are sincere in your response to an issue, patients may recall the personal response when determining where to schedule their next appointment.

⠿ Conclusion

Marketing in a medical practice is a complex balancing act between the promotion of high standards for patient service and quality while functioning within a highly regulated reimbursement system. Practice administrators who are able to promote the value of the practice, establish key relationships with clinical partners and community groups, and maintain high service and quality levels will provide the basis for personal success as well as the ongoing success of their practices.

Notes

1. A.T. Eliscu, "Marketing for Straight A's? How One Practice Created a Customer-Service Brand Identity," *MGMA Connexion* 8, no. 5 (May-June 2008): 50–53, 1.

2. "The 16 Best Things Warren Buffett Has Ever Said," *Huffington Post*, updated August 30, 2013, www.huffingtonpost.com/2013/08/30/warren -buffett-quotes_n_3842509.html.

3. Michael E. Porter, *Competitive Strategy* (New York: Free Press, 1980).

4. Porter, *Competitive Strategy*.

5. "Definition of Marketing: Marketing Research," American Marketing Association, 1995, www.marketingpower.com/.

6. Meir Liraz, *Small Business Management: Essential Ingredients for Success*, Best Business Books, 1998, www.bizmove.com/free-pdf-download/small-busi ness-management.pdf.

7. E. Jerome McCarthy, *Basic Marketing: A Managerial Approach* (Homewood, IL: R.D. Irwin, 1960).

8. "GTP Organizer Training: Training Guide #7: Organizational Structure and Culture," Gather the People, 2004, www.gatherthepeople.org/ Downloads/007_STRUCTURE_CULTURE.pdf.

9. "GTP Organizer Training."

Chapter 8

Productivity and Compensation Standards for Physicians

COMPENSATION OF PHYSICIANS and other key clinical providers is critical to the ongoing success of a medical practice. Physicians are often owners or key shareholders of the medical practice. As such, their compensation packages may significantly vary depending on the structure of the organization and the nature of the physician's employment relationship with the organization. Therefore, determination and implementation of physician compensation is often accomplished in a significantly different manner than compensation for other practice employees. This chapter covers key topics in physician compensation. For further information about compensation for other employees, please see the human resource management volume.

The competent medical practice administrator will consistently demonstrate skill in identifying types of physician compensation plans; evaluating revenue and expense allocation methods; evaluating compatibility of compensation plans with practice mission; benchmarking by specialty, location, productivity, and quality; implementing an effective allocation system; and complying with regulations including Internal Revenue Service, Stark law, and anti-kickback laws.

::: Physician Contracts

You might ask how many physicians do there need to be in a practice to make physician contracts necessary. Is it when the practice has two physicians or three or more? There is no correct answer, but when you hire any nonowner physicians, your practice has a clear need for physician contracts. Further, any practice with four or more owners should probably have contracts, but this is a guideline, not a rule.

Ask your legal counsel to help you decide whether your practice needs physician contracts. If you determine your practice needs them, preparing and executing them correctly are essential.

Contract Outline

Working with legal counsel, the group should develop a standard physician contract. You can customize the contract, especially the compensation section, for each new physician. This method allows you to create uniform contracts without them having to be identical. Counsel should also prepare a standard contract for part-time employees, one for physician's assistants and one for nurse practitioners.

Your counsel for this project must be an attorney with extensive experience in healthcare transaction law and healthcare contract law. Only a specialist will do.

Be very careful with accounting language in the compensation section. Attorneys and administrators do not always know how to write in financial terms, so ask your certified public accountant to review the compensation section before the contract is signed.

Once contract forms are developed, avoid the temptation to eliminate the involvement of your legal counsel in future physician contracts. At a minimum, your counsel should review each negotiated contract before it is signed. Compared to the original contract drafting, this review should not be expensive. Whether the practice attorney is involved in negotiations may depend on the preferences of the parties.

::: Helping Employees Understand Compensation

Compensation administration contains many risk factors for employee backlash. Most of these dilemmas can be avoided by educating employees about the practice's compensation plan and being open about the steps taken to ensure it is fair. These steps need to be simply and briefly outlined for them so that there are no surprises, and you should base them on:

- Job analysis;
- Job evaluation;
- Salary grades;
- Salary ranges;
- Salary structure;
- Salary policy;
- Manager support;
- Employee communication; and
- Monitoring, evaluation, and updating.

These steps seem mechanical, but adhering to them helps keep compensation-related emotions in check. Employees need and want to understand the key factors that influence their compensation, so use real examples to explain how factors such as experience and education work into the salary equation. For example, a person may seek a high level of compensation because he or she has a certain amount of experience or education. However, that experience or education may be unrelated to the job description. For example, someone with a doctorate in economics and six years of experience as a professor will not be able to apply much of skill and knowledge in a job as a claims processor. Despite that, the person probably feels underpaid. This example shows how important it is to match the job to the person's qualifications.

Consider another example in which a newly graduated nurse is typically paid at the entry level of the nurse job classification. If the nurse graduates as a nurse practitioner, the job classification has a higher level. Perhaps it is much higher if the person has qualifications highly demanded by a specialist medical practice, such as pediatric nursing skills with several years of related experience.

Also remember that compensation affects other HR matters, including promotion, performance management, discipline, and grievance procedures.

::: Building a Compensation System

Build the foundation for compensation administration by answering the following questions:

- Who is going to develop and oversee the compensation program?
- Who is going to provide expert advice?
- What is the budget for developing and maintaining the program?
- When will development occur and how will this ongoing task be carried out?
- Who can determine salary ranges and salary increases? How often and on what basis are these done?

It is often useful to retain a consultant to set up a compensation program and to provide ongoing consulting. Consider using a benefits consulting firm or refer questions to an industry association, such as the Medical Group Management Association® (MGMA®), for information and assistance.

Whether you use a consultant or not, it is imperative that the senior management team is involved in establishing the compensation philosophy and policy. It is also important to set up a compensation committee that represents every department to ensure adequate input across the board.

This committee should tackle the heavy-duty questions about how to establish pay structures for various types of employees. For example, should there be a difference between clinical and nonclinical staff compensation? It should also decide how benefits and incentives complement salary. Those elements of a total compensation package are what job candidates consider when deciding if they want to join your medical practice and current employees contemplate when deciding whether or not to stay with the practice.

Watching the Competition

Your medical practice needs to decide where it wants its compensation plans and policies to fit in the market, that is, whether it wants to lead, lag, or match closely with current competitive rates. By taking the pay lead for certain vital positions, the practice may attract highly qualified candidates and/or beat out the competition when candidates are in short supply. However, if a lead philosophy is used for all positions and at all times, the salary budget likely will not support it. Usually paying a premium is justified only for certain positions at specific times.

If a practice chooses to lag behind competitors by offering marginal pay, few candidates may be willing to join the practice unless the total compensation package offers something of value to certain candidates. For example, medical assistants might be offered an extremely flexible schedule that appeals to working mothers.

A match philosophy works best as long as the practice has the option of using lead and lag strategies for some positions.

Job Evaluation

Job evaluation is a systematic procedure designed to aid in establishing pay differentials among jobs within a single employer. Compensation begins with job evaluation and moves on to establishing pay, benefits, and incentives. The evaluation is based on the content of the work, the value of the work to the organization, the culture of the workplace, and external market forces.

Job evaluations take into account:

- A job's relative importance within the organization;
- The knowledge, skills, and abilities necessary to do the job;
- The difficulty of one job compared to another; and
- The education, experience, and licensing requirements for the job.

Job evaluation involves a formal comparison of the essential functions of various positions in order to rank each position in the organization. While job content is a primary factor in evaluation, market conditions, competition, supply and demand, and unemployment rates also are considered.

Using this information, an equitable and meaningful wage and salary system can be developed that complies with federal and state laws. Federal laws include the following:

- Age Discrimination in Employment Act;
- Civil Rights Act;

- Davis–Bacon Act;
- Employee Retirement Income Security Act;
- Equal Pay Act;
- Fair Labor Standards Act;
- Family and Medical Leave Act;
- Health Maintenance Organization Act;
- National Labor Relations Act;
- Pregnancy Discrimination Act;
- Social Security Act; and
- Walsh–Healey Act.

Also be aware of state laws, including minimum-wage requirements, as some states may have a higher rate than the federal rate. Also keep up to date on workers' compensation laws.

Equal Pay for Equal Work?

In 1963 Congress passed the Equal Pay Act to ensure that individuals doing the same work would receive the same pay. Since then, studies have evaluated whether men and women with similar tasks and responsibilities receive similar compensation, and the results generate heated discussion.

Sanctioned wage discrimination has virtually disappeared since the Equal Pay Act went into effect, but there are still significant differences in average compensation for men and women. In most instances, the differences relate to the dissimilarity in occupation and production, not in wages.

While the American workforce reflects societal changes in traditional occupations and the nation's ethnic and racial mix, higher education provides a clear lens for shifting demographics. In 1982 and 1983, 26.8 percent of the medical degrees were awarded to women compared with 2009 and 2010, when 48.3 percent of medical school graduates were women.[1]

Amid myriad changes the gender shift has caused, there also is a relative difference in production. The yearly published *MGMA Physician Compensation and Production Survey* has extensive information on the relative differences in the number of gross charges, encounters, total collection, and resource-based relative value scale (RBRVS) unit production for new and experienced physicians, and gender. It shows that experienced physicians are more productive than new doctors, and that male physicians are more productive than female physicians.

The survey report also shows that men have higher compensation levels than women. With the significant number of variables described in the report, it is not readily apparent whether compensation differences result from experience, workload, or other factors.

Specialty Matters

Survey data shows that, in general, women produce lower gross charges than men in the same specialty. For anesthesiology, gross charges reported for women were only 88 percent of the level reported for men. In family practice without obstetrics, women's production was 88 percent of men's production while that percentage was 82 percent for internal medicine, 93 percent for obstetrics and gynecology, 87 percent for pediatrics, and 74 percent for general surgery.

Younger, new doctors have substantially lower gross charges than older physicians, and experience increases productivity.

Arguably the most interesting observation from these data is that there appears to be a gender pay gap in many specialties. Female compensation, as a percentage of male compensation, generally lags beyond differences in productivity. For example, in anesthesia, gross charges for women were 88 percent of men, but compensation was only 83 percent as much.

General surgery was the major exception. Female surgeons reported pay that was 77 percent of their male counterparts with production that was 74 percent. Internal medicine was relatively neutral with the percentage amounts of compensation and production being almost equal at 83 percent and 82 percent, respectively.

The differences in productivity for men and women have been studied and often explained through differences in hours worked per week, time spent with patients, patient acuity, and age mix and societal factors.

The difference in compensation is much more difficult to understand. Logically, physician compensation systems pay less for a lesser amount of work and more for additional output and are blind as to who performs the labor. At the same time, a gap exists in the relative amounts of compensation related to production.

Perhaps the best explanation is not that doctors receive equal pay for equal work, but that they receive unequal pay for unequal work.

⠿ Understanding the Stark Law

The federal physician self-referral law (the Stark law)[2] is now almost 25 years old, but time has not produced clarity or certainty in many aspects of its implementation. After original enactment in 1989, significant amendment in 1992, and various efforts to curtail or expand the scope of the law since, Congress never seems quite finished with its policy-making function. Similarly, the Stark law has produced a long and tortured history of rule-making by the Centers for Medicare & Medicaid Services (CMS), including, among others, Stark law 1 and Stark law 2, and within Stark law 2, phases I, II, and III (collectively, "the regulations").[3]

More recently, the courts have begun to add their paint to an already crowded canvas. Two recent cases have generated considerable notoriety in the healthcare trade press and are the subjects of hot debate among healthcare lawyers, institutional compliance officers, and others concerned with ensuring compliance of physician compensation arrangements in diverse practice settings.

Both cases (discussed in the sections that follow) involved physician compensation relationships with hospital systems that were structured as employment relationships, not compensation plans in physician-owned medical groups. Similar facts would likely have produced different legal outcomes in a physician-owned group setting.

In less than six months' time, two federal district courts have interpreted critically important provisions of the Stark law's exception for compensation paid to bona fide employees and have sided with the government's interpretation of the law in both instances, which was adverse to hospitals and more restrictive than what at least some healthcare lawyers, consultants, and appraisers previously thought the law to be. Both of these cases are only district court decisions. One has been settled without the benefit of an appellate review of the lower court's reasoning, and the other might be settled before an appeal is ultimately decided. Thus the full legal significance of these decisions in other jurisdictions remains an open question. Other judges confronted by similar facts (facts are virtually never identical) might reach different conclusions. Suffice it to say, however, that these decisions, and particularly the dollar amount of both, have driven fear into the hearts of hospital management, legal counsel, compliance officers, and valuation consultants, and perhaps hospital-employed physicians as well. Going forward, all parties involved are likely to approach hospital-physician employment negotiations with greater caution and with a more conservative approach to permissible compensation formulas.

The *Tuomey* Case

On Sept. 30, 2013, a federal judge in South Carolina issued a $237.5 million judgment against Tuomey Healthcare System Inc.[4]

The *Tuomey* case involved a number of factual and legal disputes leading up to the blockbuster decision. The central issue among these was the manner in which that hospital system paid a group of part-time employee physicians for professional surgical services rendered at the hospital. The hospital billed and collected for their professional services and compensated the physicians through a combination of base and incentive pay. The formula was a rich one indeed, resulting in compensation dollars that, on average, exceeded the physicians' professional collections by 31 percent. In other words, as designed and operated, it virtually ensured a significant hospital subsidy in favor of the physicians as compared with what a physician in a free-standing group practice, doing his or her own billing and collections for the same services, could have realized.

Tuomey is particularly significant because of the size of the judgment and because it suggests a new criterion for determining whether a given compensation arrangement will be considered to exceed fair market value or not be "commercially reasonable." To the extent that this court focused heavily on the compensation being in excess of professional collections, it suggests a new standard not found anywhere in the Stark law statute, the regulations, or prior CMS commentary on physician compensation. The *Tuomey* decision is currently on appeal to the U.S. Circuit Court of Appeals for the Fourth Circuit. Given the size of the judgment, which would be catastrophic to virtually any hospital system, it seems likely the case will at some point be settled. The government has asked the hospital to escrow $50 million while the appeal and, presumably, settlement talks continue.

The *Halifax* Case

Shortly after the *Tuomey* decision, a federal district court in Florida issued a similarly significant judgment against Halifax Hospital.[5]

This case involved, among other issues, compensation paid to a group of six employed, full-time medical oncologists who practiced at the hospital. Those oncologists were eligible for an incentive bonus as part of their total compensation. The bonus was characterized as a productivity incentive, and it was apportioned between and among the six physicians in proportion to their individual professional productivity as measured by personally performed services. However, the bonus pool being thus distributed was derived from 15 percent of the operating margin of the hospital's medical oncology program. That margin included not just personally performed services, but also designated health services, including hospital outpatient charges and oncology drugs.

Unlike *Tuomey*, where the principal legal issue was whether the physician compensation met the Stark law's test for fair market value payment, the legal issue in *Halifax* was whether the bonuses reflected the volume or value of the physicians' referrals to the hospital. The court concluded that it did because the bonus pool included profits from hospital department operations, not just professional billings. As a result, even though the resulting compensation might have been within relevant salary survey ranges, the traditional determinant of fair market value (and each physician's share was determined by looking only at his or her professional productivity, not including hospital referrals), the formula was effectively tainted by virtue of how the productivity bonuses were funded.

Also, unlike the decision in *Tuomey* where the judge and jury assessed damages, the *Halifax* decision simply ruled on what it considered to be the relevant legal issue, leaving a determination of damages to be assessed against the hospital system to a subsequent trial. The day before that trial was scheduled to begin, the hospital system and the government announced a settlement agreement pursuant to which the hospital system agreed to pay the government $85 million to settle the medical oncology compensation and certain other issues in the case. Because of the other issues, it is not possible to determine precisely how much of the total settlement amount relates to the bonus compensation paid to the oncologists. However, based on the publicity surrounding the case, one can assume that a very substantial portion of the settlement relates to that aspect of the case.

Implications for Group Practices

The obvious question is the significance of these judicial developments for existing compensation plans in group practices throughout the country. Both cases interpreted the Stark law's employment exception, on which most hospital-employed physicians and their employers rely.

Physician-owned group practices, conversely, do not and cannot rely principally on the employment exception for their Stark law compliance strategies because it protects only a physician's compensation relationship with an employer and not whatever ownership interest a physician might have in the practice. Most, if not all, physician-owned practices, therefore, rely on the exception for in-office ancillary services found in 42 C.F.R. 411.355 (b) of the regulations, which exception protects both ownership and compensation relationships. And in most instances, for group physicians ordering ancillary services from their own groups to rely on that exception, the group itself must meet the Stark law's definition of what constitutes a bona fide medical group practice. That definition is found in 42 C.F.R. 411.352 of the regulations.

The rules governing compensation practices in such groups are found not in the in-office exception, but in the group practice definition, and specifically in subsections (g) and (i) of Section 411.352, which provide compensation alternatives that are in some respects similar to, and in other respects distinct from, the compensation test in the employment exception. Those distinctions provide more flexible treatment to group practices in several important respects.

As a general matter, they permit compensation formulas that indirectly reflect the volume or value of a physician's referrals to his or her own practice as long as the method falls under either (1) permissible productivity bonus provisions of the definition or (2) permissible profit-sharing methods. That greater flexibility is found principally in these attributes of the definition, all of which differ from the employment exception:

- There is no fair market value test in the group practice definition;
- Productivity bonus formulas might include services "incident to" a physician's professional service in addition to personally performed professional services;

- There is protection for any productivity bonus calculated in a "reasonable and verifiable" manner that is not directly related to the volume or value of a physician's referrals for designated services;

- Certain "deeming provisions" provide regulatory certainty for particular productivity bonus approaches that might otherwise be subject to potential scrutiny; and

- Profit-sharing formulas, as opposed to productivity bonus mechanisms, are permitted if they do not relate directly to the volume or value of referrals, provided the profits being distributed derive either from the designated services provided by the entire group or a component of the group consisting of five or more physicians.

That the compensation provisions of the group practice definition are more permissive than those in the employment exception is by no means accidental. The law was written this way as a result of advocacy efforts by MGMA and others, with both Congress and the regulators in the early days of the Stark law's development.

So what are the implications of the recent *Tuomey* and *Halifax* cases for physician-owned groups relying on the in-office ancillary services exception and the compensation provisions in the definition of group practice? The *Tuomey* case appears to have little substantive significance since the court's decision turned largely on an analysis of the employment exception's fair market value standard, and fair market value is not an element of the compensation provisions in the group practice definition. Similarly, *Halifax's* "tainted" funding source reasoning should be less applicable to groups, given the greater flexibility for productivity bonuses that relate indirectly to referrals and the express provision supporting profit-sharing mechanisms.

Conversely, one can imagine a challenge based on a blending of the two case theories: If a productivity bonus mechanism is funded in part with ancillary profits (*Halifax*) and results in compensation in excess of professional collections (*Tuomey*), then is it really a productivity mechanism at all, or is it a profit-sharing plan in sheep's clothing? In other words, might the outcome turn on proper characterization of the plan, and does that favor use of the Stark law's permissive provisions for profit sharing rather than, or in addition to, production-based bonuses?

Unfortunately, as with everything that is Stark law related, some uncertainty will remain unless and until courts are asked to interpret in an adversarial context a government challenge to a group's compensation system.

One aspect of both cases likely does have significant implications for any challenge to a group's compensation methods and that aspect is not substantive but procedural. In both cases, the respective judges placed the burden of proof on the defendants to prove compliance with an exception. The government's burden was limited to proving that a financial relationship existed and that there were referrals for designated health services subject to the Stark law.

Another possible implication of these two rulings relates to hospital-physician service contracts as opposed to employment relationships. For a variety of reasons, some hospitals contract with medical groups to purchase professional services. Group physicians serve hospital patients, the hospital bills and collects for its professional services, and the hospital pays the group as outlined by the contract. These arrangements are typically protected under the Stark law's exception for "personal service arrangements" found in 411.357 (d) of the regulations or for "fair market value compensation" found in 411.357 (l) of the rules.

Like the employment exception, both of these contract exceptions have a fair market value test and prohibit compensation that takes referrals into account. The fair market value exception also has a commercial reasonableness test. These are precisely the factors that became problematic when interpreted in *Tuomey* and *Halifax*. Were a court asked to interpret these compliance factors in the context of a professional services contract rather than employment, it might reach similar conclusions. It is not hard to imagine a future case in which a hospital that pays more for professional services than it collects for those same services finds itself accused of paying more than fair market value. Similarly, production-driven payments funded from sources other than mere professional collections may well be challenged as inevitably volume related.

Finally, we should not leave *Tuomey* and *Halifax* without noting that many hospital systems employing large numbers of doctors might be able to structure their physician practices to qualify as bona fide groups under the Stark law definition. These hospitals and their physician practice managers should explore compliance strategies based on the combination of the group practice definition and the in-office ancillary services exception instead of relying on what, prior to *Tuomey* and *Halifax*, legitimately seemed like the much simpler approach of reliance only on the employment exception.

⠿ Job Evaluation Methods

Not all jobs are created equal, and when determining pay levels, it is helpful to separate the jobs performed in your practice based on a number of factors. The four most popular job evaluation methods are ranking, classification, factor comparison, and point factor. There are advantages and disadvantages for each. In all cases, results should be compared with industry market data to make sure the practice is doing as well or better than its peers in key areas.

Ranking Method

The ranking method involves ranking the job descriptions in order from highest to lowest in each department based on a definition of value or contribution. It works best when there are just a few jobs (less than 30) to be evaluated. A matrix is developed to show the compensation committee how the jobs rank across departments.

The advantages are that it is the:

- Simplest;
- Fastest;
- Easiest to understand and explain to employees; and
- Least expensive job evaluation method.

The disadvantages are:

- It is subjective. It involves making nonquantitative decisions rather than making judgments or comparisons based on essential functions or the necessary knowledge, skills, and abilities needed for a job. No standards are used for comparison, which makes the process particularly difficult when a new job is created.

- It is cumbersome to use when there are many jobs to evaluate. If there are more than 30 jobs, the process usually takes too long.

Using Ranking

An individual or a committee can do the ranking department by department. The ranker writes down the job titles and puts them in order by value. A weighting system could also be used. Jobs are subjectively given "weights" to reflect what the rankers believe they are worth. Jobs can also be compared in pairs, meaning two jobs are put side by side and then one is chosen as more valuable than the other.

Develop a chart showing all the jobs in all the departments for the compensation committee to review. Then the jobs can be ranked. After the jobs are ranked from least to most valuable by one of these ranking methods, pay grades are established (entry level/beginner, junior, middle, and senior) for each position in each department.

Pay scales can be assigned for these grades after checking to see how similar jobs in the community are compensated. In this competitive analysis process, using benchmarks is helpful.

A few benchmark jobs (also known as key jobs) can be chosen and compared with what other medical groups pay. For example, an X-ray technician position, which has similar functions across medical practices, can be used when checking the average pay in the community. Then a pay scale can be set based on these benchmark jobs, placing other jobs in between the benchmarks based on ranking.

Benchmark jobs have:

- Well-known characteristics and are relatively stable over time;
- Commonalties across employers;
- Components representative of an entire range of jobs; and
- Acceptance in the external market for setting wages.

By reviewing the market price of benchmark jobs within the medical practice industry and one's community, a trend line can be established that fits for the group.

Classification Method

Classification is similar to ranking. It involves putting jobs in broad classes or categories based on job analysis findings and building a hierarchy. It uses some comparison standards, such as the complexity of the work and the amount of supervisory responsibility.

The advantages of this method are that it is:

- Simple;
- Fairly easy and fast to do; and
- Easy to understand.

The disadvantages are:

- The standards used are not exact, so the level of complexity may not be an exact yardstick. As a result, jobs may be forced into a slot that is not an exact fit; and
- It relies on subjective judgments and may build in biases based on gender, race, or other factors.

Although steadily improving, the national average for women's wages is still about 75 percent that of men. To prevent suspicion of gender bias, use the appropriate methods for determining job worth.

Using Classification

Classification can be applied by an individual or involve a committee. Job descriptions are slotted into a series of classes that cover the range of jobs. These classes are like a series of labeled shelves in a bookcase. Use the following steps:

1. Define each class;
2. Identify and slot benchmarks as reference points;
3. Prepare a classification plan; and
4. Apply the system to non-benchmark jobs.

Typically up to 14 classes are adequate. Many classes allow variability and diversity. Too many classes, however, inhibit their use as common denominators. Like job descriptions, class descriptions are only useful when they reflect the real work involved and when they represent meaningful similarities and differences among jobs.

Classification methods are typically occupation or industry specific. The government, for example, has a Defense Civilian Intelligence Personnel System based on job classifications.

Factor Comparison Method

The factor comparison method is used to evaluate jobs using two criteria: (1) a set of compensable factors, and (2) wages for benchmark jobs.

These two criteria combine to form a job comparison scale that can be used to set wages for non-benchmark jobs. This method is complex and unpopular.

Using Factor Comparison

A compensation committee is usually the group assigned to use this method, which involves dividing hourly pay into pay for each of the factors.

There are several steps in this process:

1. Begin as usual with job analysis, but put a twist on it by describing each job in terms of compensable factors. There are four universal ones: skill requirements, effort (physical and mental), responsibility, and working conditions.

2. Select benchmark jobs.

3. Rank benchmark jobs on each factor, assigning points for each one.

4. Assign benchmark wages to the factors. Decide how much of the wage rate for each benchmark job is associated with mental demand, responsibility, and so on.

The wage rate for an administrative assistant, for example, may be $15.00 per hour with $6 designated as pay for mental requirements, $4.00 for skill, $3.00 for responsibility, $1.50 for physical effort, and $0.50 for working conditions.

Point Factor Method

This popular system looks at a job's specific duties and responsibilities (essential functions) and awards points to each. It is an extension of the factor comparison method. The points are arbitrary, but they reflect the value that a medical practice attaches to each function. For example, if a practice values customer service highly, it would assign many points to this function.

The advantages are:

- The job value can be expressed in monetary terms;
- The method can be applied to a wide range of jobs; and
- It can be used with new jobs.

The disadvantages are:

- Pay judgments are subjective; and

- Standards for determining pay may have built-in biases.

Using the Point Factor Method

The typical set of compensable factors includes skill, responsibilities, effort, and working conditions:

- Skill equals experience, education, and ability.

- Responsibilities typically include fiscal and supervisory.

- Effort includes mental and physical.

- Working conditions include location, hazards, and extremes in environment.

Each factor is divided into levels or degrees and then assigned points. Each job is rated using the job evaluation instrument. The points for each factor are added to a total point score for the job.

Jobs are then grouped by total point scores and assigned to wage or salary grades. Similarly rated jobs are placed in the same wage or salary grade.

::: Computing Pay

After each job has been evaluated, the dollar value that each position is worth can be determined. This process is called pay computation, and requires you determine the:

- Number of pay structures needed;

- Number of pay grades within each structure;

- Minimum, midpoint, and maximum pay for each grade;

- Ways individuals can advance in pay grades;

- Record-keeping and reporting requirements; and

- Methods for communicating to employees about compensation.

A practice's compensation committee determines where it wants each job on the pay scale using the following categories:

- Premium (6 to 10 percent above market rates);
- Fully competitive (5 percent above market rates);
- Competitive (equal to market rates); or
- Marginal (1 to 5 percent below market rates).

Pay Grades

The compensation committee sets minimum, midpoint, and maximum pay levels for each pay grade. The minimum is typically set at a level that would be acceptable as a starting salary by 80 to 90 percent of potential candidates. The midpoint should be high enough to retain employees when they have reached a high level of proficiency. The maximum is used to retain the most competent employees.

For entry-level jobs, the range between each of the three levels is small (e.g., 20 to 25 percent). With higher-level positions, the range is broader (e.g., 35 to 40 percent) to ensure the flexibility needed to retain managers and administrators.

Setting Pay Grade Boundaries

A standard percentage difference should be used between midpoints for adjoining pay grades to ensure consistency in the pay structure. In healthcare organizations, there often is a small differential for lower-skilled employees, which is perhaps as low as 3 to 5 percent. At higher levels of skill, there are usually higher midpoint differences. The pay range within each pay grade should provide opportunities for employee growth. Ranges typically vary from 10 to 25 percent on either side of the midpoint. After the midpoint and the spread of each pay grade have been established, the minimum and maximum pay rates for each grade can be determined. For the maximum rate, multiply the midpoint value by the square root of the spread of the change; for the minimum rate, divide the midpoint value by the square root of the spread.

Setting Pay Steps within the Boundaries

After the boundaries of the pay grade are set, the number of pay steps in the range can be determined. Typically, the number of steps varies from 5 to 12 within each pay grade. The percentage increase within steps varies from about 2.5 to 5 percent. The compensation committees may decide to pay for performance or for longevity and set a wider range to reflect these objectives.

Determining Raises

How long should it take for an employee to move from the minimum to the maximum pay rate? Typically an employee starts at the lower end of the range and moves to the midpoint (the competitive market rate) within two or three years, assuming the employee's performance is satisfactory. Thereafter, the rate of advancement slows, with increases given for exceptional performance. For example, if the pay grade has a range of 10 steps, the employee would only move to the 7th step based on satisfactory performance and longevity. The remaining steps would be earned only for exceptional performance.

Determining How Many Pay Grades Are Appropriate

In large groups it is common to have one or more pay structures for different categories of workers, for example, a different one for higher-level administrators than for entry-level employees. In small groups a single pay structure is usually adequate.

For a larger group, there may be as many as 40 pay grades. For a small group, four to five pay grades work well. Regardless of the number of pay grades, use the following tips when establishing them:

1. Cluster positions so that those of the same general value are assigned to the same pay grade;

2. Place positions that are different in value in different pay grades; and

3. Ensure that pay grades reasonably conform to pay patterns in the labor market area.

Broad banding of pay grades is another possibility. This method reduces the number of pay grades to a few wide ones, such as one for salaried exempt, one for salaried nonexempt, and one for hourly employees.

Merit Pay

This traditional method is a performance-based system with financial rewards for employees who work harder and perform the best. Salary increases are scheduled at specific times, such as the anniversary date of employment, and the salary progresses from the pay-grade minimum to midpoint to maximum rate. Typically salary increases are more rapid and larger in the minimum to midpoint range and stay relatively stable around the midpoint, which is set at the local competitive market rate.

Pay raise criteria in this system include:

- Merit;
- Length of service;
- Experience;
- Productivity; and
- Performance.

Merit pay is designed to reward extraordinary performance. Over the years, however, economic rewards evolve into entitlements. This trend is fueled by the tendency of organizations to give almost everyone the same percentage increase in salary. This automatic approach has generated an increasing demand by employees for such material rewards, thus eroding their usefulness as incentives and managerial tools.

Longevity and Seniority Pay

This traditional system rewards length of service with steady increases in pay at set intervals. Increases tend to be the same for every employee with a satisfactory performance report. This system reduces conflicts between the supervisor and the employee, and with unions. The downside is that it does not reward employees for excellent performance, and it is falling out of favor.

If raises in this system are not monitored carefully, employees may be put in jeopardy of becoming ineligible for a pay raise because they reach the maximum end of the pay range. If a raise is given beyond the maximum, the salary is indicated as out of range and puts the employee and his or her supervisor in an awkward spot. Remind supervisors to stay out of this spot by helping them to work with employees to get the training and assistance needed to move up to another pay grade before they reach the end of the range. Some employees may not have the qualifications or desire to move up, and their salaries must remain capped.

Pay for Performance

If a medical practice is committed to rewarding performance, a system should be designed to give salary increases based on a negotiated plan between managers and employees for earning more responsibilities and achieving goals. With such a system, salary increases are neither automatic nor based on seniority or longevity.

A performance-appraisal system based on sound principles is the only way to avoid equal employment opportunity challenges. Such a plan typically sets standards to measure performance, encourages managers to give continual feedback about performance, corrects poor performance, reinforces goals, and rewards results.

One approach is to use a management-by-objectives system to establish result targets and to measure degrees of merit. Financial models (usually calculated on net collections) tend to work well in a practice with like workloads. Unit-based models (such as a relative-value model) often work better in a practice with differential workloads. There are many fine consultants available to structure productivity plans.

Most group practices now use some type of pay-for-performance method. Some physicians regard productivity measurement as an economic necessity, while others see it as crass commercialism that degrades the profession and dehumanizes the patients. The haphazard, "ready-fire-aim" approach to starting a practice leaves the group vulnerable when disagreements emerge.

Value-Based Physician Compensation

Developing a value-based physician compensation plan may be the best defense in the face of the emerging payer reimbursement models from Medicare and other payers.

Value-based plans can come in many forms — from pay-for-performance to a patient-centered medical home model — but there are a few important steps practices can take when implementing a value-based compensation plan.

Involve Physicians as Soon as Possible

If you're interested in implementing a value-based compensation model for your physicians, you'll want to involve them in the decision and development immediately. Communication should be clear at each step of the way, and it is usually better to err on the side of too much information rather than too little.

For resistant physicians, commit to working with them without sacrificing the entire plan. For example, physicians receiving a pay increase rarely complain unless it isn't enough. Physicians receiving less may accept a small decline, but will generally resist any material decline regardless of the reasons.

In these cases, changes may have to be phased in to allow for individual adjustment. For example, if someone's salary needs to be decreased by 15 percent, phase it in at 5 percent per year for three years.

It is important to try to make any reductions somewhat equal for all physicians. Physicians may need to accept a plan that is "equally unfair" with no one or two physicians benefiting more than the others.

Create a Compensation Plan Committee

An in-house compensation plan committee should develop the value-based compensation plan. For smaller practices, the committee should include the following:

- A physician leader and administrator;
- Some other type of administrator-physician team; and
- All physicians in the practice.

For larger practices, the committee should include:

- A subset of the organization, including physicians and administrative personnel;
- An outside consultant to promote objectivity and "absorb some of the unhappiness" or "take the heat" if needed; and
- A financial officer or accountant.

Other considerations include making sure the committee is separate from your governing board or approval authority body to ensure a different representation, but have at least one member of your governing board or approval authority serve on the committee. Involve a diverse physician mix to bring different viewpoints of what is considered fair.

Use Data to Build Your Plan

Data used to determine incentive payments and bonuses must be perceived as relevant by physicians. If physicians distrust the information that's driving compensation, they will reject the entire plan. For example, rather than just saying patient satisfaction is a part of the plan, include a number of patient care measures, the number of referrals, inpatient admissions, length of stay, ancillary services, patient panel size, and patient satisfaction survey results.

Incentive amounts should make sense to your particular type of doctor; a bonus that is meaningful and appropriate for a pediatrician might be too small for a cardiovascular surgeon because of the relative differences in their specialty-based compensation.

Pay Surveys

To ensure that pay grades and salary ranges are competitive, gather current data on rates and ranges for comparable jobs in the industry and community. Salary surveys can confirm that the practice's pay structure is competitive and assure the employees that it is fair.

A practice can use pay surveys published by compensation organizations and by the government. Examples include the American Management Association, the Society for Human Resource Management, MGMA, the U.S. Department of Labor, local chambers of commerce, and many private consulting firms. Such surveys are conducted by experts and include data from a large number of participants, resulting in a more accurate analysis. Compared to do-it-yourself surveys, these external surveys are less expensive, protect the anonymity of the participants, and are perceived as more credible.

For small- or medium-sized medical practices, external surveys are effective tools and should contain the following:

- Industry-specific job titles;
- A sufficient number of responses;
- The median and mean average salary for each job; and
- Results by job title, industry, and geographic area.

One way to learn about salary surveys is to participate in one. They require you to:

- Match your organization's job titles as closely as possible with those on the survey;
- Match your organization's structure with the structure on the survey, for example, how you group jobs such as accounting jobs;

- Match your job descriptions with those listed in the survey; and
- Make a copy of the survey before sending it in.

Compensation and Record-Keeping

The compensation information needed for budget purposes includes:

- Gross and net pay for each employee;
- Ratio of gross pay to net pay for the entire medical practice;
- Comparison of budgeted pay to actual pay;
- Breakdowns of compensation by team, department, classification, and pay grade; and
- Other pay statistics used for monitoring the group's performance.

Payroll information needed to comply with governmental laws and regulations and to inform employees about their compensation includes:

- Employee identification number (if used by the medical practice);
- Social Security number;
- Base pay;
- Time worked;
- Premium pay, incentive pay, and bonuses;
- Tax deductions; and
- Benefits.

⠿ Payroll Processing

Payroll processing can be quite complex for medical practices because of the array of options such as flexible benefits, various retirement savings plans, leaves of absence, shift differentials, and other offerings. It can be beneficial to use a payroll vendor for processing. No matter what choice is made, internal staff will need to collect, input, and report compensation data and be available to answer employee questions.

One payroll decision that must be made is the timing of paychecks. Should they be issued every Friday or every other Friday, or on the 15th of the month and the last day of the month? The finance department can help determine the best schedule for a medical practice. The pay calendar should be posted at the beginning of the year for all employees and supervisors to see.

You must also decide if you will offer direct deposits. This is convenient for both the employees and the organization. In fact, some companies mandate this step. The payroll department or payroll-processing vendor can help determine the pros and cons for your medical practice.

Bundling

With new payment models evolving, one of the biggest questions to be addressed is how to compensate physicians and align their interests and performance with the overall objectives of these new models, such as bundling.

First of all, let's assume that there will not be a total change from fee-for-service reimbursement to bundling overnight. The concept is still a work in progress and will probably result in a multitude of different models based on individual situations. In other words, there is a strong probability that you will be running your current physician compensation plan for some time now while incorporating additional components to address different payment methodologies. Additional components may include positive revenue sharing; negative loss allocation; and positive, neutral, or negative incentives for quality metric attainment.

There isn't going to be an easy one-size-fits-all, off-the-shelf method to compensate physicians for participation in bundled payment arrangements. Payers are going to want bundled reimbursement for a procedure or a menu of procedures to be discounted from current fee-for-service costs and will likely impose quality metric requirements to ensure that quality standards are met. Conversely, physicians want to be reasonably compensated for their efforts and training and are going to look at the proposal for bundled services payment and compare it with fee-for-service reimbursements. In addition, physicians should evaluate the potential risks and costs of meeting quality guidelines in terms of time and resources.

The physician and practice entity will need to evaluate each bundled service to determine how much of the payment (or loss) will accrue to the individual physician and/or practice entity. One possible scenario is to have all bundled service reimbursement segregated into a special account that participating physicians would draw on under a discounted fee-for-service basis. The practice would receive compensation to cover overhead, and any remaining funds (profits) could be allocated to physicians. This methodology could complement a primary physician compensation plan that is totally or partially based on production.

Another scenario includes physicians who are employed by an integrated delivery system and have straight salary compensation. A bundled services component that would allow risk and reward sharing could be added to that base salary.

The incentive or disincentive would have to be substantial enough to encourage physicians to actively participate in managing the bundled services.

Compensation Information for Employees

Employees want basic information about when and how they are paid, as well as information on how to read pay-stub information related to deductions and the other listed items. Some organizations provide an annual compensation report for employees that details not only pay elements, but also benefits and incentives.

The amount of information shared with employees about compensation depends on the group's philosophy. Do the managers emphasize open communication? Do they believe that the more information provided formally by management, the more employees will understand and the less they will seek out information through the grapevine?

Before sharing payroll information, ensure that a solid compensation program based on well-developed pay structures, pay grades, and salary rates and ranges is in place. It must stand up to employee scrutiny as they compare what the group offers with other organizations in the community.

Employees also want to know about payroll mechanics. What is the pay schedule? Is the option of direct deposit offered? Is it required? Are timesheets required? Which employees are required to submit them? What is the deadline for timesheet submission? These matters must be made clear.

Pay Adjustments

Pay structures need to be adjusted when medical practice or environmental variations occur. These include changes in inflationary rates, changes in the relative value of a job to the medical group, adjustments to job tasks and responsibilities, and developments of new technology. Adjustments may also need to be made to ensure that the medical practice achieves the three classic compensation goals:

1. Equal pay for equal work;

2. Competitive salaries; and

3. Rewards for performance.

The group can continually accomplish these goals by adjusting salary structures, pay grades, and individual salaries in the following ways:

- Remaining competitive by annually reviewing the labor market's prevailing pay rates for comparable jobs and adjusting the medical group's salary structure in unbiased ways;

- Retaining employees by rewarding outstanding performance through a competitive salary structure; and

- Making equitable adjustments to employee salaries when promotions or demotions occur.

Listed here are the three types of pay adjustments.

1. Across-the-board increases to all employees because of inflationary, cost-of-living adjustment (COLA), or labor market factors. These increases are typically an equal percentage to all employees. This changes the dollar amounts for each grade and step in the salary structure but does not move any employee or job within the structure. A COLA increase was common in the past but is less popular today.

2. Individual performance increases or longevity increases. Merit pay was designed to reward performance but is often given automatically. Using a pay-for-performance system, an employee meets prenegotiated goals and earns rewards. The manager teams with the employee to set performance standards and to give continuous feedback so that the employee feels he or she has earned the increase.

Adjustments are typically made when an employee is promoted and accepts higher-level job duties and responsibilities. Conversely, if an employee is demoted to a lower-level position, a salary decrease should occur. An employee may seek a less demanding position for personal reasons.

3. Job classification increases. These occur when the supply of available candidates for a job is so tight that the job becomes more valuable in the labor market. For example, the current national shortage of nurses has caused the value of this job category to increase.

Work Premiums and Overtime

Healthcare organizations often ask employees to work outside the standard 8-to-5 routine. To compensate for these "off hours," work premiums may be used to pay for overtime, weekend and holiday work, and on-call or standby work. Work premium policies must comply with federal overtime wage and hour laws.

Under the Fair Labor Standards Act (FLSA), organizations must pay a time-and-one-half premium for the hours beyond 40 that a nonexempt employee works in one workweek. This means overtime. This type of pay can help manage costs; having an employee work a few more hours means the practice does not have to hire another employee.

Overtime authorization can inadvertently become automatic, however, and costs can mount quickly. Note whether employees are stretching out their work to get overtime work or whether managers are slow to recognize that additional staff is needed.

Employees can quickly burn out if asked to do extra hours on a regular basis. This has become a problem, for example, for nurses working in short-staffed hospitals. It is best to assign overtime work only to those qualified employees who voluntarily request extra hours of work.

Be aware of the various compensation compliance issues. For specifics, refer to FLSA regulations. The FLSA does allow inpatient healthcare providers to use an 8/80 pay period system. However, few medical practices have such facilities.

Shift, Weekend, and Holiday Work

Some groups have irregular shifts at the medical practice, for example, from 4 p.m. to midnight or from midnight to 8 a.m. This scenario occurs more in a hospital setting, but some groups, such as those that do cosmetic surgery, have patients stay overnight. In these cases, it is common to add a shift differential rate of pay to the normal rate paid to nonexempt employees. This could be either a flat amount or a percentage. Salaried employees doing shift work sometimes receive an additional monthly increment to their base pay.

Some employees who work Monday through Friday receive premium pay for working on weekends or holidays even though the hours worked during the week do not exceed 40. Such after-hours work is often compensated at time and one-half. It is rare that an employee receives both overtime and weekend or holiday pay.

Call-in and Standby Premiums

Occasionally medical practices need employees to stand by to perform work assignments outside of normal working hours. Because such on-call assignments are an inconvenience to employees, premium compensation should be provided — usually at one and one-half times their regular hourly rate.

As an alternative, a minimum reporting premium policy may be established that guarantees a certain amount of pay for being on call. A standard reporting premium is two to four hours of pay for reporting to work outside of normal working hours, regardless of how long the employee works.

Such policies may also apply to other types of jobs in the medical practice, particularly jobs in an information systems department. Like most companies, healthcare organizations are dangerously vulnerable to computer breakdowns. For that reason, most medical practices have computer staff members on call 24 hours a day and provide premium pay for their availability.

Dispute Resolution

No matter how carefully a compensation system is crafted and implemented, someone will eventually become unhappy. If you can't resolve this type of dissatisfaction, it can lead to a great deal of conflict in the practice. Your governance documents should have a clear system for appeals and disputes. Even with these precautions, disputes may become unsolvable, at which point you should seek legal counsel.

⸬ Creating a Compensation Plan: A Step-by-Step Case Study

To put everything discussed into context, consider the following case study of Hometown Surgical, which used this step-by-step process to create a fair and equitable physician compensation plan that advanced the practice's mission and vision.

Step 1: Define the Problem

Charged with developing an acceptable physician compensation plan for its newly merged practice, members of Hometown Surgical's compensation committee jumped right into step 1 of the evidence-based management decision-making methodology, which is to define the problem at hand.

Even though one of the pre-merged practices had followed an equal-share compensation plan for years, most of the new group voted to consider an exclusively production-based compensation model. Truthfully, the two most productive surgeons in the equal-share practice had grown to resent the existing compensation plan.

In creating a plan that all of the physicians — or at least a strong majority — would perceive as fair, the committee's challenge lay in arriving at a group definition of "fair." In pursuit of that definition, the practice administrator led a brainstorming session, during which the group identified the issues that a good compensation scheme would effectively address. In other words, what were the new plan's objectives? What did the group want to accomplish with its compensation scheme?

With all of the ideas on a whiteboard, committee members reviewed the list and eliminated or combined duplicate and closely related issues. Finally, they sorted the list into three categories:

1. Nonnegotiable (deal breakers);

2. Extremely important; and

3. Desirable but not essential.

Nonnegotiable Criteria

The committee determined that its recommended compensation must meet each of the following criteria:

- Every physician has the opportunity to earn an income that compares favorably to surgeons in similar practice settings locally, regionally, and nationally;

- The plan clearly rewards greater productivity with higher pay; and

- The plan does not penalize individual physicians for lost productivity caused by their involvement in group-sanctioned projects or activities (e.g., agreeing to see patients in a new satellite office with low start-up patient volume).

Extremely Important Criteria

Although meeting *all* of the following criteria was not essential, the group decided it would not likely recommend any compensation plan that missed the mark on two or three:

1. Every physician has the opportunity to maintain his or her pre-implementation income level without seriously disrupting his or her personal financial planning.

2. The plan sets clear minimum production expectations, with financial penalties assessed to those physicians failing to meet them.

3. The plan provides financial incentives for physician behaviors that support the group's vision and strategic plans.

Desirable but Not Essential Criteria

The committee members decided they would make every effort to craft a plan that would meet these criteria as well; however, the doctors would not reject a formula that proved not to *fully* meet them:

- The plan provides bonus pay for nonclinical activities that promote the practice (e.g., public-relations events, marketing efforts, developing and retaining referring physicians, community and hospital involvement, other "good citizenship" behavior);

- The plan pays bonuses to physicians who meet measurable quality-improvement, patient-satisfaction, and safety goals; and

- The plan rewards physicians for effectively using resources and controlling overhead costs.

Overall, the committee determined that the ideal compensation plan was one that gave every physician a fighting chance at maintaining or growing his or her income in exchange for each physician's best efforts to produce revenue on par with other surgeons in similar practice settings. Financial incentives would focus on factors more or less within each physician's personal control and always with an eye toward advancing the group's overall agenda.

Step 2: Explore Information Needs

Members of Hometown Surgical's compensation committee used an evidence-based approach for modifying the practice's compensation strategy. Identifying the project's scope and objectives provided a clearer picture of the kinds of data and information necessary to achieve the project's goals. Each goal prompted a series of natural questions that led to a search for useful information:

- **Overall goal** — Construct a production-based compensation plan that encourages physicians to maintain reasonable productivity and rewards them with optimum pay:

  - What issues have other practices faced when creating or revising their compensation plans?

  - Rather than building a plan from scratch, can we find a ready-made profit-distribution formula that we can adapt and implement in our practice?

- **Nonnegotiable goal 1** — Provide the opportunity for physicians to earn competitive incomes locally, regionally, and nationally:

  - How much do general surgeons in comparable practice settings earn in our locale, in our region, and across the United States?

  - How have our surgeons' historical incomes compared to national and regional averages?

- **Nonnegotiable goal 2** — Reward higher productivity with higher pay:

  - How do other groups measure physician productivity?

  - What is the relationship between productivity and compensation for surgeons in similar practice settings?

- **Nonnegotiable goal 3** — Avoid penalizing physicians when serving the group results in lower productivity:
  - What kinds of strategic activities could impair a physician's productivity?
  - How can we measure or estimate the potential negative effect of such activities?
  - How can or should we make up the difference?
- **Secondary goal 1** — Provide the opportunity for physicians to maintain current (pre-implementation) income levels:
  - How much did each physician earn (including both direct and indirect compensation) in the previous two or three years?
  - What are reasonable income expectations over the next two or three years?
  - How have other practices successfully managed compensation plan transitions?
- **Secondary goal 2** — Set clear minimum-production standards and provide penalties for failing to meet standards:
  - How much productivity do general surgeons report in comparable practice settings and in our locale, in our region, and across the United States?
  - Historically, what has been each physician's production for the past two or three years?
- **Secondary goal 3** — Provide financial incentives for behaviors that support the group's vision and strategic plans:
  - What kinds of physician behaviors do other practices recognize and reward?
  - What kinds of physician behaviors do other practices penalize?
  - How do other practices structure rewards and penalties?
- **Additional goal 1** — Provide bonus incentives for "good citizenship" activities and behaviors:
  - Do other practices reward nonclinical efforts such as marketing, educational presentations, and other activities?
  - How do they structure bonuses to reward good citizenship?

- **Additional goal 2** — Provide incentives for meeting quality, safety, and patient-satisfaction goals:
  - How do other practices quantify quality and excellence measures?
  - How do they structure bonuses for meeting quality and excellence goals?
- **Additional goal 3** — Reward physicians for practice overhead cost containment:
  - How do other practices allocate overhead expenses?
  - How do other practices reward or penalize physician behaviors that positively or negatively impact practice costs?

Step 3: Collect the Data

The Hometown Surgical compensation committee's data needs were sizeable, so the practice administrator tapped several staff members to help collect and organize it. Staffers secured copies of articles and Web pages with reports, commentary, and instructions, and made copies for each physician committee member. The practice administrator prefaced report and article excerpts with a brief cover memo that highlighted pertinent information on which the physicians could focus.

Meanwhile, the practice administrator collected internal data from the group's practice management system (PMS). When the two previously separate practices had merged, the group had decided to maintain historic PMS information in two original databases, starting the new, combined practice with a clean information technology system. Consequently, the practice administrator had to collect and recap data from three separate systems.

Using the computer systems' individual data-export functions, the practice administrator used many of the standard charge, payment, and adjustment reports; accounts-receivable reports; appointment schedule and encounter reports; and procedure analysis reports. Each system could export the report data in CSV (comma-separated value) format for easy conversion to Microsoft® Excel or another spreadsheet program.

Whenever possible, the practice administrator sorted the report results by physician and location to help highlight any outliers. An outlying data point could inadvertently give a physician an unfair advantage or disadvantage if the profit-distribution formula didn't account for the anomaly. The main data reports the practice administrator ran included:

- **Aged accounts receivable** — by physician, payer type, and service location;

- **Charge analysis** — by physician, procedure code, payer type, and service location;

- **Payment analysis** — by physician, procedure code, payer type, and service location;

- **Adjustment report** — by physician, procedure code, payer type, and service location;

- **Appointment/encounter report** — by physician, payer type, and service location, including next-available appointment analysis and a no-show report; and

- **Referring physician report** — by physician.

In addition to the revenue-cycle reports, the practice administrator exported data from the practice accounting software to Excel, showing the past three years' data from each practice. These reports detailed practice expenses and physician compensation.

Step 4: Interpret the Data

By now, Hometown Surgical's administrator and its compensation committee had amassed significant information and raw data to assist with its evidence-based approach to modifying the practice's compensation strategy. As it quickly became obvious that making sense of it all would require significant effort, the group divided the work among its members. Two physicians focused on articles, books, and reports about compensation plans, while two others studied statistical data about physician compensation and productivity. The administrator concentrated on developing spreadsheets to present internal data to the rest of the committee, which would allow members to compare the practice's statistics with national and regional benchmarks.

Looking for Models

The subcommittee charged with perusing general compensation-planning information spent significant time reviewing the various types of compensation plans, their strengths and weaknesses, and different ways to measure physician productivity. It distributed summary notes to the rest of the committee.

The subcommittee also worked with the rest of the committee to determine what statistical data regarding productivity, revenue management, and practice costs comprised the critical framework for comparing and designing compensation plans, projecting how variations in those data points would impact physician income for better or worse.

Benchmarking for Compensation Design

The administrator reviewed benchmarking principles as he organized the PMS and accounting-system data into spreadsheets for comparison purposes.

Understanding the Statistics

The physicians studying survey data familiarized themselves with the numbers reported by surgeons in similar practice settings. They noted that certain factors affected productivity and compensation levels:

- Geographic region;
- Group size;
- Single vs. multispecialty;
- Physician owned vs. hospital or system owned; and
- Years in practice.

Similarly, practice-setting characteristics seemed to affect practice expenses and total profitability. Even revenue-cycle statistics varied somewhat by practice characteristics. The physicians studying the data noted patterns that emerged from the sea of numbers included in the reports.

When the practice administrator provided similar data points specific to Hometown Surgical, the physicians led a discussion comparing the practice's numbers to the nationally reported benchmarks.

Key Performance Indicators

Armed with a wide variety of information, the committee regrouped to begin serious discussions about appropriate key performance indicators (KPIs) for Hometown Surgical. The most important indicator — how to measure productivity — posed some difficult challenges. Possible measures included:

- Gross and/or net charges;
- Gross and/or net collections;
- Relative value units (RVUs);
- Patient encounters; and
- Hours worked in various settings (clinic, operating room, night call, etc.).

No measure was perfect. Each standard had various effects beyond the individual physician's control (e.g., collections can increase or decrease because of payer mix and revenue-cycle management instead of how much the physician actually worked). Some measures had aspects that a physician could possibly "rig" or "game" (e.g., by overcoding, overutilization, or pushing the medically necessary boundaries).

The doctors found RVUs to be an attractive measure because most payers had gravitated toward CMS's resource-based system. Some of the physicians, though, noted that through the years, CMS's Medicare Payment Advisory Commission had taken aim at specific procedures and depressed their values (and reimbursement), even when the rest of the payer community continued to pay at a higher rate.

Using the PMS procedure data presented by the administrator, the committee developed a list representing the practice's top Current Procedural Terminology (CPT®)* codes, which represented 80 percent of the practice's productivity. They then turned to the payment and adjustment reports to compare reimbursement by payer. Some hernia surgery and gallbladder surgery codes showed relatively higher values among commercial payers.

In the end, the group decided to recommend using a modified RVU scale to measure physicians' primary productivity. The relative values for some codes were adjusted to offset the depressed values in Medicare's RBRVS (resource-based relative value scale).

---

* CPT © 2015 American Medical Association. All rights reserved.

Step 5: Size Up the Alternatives

By now, members of Hometown Surgical's compensation committee had a more thorough knowledge than ever of the key issues surrounding the design of an effective physician compensation plan. They had studied:

- Benchmarking data from across the nation;

- Internal data and how it compared to national benchmarks;

- Compensation plan types and philosophies;

- KPIs; and

- Specific issues facing general surgery and their own practice.

Now it was time to create the general framework for the plan. Two production-based models rose to the top among the plans under consideration, and the committee narrowed their choices down to two schemes.

The committee members liked the "guaranteed base plus incentive" option shown in Exhibit 8.1 because it provided a predictable base salary each month and relied on RVUs to calculate physician productivity. The plan assigned a compensation conversion factor to production RVUs, paying each physician $25.29 for every RVU that he or she produced, *including* the base salary. In other words, the physician had to produce enough RVUs to cover his or her base salary before the bonus kicked in.

The alternative model, "base plus incentive with expense consideration" as shown in Exhibit 8.2, featured a variable base salary calculated on the practice's overall revenue production in the previous period. The base salary more or less functioned as a "draw" against the physician's share in the practice's net profit (revenue less expenses). The doctors' shares in the excess (profit) increased dramatically as the profit margin grew.

In studying the strengths and weaknesses of each model, the committee ended up creating a hybrid of the two. Committee members decided to recommend a plan that started with an annual base salary that represented 80 percent of the physicians' prior-year salaries. The base salary would serve as a draw against each physician's total compensation, which would amount to his or her share in the practice's net profits, commensurate with his or her share in the practice's total RVU production.

EXHIBIT 8.1

Guaranteed Base Plus Incentive[6]

Base and incentive compensation example	Example	
■ Base salary set at defined level (e.g., $400,000)	Mean	$24.40
■ Incentive paid where $ per total RVU (TRVU) × TRVU production exceeds base salary	25th	$21.34
■ Incentive compensation comp/TRVU conversion factor calculated at average of 25th percentile, mean, median, 75th percentile, and 90th percentile using MGMA survey data for specialty	Median	$25.45
	74th	$26.98
	90th	$28.29
	Average	$25.29
Example		
■ TRVU for quarter	TRVU	3,450.00
■ TRVU × conversion factor = compensation earned	$ per TRVU	$25.29
■ Base salary = $400,000 ($100,000 per quarter)	Total for quarter	$87,250
■ Physician compensation using $ per TRVU does not meet base compensation for quarter, so he/she receives base only ($100,000)		

RVU – relative value unit
TRVU – total RVUs

Some concerns were raised regarding the fairest way to allocate expenses. Higher producers worried that they would, in effect, be paying a disproportionately high share of practice costs. They believed their increased productivity did not affect costs at the same rate. To offset this concern, the committee decided to follow a tiered bonus distribution.

Step 6: Present the Information

To prepare an effective presentation for the practice's fellow partners, Hometown Surgical's compensation committee scheduled its next meeting on a Saturday morning when they could spend several hours without interruption. They were reasonably comfortable with the plan they intended to recommend, but they knew that the partners would ask tough questions and any compensation scheme would be a hard sell.

EXHIBIT 8.2

Base Plus Incentive with Expense Consideration[7]

Base salary	Example	
■ Set in relation to net practice revenues (NPR) in prior period	Under $350,000	= $120,000
■ NPR includes revenues from direct professional services (including managed care bonus/deficit), excluding ancillary services	$350,001–$400,000	= $140,000
	More than $401,000	= $160,000
■ Incentive compensation comp/TRVU conversion factor calculated at average of 25th percentile, mean, median, 75th percentile, and 90th percentile using MGMA survey data for specialty		

Incentive compensation

- ■ Equal to NPR less allocated practice-related expenses
- ■ If net surplus, the physician receives
  - > 15 percent of first $15,000
  - > 75 percent of next up to $50,000
  - > 80 percent of remainder over $50,000

NPR – net practice revenues
TRVU – total RVUs

Organizing the Team

The committee determined that physicians might be less resistant to the proposed plan if a fellow doctor served as point person during the presentation. One physician on the team, Dr. Brown, had a knack for numbers and was an obvious choice for this role, with the administrator handling technical details about data reports, spreadsheets, and the Microsoft® PowerPoint presentation.

Other committee members were assigned specific topics on which to focus in their preparations. The subcommittee members who worked with conceptual design reports would try to answer questions about philosophies and design issues. Those who had pored over survey reports were charged with presenting comparative data.

Refining the Reports

The practice administrator created a spreadsheet that would take center stage at the partnership meeting. First, he constructed the spreadsheet to perform the calculations necessary for processing practice financial data through the new profit-distribution formula. To test the cell calculations, he used simple, round numbers to make it easier to track the effects caused by any adjustments in the data.

Satisfied that the spreadsheet was functioning properly, he plugged in real, historical data from the pre-merged practices to show the physicians what they would have earned if they had used the proposed compensation plan during the 12 months before the merger. The presentation included three components:

1. Introduction to physician compensation planning;

2. Comparison of Hometown Surgical's financial performance with national survey statistics (benchmarking to discover opportunities for improvement); and

3. The recommended plan, how it works, and why the committee recommends it.

The practice administrator focused on simplicity and accuracy. Top-performing practices have often refined their compensation plans to the point that nearly any member of the practice can describe in simple terms how he or she gets paid. He minimized verbiage and relied on diagrams, charts, and graphs wherever possible.

Finally, the practice administrator and the committee designed a pre-meeting packet to distribute one week before the event. This report included background information about compensation philosophy and a few simplified sample schemes. It included a one-page summary showing Hometown Surgical's KPIs compared to national survey data and a diagram that explained, without fine details, the compensation plan's main features. A cover memo strongly urged the physicians to study the handouts before the meeting.

Moderating the Meeting

The group's president and the administrator scheduled a special partner meeting with no other items on the agenda. They contacted each partner to verify availability, because they believed they couldn't complete the task without everyone's attendance.

Once the meeting opened, the president made very few remarks and turned the podium over to Dr. Brown. Using the presentation the practice administrator had prepared as a focal point and guide, Dr. Brown led the presentation and discussion.

Step 7: Determine the Outcome

The Hometown Surgical compensation committee's presentation to the other physicians, highlighting its recommendations for a new physician compensation model, went well. The questions and discussions during the introduction and theoretical portions of the presentation seemed almost academic at times. It wasn't particularly difficult to arrive at a general consensus regarding the goals and principles behind the committee's recommended plan. They all agreed, with varying levels of enthusiasm, that:

- Their plan should follow a production-based scheme;

- RVUs seemed the most neutral way to measure physician productivity;

- The plan should include an expense-sharing component; and

- High producers should not bear an unfair portion of shared expenses.

The discussion's tone shifted, however, when the administrator distributed the spreadsheet report comparing individual physicians' actual incomes during the previous 12 months to what they *would have been paid* if the proposed plan were in place. Predictably, lower producers didn't like seeing that their incomes would have been lower under the new compensation formula.

Evidence Pays Off

Thanks to the extensive research, that is, gathering evidence on which the committee based its recommendations, the committee was able to respond to doubters with sensible answers that helped mitigate some of the concerns. They could:

- Show how production-based reimbursement has almost always had a positive effect on the success of group practices;

- Explain how the formula's features helped control the physicians' share of practice overhead expense;

- Offer sound arguments for how the formula would benefit the practice in the future as it recruited new physicians just starting out in the practice; and

- Even show how the group's strategic expense consolidation plans for the near future should enhance the bottom line, resulting in higher incomes for the physicians in the merged practice, which meant the lower-producing doctors' incomes would not drop sharply.

Another advantage to the committee's extensive preparations arose when questions and comments from the partners suggested modifying or tweaking the formula. When a partner would ask "What if ...?," the administrator could enter the "what-if" numbers into the spreadsheet and the group could view the results on the projected image. This way, the entire group had direct input regarding some of the final details of the proposed formula. They set base salary levels, scheduled bonus payments, and determined the tiers for bonus distributions. They also agreed to use retained earnings as a secondary bonus pool to compensate and incentivize partners for nonclinical activities.

In the end, the vote was almost unanimous in accepting the now-modified formula as recommended by the committee. One physician dissented, though he assured his colleagues that he would go along with the majority without complaint. The official practice minutes showed that the partners resolved to:

- Adopt the committee's recommended formula as modified during the meeting;

- Have the practice's legal counsel and CPA create the exact wording for the agreement that everyone would sign;

- Implement the plan at the beginning of the next quarter and continue testing and comparing the new plan's formula against actual compensation for the 90 days before going live;

- Monitor the plan closely for three to six months after the go-live date to make further adjustments; and

- Review the plan's performance six months after going live, at which time the group would vote again to continue with the plan, modify it radically, or replace it entirely.

Step 8: Evaluate the Effect and Outcome

Within a week of Hometown Surgical's partner meeting, during which the physicians had voted in favor of the new physician compensation plan, the group received a draft agreement for review, along with a one-week turnaround for comments. Two doctors wanted to run the agreement by their personal attorneys before weighing in.

In the meantime, the practice administrator modified his master spreadsheet to reflect the plan adjustments the partners had made during the meeting. He formatted a summary page that highlighted the key data points from month to month and allowed each physician to clearly see not only how much he or she earned but also to understand how the figure was calculated. He made sure that the report clearly displayed both the RVUs credited to each physician and the dollar value for his or her gross charges and collections. The practice administrator hoped that seeing actual dollar amounts would help the lower-producing physicians avoid a sense of unfairness on seeing their more productive colleagues earning more.

Going Live

After the three-month dry run, during which physicians could compare their actual incomes to what they would have earned under the new formula, the group was ready to go live. In keeping with their resolution, the physicians discussed the new plan's effect at each of their monthly meetings.

At first, the charges and collections posted on their income reports caused some confusion. Some physicians saw no clear pattern in the relationship between charges and payments. The practice administrator explained that charges and collections reported in any given month actually aren't closely connected. The bulk of any month's collection activity really pertains to charges submitted one to three months earlier. The group's average days in accounts receivable normally ran about 50 days, so he created a six-month rolling report with a graphic display of charge and collection amounts. The doctors could see how rising and falling collections each month shadowed charges by one or two months on the graph.

As the months went by, the group asked questions, and individual physicians occasionally proposed changing or tweaking the plan here or there, but in the end, the only changes approved had to do with adjusting the bonus tiers slightly and further refining the reports for clarity.

Sixth-Month Review

As promised, the president put "re-evaluation of profit formula" on the monthly partner meeting six months after the go-live date. By then, the physicians had grown accustomed to the new plan, believed they understood it well, and decided to keep it.

Merging the two practices had produced some overhead reduction as the new entity was able to eliminate some resource redundancy and gain some volume-based price breaks on supplies. Overall productivity was up, possibly spurred on by the new plan. Most, but not all, of the increased volume was seen among the lower producers. The youngest member of the group built his new practice rather quickly, and older members suspected that the production formula provided the "carrot on a stick" that enhanced the new surgeon's motivation.

Six months into the plan, the physicians voted unanimously to keep the plan without major modification. Even the physician who had dissented earlier voted to stay the course, albeit with some reluctance, saying, "It's clear we'll never go back to an equal-share plan, so I might as well show my support for our group."

⁝ Conclusion

The effective management of physician compensation is complex, requiring sophisticated interpersonal and technical skills. The practice administrator demonstrates leadership in this area by identifying and implementing compensation packages that support the mission of the practice as well as the motivation of physicians and the quality of patient care delivery.

Notes

1. "Data Book," Association of American Medical Colleges (AAMC), http:// aamc.org/ publications; "AAMC FACTS: Applicants, Matriculants, Enrollment, Graduates, MD/PhD, and Residency Applicants Data," AAMC, www.aamc.org/data/facts/.

2. Social Security Act Section 1877, 42 U.S.C. 1395 nn.

3. 42 C.F.R. 411.351 *et seq.*

4. U.S. *ex rel. Drakeford v. Tuomey Healthcare System,* 2013 WL 5503695 (D.S.C. 2013).

5. U.S. *ex rel. Baklid-Kunz v. Halifax Hosp. Med. Ctr.,* 2013 WL 6017329 (M.D. Fla. filed Nov. 13, 2013).

6. Bruce A. Johnson and Deborah Walker Keegan, *Physician Compensation Plans: State-of-the-Art Strategies* (Englewood, CO: MGMA, 2009).

7. Johnson and Keegan, *Physician Compensation Plans.*

Chapter 9

Monitoring Physician Conduct and Performance

PHYSICIANS ARE KEY to the quality of patient care delivery and the overall health of the medical practice. As leaders, their behavior sets the tone for the entire organization. It is therefore critically important for the practice administrator to ensure that consistent performance expectations and professional codes of conduct are adhered to by physicians as well as other staff. The competent administration of these standards includes skill in developing and implementing policies, communicating and clarifying performance expectations, supporting organizational and professional leadership groups to implement standards, facilitating conflict resolution, and fostering the growth and development of physician leaders as knowledgeable, participative stakeholders.

::: Managing Clinical Staff Conduct and Performance Expectations

Written standards of conduct and expectations should be developed and implemented within every well-managed medical group. This forms the basis for what is expected of the group's members and is also essential for the continuation of group culture.

Professional Standards Committee

The professional standards committee consists of the department chiefs from each division (or, in smaller organizations, this might be the duty of the managing partner or senior partner). Each department must have procedures in place to deal with performance and behavioral issues that do not merit escalation to the executive board level.

Professional Standards Documentation for Physicians

A professional standards document similar to the one presented here should be signed and become part of each physician's personnel file. A professional standards document for physicians could include the following expectations:

- Provide high-quality health services that respond to individual, family, and community needs;
- Maintain the integrity and quality of job performance by giving the best effort possible on the job;
- Provide healthcare services in compliance with all applicable laws, regulations, and standards, including state and federal legislation regarding patients' rights;
- Ensure that each clinical assessment is undertaken by individuals qualified to conduct such assessment;
- Maintain medical records and documentation to meet the requirements of the medical staff bylaws, facilities policies, accreditation standards, and all applicable laws and regulations;
- Maintain medical records in a legible manner;
- Provide required documentation that the services were, in fact, provided and use billing codes that accurately describe the services provided;
- Preserve the practice's property, facilities, equipment, and supplies, whether owned or leased;
- Encourage fellow physicians to develop their skills and potential;
- Actively strive to create a professional atmosphere that will be admired by physicians, patients, and visitors;
- Show respect and consideration for one another, regardless of position, station, or relationship;

- Recognize and support the diversity of the practice's physicians, staff, patients, and communities as a valuable asset;
- Use conflict resolution skills in managing disagreements;
- Address dissatisfaction with policies through appropriate channels;
- Communicate with others clearly and directly, displaying respect for their dignity;
- Address concerns about clinical judgment with associates directly and privately;
- Support policies promoting cooperation and teamwork;
- Address concerns about operational or physician performance issues in an appropriate setting and in a respectful manner;
- Dress in a professional manner; and
- Disclose and avoid conflicts of interest.

Regarding the last expectation, conflicts of interest occur when a physician's outside interests or activities might compromise his or her obligations to patients or the practice. Because of the wide variety of activities that may constitute a conflict, a physician should consult the executive board if uncertain about a particular activity. If a conflict is identified, the preferred action is to terminate the outside activity or remove oneself from any activity in patient care or the practice that may constitute a conflict. If this is not possible, measures should be taken in consultation with the executive board to minimize the effects of such a conflict.

Dealing with Unreasonable Behaviors

In general, an unreasonable behavior is any activity that:

- Undermines practice morale;
- Heightens physician turnover;
- Detracts from productive activities;
- Increases the risk of ineffective or substandard practices;
- Generates poor patient satisfaction;
- Intimidates or threatens harm to others; or
- Disproportionately causes distress to others in the work environment.

Unreasonable behavior includes, but is certainly not limited to, such behaviors as:

- Failing to comply with professional standards;

- Addressing nonconstructive criticism in such a way as to intimidate, undermine confidence, belittle, or to impute stupidity or incompetence;

- Imposing idiosyncratic requirements on nurses or other staff members that does not add to quality patient care but serves only to burden them with special treatment for the physician;

- Using foul or abusive language directed at staff members or others associated with the practice, such as hospital personnel, vendors, and so on;

- Arbitrarily sidestepping policies;

- Acting in ways that could be perceived as sexual harassment;

- Criticizing staff in front of others;

- Showing disrespect or being discourteous;

- Relying on intimidation to get his or her way;

- Leveling attacks that are personal, irrelevant, or go beyond the bounds of fair, professional comments at others (respectful confrontations are helpful and encouraged, but personal attacks are out of bounds);

- Purposefully violating or ordering an employee to violate the practice's employment or physician policies;

- Retaliating in any way, at present or in the future, against any employee who reports an incident to the professional standards committee;

- Performing actions in the name of the group without the group's authorization; and

- Engaging in any other behavior, not specifically just listed, which, after report and investigation, is deemed disruptive by the professional standards committee.

Professional Standards Violation Policy for Physicians

The professional standards violation policy for physicians outlines collegial steps that can be taken in an attempt to resolve complaints about inappropriate conduct exhibited by physicians. There could, however, be a single incident of inappropriate conduct or a continuation of conduct that is so unacceptable as to make such collegial steps inappropriate. Therefore, nothing in this policy precludes immediate referral to the executive board, if warranted. It is the responsibility of the president or other physician leader of the medical group to refer the matter to the board.

The goal of this policy is to address and motivate a change in behavior that would be consistent with the professional standards, mission, vision, and core values established by the practice. Specifically, such a policy promotes collegial cooperation, recruitment and retention of quality physicians and staff, and incentives to achieve the practice's strategic goals.

If there is a report of a second incident about a similar issue for the same physician within a two-year period and a determination that inappropriate conduct has occurred, the professional standards committee may issue a report and recommendation to the executive board that could include a financial assessment. The recommended assessment amount should be determined by an average of the committee members' inputs through secret ballot, but should be within a predetermined upper and lower boundary. This possible assessment would be deducted from the physician's paycheck on the payday following the executive board's approval.

If there is a report of a third infraction of a similar nature, and if the committee determines that inappropriate conduct has occurred, the matter is then sent to the executive board for further action.

It is important to document a plan of correction that clearly addresses the desired improvement expected of the physician. This might include the following guidelines:

- Do not pass off work to other partners, either junior or senior, that you can or should do yourself;
- Provide comprehensive and careful patient care;

- Avoid comments to office staff that might have sexual connotations;

- Pay strict attention to patient confidentiality;

- Provide sole call coverage — only rarely should a call be made to partners at home regarding patients when these physicians are not on call;

- Avoid confrontational behavior with others in the office and hospital;

- Avoid "accounting" of procedures (e.g., who has done the most or least procedures or patient visits);

- Be courteous on the telephone and to all staff, physicians, and partners at any location; and

- Be a team player — be punctual and do not leave before the normal work day is over without checking with partners to see if all work is completed.

Dealing with Problem Physicians

A large part of the art of group practice management involves the administrator's ability to work successfully with the physician members of the group and the formal physician leadership structure, especially when matters of conflict arise involving an individual doctor.

In many groups, the biggest and thorniest issue that administrators face is "the problem physician." How do practices define objectively the nature of the problem, identify the possible solutions, determine responsibilities, and create a process for resolution? In virtually all cases, the practice will achieve a successful result through a concerted effort by the physician and administrator team. Although the nature of the problem determines the predominant player — for clinical problems usually the physician, for economic problems the administrator — almost always it's a combination.

Four Categories of Problems

We can place potential group practice problems in four broad categories: clinical (including ethical), behavioral, legal and/or regulatory, and economic. Judgment plays a key role in determining which incidents the practice should address in a formal way and which can be properly addressed informally or privately. Common sense plays a role in these decisions, and the recognition that you can't turn every molehill into a mountain. The size of the group often determines the degree of formality associated with the problem-identification and problem-solving processes, but the basic approaches and processes outlined apply to groups of all sizes and types.

Problems in the clinical category include:

- Clinical competence;

- Quality of care or adverse outcomes;

- Medical ethics; and

- Adherence to medical staff bylaws, such as chart completion.

Behavioral problems are the most common and include:

- Immaturity;

- Psychiatric diagnosis;

- Impairment through substance abuse; and

- Sexual or other forms of harassment.

Practice leaders may have difficulty determining whether a behavioral problem calls for informal or formal intervention. We all have occasional bad days. We can overlook another's minor failings with the assumption that they will reciprocate when it is our turn. Sometimes a young and immature new member of the group just needs a kindly chat with one of the senior physicians.

The need for formal intervention becomes clear when patterns of disruptive or inappropriate behavior emerge, infringing on the rights of others or the maintenance of a proper office environment.

In the legal and/or regulatory problem area:

- The most common concern is coding compliance; and

- Less frequent and potentially far more serious are issues relating to malpractice and medication-prescribing patterns.

The best approach to dealing with potential compliance issues is through a vigorous, ongoing, mandatory compliance program. From a quality and risk management standpoint, a meaningful and continuous internal quality management program is the best preventive approach.

Economic issues regarding physicians in a practice are interrelated. They also have counterparts, such as too much productivity, which are infrequently discussed and usually regarded as a quality-of-care matter. Economic problems in a medical practice include:

- Lack of individual productivity;
- Perceived poor work ethic; and
- Failure to do one's fair share.

In most groups, following a physician's guaranteed-salary period of employment, individual productivity plays a significant role in determining personal income, so it often is self-policed. Failure to do one's fair share can be more subjective.

What Is the Norm?

A *norm* is a general standard; a *problem* is behavior that deviates from the norm beyond an acceptable degree. For example, most groups would have zero tolerance for any level of sexual harassment, while many groups will overlook minor transgressions of policy or procedure.

The mission, values, and objectives of the group represent the foundation of a norm for behavior: They both reflect and form a blueprint for the organization's culture. The behavior of the perceived superior physicians also establishes an informal norm or role model. The bylaws of a group or hospital often establish specific criteria, such as medical record completion within a certain time.

The Mechanics of Problem Solving

To solve a bad-behavior issue, the practice must:

1. Determine that a legitimate problem exists, based on an objective assessment of the relevant facts;

2. Decide — at the physician leadership level — to deal with the problem and establish a timetable to achieve the desired outcome;

3. Obtain a commitment from the group to support problem resolution;

4. Identify who is responsible for dealing with particular aspects of the problem (normally, this will be a designated physician leader, the administrator, or a collaboration by the two); and

5. Document the various interactions.

How the Process Works: A Case Study

To gain a better understanding of the complexity involved in handling a problematic physician, consider the following case study.

Dr. Davis is an orthopedic surgeon who joined XYZ Clinic on completion of his training two years ago. XYZ Clinic is a four-physician group practice in a small Midwestern city. Dr. Davis is an excellent surgeon and brought many new skills to the group and the community. His patients liked him and the clinic employees worked well with him, except when he had what the staff referred to as "tantrums." For example, on one occasion Dr. Davis requested a certain width of casting tape and was handed a different width. He threw the roll across the procedure room, used bad language, quickly finished the procedure, and stormed out of the room.

The incident was the latest in a series of conflicts between Dr. Davis and the support staff. The senior orthopedist, Dr. Moss, had tried numerous times to counsel Dr. Davis informally and avoid direct confrontation. In those conversations, Dr. Davis would state differing views of the problem encounters with support staff and decline to accept any responsibility. Separately, the administrator of the group, Ms. Graham, had met with the involved support staff members following each problem encounter with Dr. Davis, and documented in writing their versions of the facts of each confrontation.

Dr. Moss was frustrated that his friendly advice had not been well received and decided that Dr. Davis's behavior was a serious problem. Dr. Moss began to speak personally with his orthopedic colleagues, some other physicians in the group, and the administrator. These discussions indicated that Dr. Davis's behavior was creating problems with support staff and other departments and was not isolated within the orthopedic department.

Solving the Problem

Dr. Moss met with Ms. Graham, discussed the situation, and reviewed notes describing the previous events. Both Dr. Moss and Ms. Graham agreed that the pattern was a cause for concern and informal counseling had not proven effective.

Dr. Moss and Ms. Graham brought up the issue at the next meeting of the executive committee. This body agreed that Dr. Davis's behavior was inappropriate and unacceptable, that the version of the conflicts presented by the support staff were accurate, and that the repetitive nature of the conflict suggested the need for a structured, formal process to change the behavior permanently. The executive committee asked that the matter be dealt with immediately and directed Ms. Graham to prepare a summary of the circumstances of the conflicts.

Dr. Moss and Ms. Graham met with Dr. Davis to discuss specific occasions of conflict. Dr. Davis was defensive and expressed a completely different view of the situations. In his opinion, the main problem was the lack of training of the support staff; in his mind his behavior was reasonable. The discussion quickly reached an impasse.

Dr. Moss excused Ms. Graham so that he and Dr. Davis could discuss the matter on a physician-to-physician basis. Dr. Davis continued his denials, and the two reached another impasse.

Dr. Moss asked for a special meeting of the executive committee. Dr. Davis was invited to join the meeting following some initial discussion. The president of the group explained the position of the executive committee: There was indeed a problem with Dr. Davis's disruptive behavior and his denials were more troubling than the conflicts themselves. The committee presented Dr. Davis with three choices and gave him one week to make a decision:

1. Make a commitment to work with Dr. Moss and Ms. Graham to address the problems in a constructive way and to accept responsibility for behavior consistent with the expectations of the group;

2. Seek outside counseling at the group's expense; or

3. Resign from the group.

Dr. Davis elected to pursue counseling. It gave him the coping mechanisms he needed to become a productive member of the group. He repaired his relationships with support staff and his colleagues and is thankful that the group had the wisdom to recognize the problem and the fortitude to insist that he deal with it appropriately.

The aspects of the preceding problem-solving case study that are most applicable to situations involving problem physicians are:

- The problems were identified objectively and documented;

- The physician leadership of the group determined that the problem behavior was inconsistent with the norms of the group and required remedial action;

- The team approach of the administrator and a physician addressed the matter definitively;

- Specific tasks and responsibilities were assigned and a timetable was established; and

- The problem physician received a set of specific choices and a goal to resolve the problem behavior definitively and permanently.

No matter how large or small your medical group, how formal or informal your structure, you can address problem situations with the same type of organized and common sense approach.

::: Medical Malpractice and Physician Misconduct

Physicians must become strong members of the team in an effort to prevent malpractice. The challenge is huge. Nearly 90 percent of 1,500 physician executives surveyed by the American Association for Physician Leadership said they were "very concerned" or "moderately concerned" that the U.S. healthcare system was rife with ethical lapses, conflicts of interest, and dishonest business practices.[1]

Medical malpractice is professional negligence committed by a physician or other healthcare provider resulting in an injured patient. A verdict of malpractice requires a finding of negligence and conduct that causes a negative outcome to the patient. If no injury occurs, there is no cause for a lawsuit.

Practice administrators and physicians alike must keep in mind that this topic will demand thorough and continuous awareness and action throughout their medical careers. Common causes of medical malpractice include:

- Medical errors — diagnosis and treatment failures;

- Prescription and medication errors;

- Inadequate physician and staff training (working beyond the scope of training);

- Physician misconduct;

- Physician impairment;

- Equipment malfunction; and

- Inadequate documentation.

Understanding these causes helps a practice develop administrative systems for better medical care to prevent malpractice occurrences. Physicians must also remain ever vigilant.

Malpractice Insurance

Physicians should understand the malpractice insurance coverage the practice carries and what their responsibilities are for their coverage. Several different types of professional liability policies are available to physicians today. Most are claims-made (also known as discovery) policies. However, there also are occurrence policies, which may be harder to acquire.

Claims-Made Policies

Claims-made policies cover claims made against the policyholder during the period in which the policy is in effect. Under these policies, the date on which the event took place that gave rise to the claim is irrelevant; only the date on which the claim is made matters.

Malpractice benefits should cover the practice as an entity as well as the individual physicians. Most insurance contracts require a minimum amount of coverage, typically $1 million per claim and $3 million per claim period.

Occurrence Policies

Occurrence policies are also available in some areas. Under occurrence policies, the insurer is responsible for covering a claim if the event that gave rise to the claim takes place during the term of the occurrence policy, even if the policy is no longer in force. In many states, it is difficult, if not impossible, to obtain occurrence insurance.

Tail Coverage

Tail coverage, which protects physicians with (claims-made policies) who change jobs or whose coverage is terminated, is a key consideration for many physicians. It is sometimes possible to get tail coverage without having to pay for it. If the physician maintains coverage with the same insurer in his or her new position, the insurer might not charge for the tail, or the physician might find an insurer willing to add tail coverage to a new claims-made policy as an incentive to buy the policy. However, in most cases, tail coverage comes with a price tag, and not all employers are willing to pay it.

Malpractice claims coverage is usually a benefit of a physician's employment and should be stipulated in the employment agreement. However, a practice does not always provide tail coverage insurance for claims made in a prior time period.[2] Some practices consider tail coverage to be the individual physician's responsibility.

Malpractice insurance applications must be completed thoroughly and accurately so as not to jeopardize coverage in the event of a claim.

Rating the Insurer

A.M. Best Company ratings are recognized as the industry benchmark. These ratings assess an insurer's financial strength based on a review of the company's balance sheet, operating performance, and business profile. It is important to use an insurance company that has a secure rating of B++ through A++. The A.M. Best Website at www.ambest.com allows users to search for a list of insurers with secure ratings.

Coverage and Exclusions

When comparing rates for the same coverage from two or more insurance companies, it is important to review the coverage and exclusion sections of the policies as well. To do this, be sure to ask for a copy of the insurance policy that each company would issue as if it were writing the policy today.

Some will cover not only claims of professional negligence but also claims of unprofessional conduct made to bodies such as state licensing boards. Some evidence suggests that these entities will become more proactive in disciplining physicians as a result of certain claims, which may make expanded coverage beneficial.

Most policies exclude claims involving punitive damages, intentional misconduct, and contractual indemnity claims. Compare the language of each such exclusion in the policies under consideration and seek advice from an insurance agent or attorney.

Corporate Coverage

As the malpractice crisis has worsened, the cost of covering a professional entity today can be substantial.

Physicians often ask whether, given its cost, corporate malpractice coverage is necessary. Although this coverage may not be mandated by state rules or regulations (which may require individual coverage), it remains important. The professional corporation or limited liability company can be held liable on its own for the acts of its employees within the scope of their employment. The additional coverage held by the entity can ensure that the resources are sufficient to settle a claim or, in the worst case, help to prevent a verdict from exceeding the coverage limits. Plus, if the entity does not maintain malpractice insurance but is included in a lawsuit against a physician (which is almost always the case), the entity will have to engage and pay for an attorney to defend its interests. Corporate malpractice insurance would cover this expense. Whether to maintain corporate coverage may come down to a cost vs. benefit decision for the practice's shareholders, but is recommended.

Medical Errors

The Institute of Medicine (IOM) reports that preventable healthcare injuries cost the economy up to $29 *billion* annually, of which half are direct healthcare costs. The IOM report estimates that up to 98,000 people each year die from medical errors.

Common medical errors include:

- Failure to diagnose or a delay in diagnosis, which is the number one malpractice allegation;

- Negligent maternity care;

- Negligent fracture or trauma care;

- Failure to consult an expert in a timely manner;

- Negligent drug treatment;

- Negligent procedures;

- Failure to obtain an informed consent;

- Failure to obtain and act on laboratory results; and

- Failure of administrative systems, such as misfiled laboratory reports.

Prescription and Medication Errors

More than 7,000 deaths each year are attributed to medication or prescription errors.[3] This number points to the magnitude of the prescription and medication error problem.

Contraindicated medications, wrong dosages, and allergic reactions are the most common prescription errors. Prescription mistakes often result from illegible handwriting or because a rushed and distracted physician makes errors in drug dosages and/or neglects to ask about drug allergies.

Reducing Errors with Medication Lists

Medication lists are an easy way to reduce prescription errors. Clinical support staff should put one in each chart to record all of a patient's current prescriptions. The nurse, physician assistant, or nurse practitioner should review the list with the patient prior to the physician's visit.

Advantages of a medication list include:

- Efficient charting;

- Safer refills;

- Better communication among physicians;

- Allergy documentation; and

- Documentation of over-the-counter medications, supplements, herbal therapies, and vitamins, as these are often overlooked.

Inadequate Physician and Staff Training

A physician who performs a procedure that he or she is not adequately trained for puts the patient at risk. Physicians may do this out of a desire for additional income or from overconfidence. Performing procedures when a physician is tired or distracted, which can be viewed as a temporary impairment, can also cause an adverse outcome.

Always remember that all patient care is ultimately under the direct supervision of the physician. It is important that the physician and/or practice manager assigns tasks for each employee at his or her appropriate skill level.

Physician Misconduct

Physicians are people and are therefore not immune from engaging in behavior that is detrimental to patients, employees, and the practice as a whole. Major examples of medical misconduct include the following:

- **Sexual misconduct.** Sexual contact that is concurrent within the physician–patient relationship is considered misconduct. A physician must terminate his or her professional relationship with a patient before beginning any personal relationship.

- **Credentialing and licensure fraud.** Any misrepresentation a physician makes when applying for credentialing, licensure, or medical malpractice coverage is considered misconduct. Practicing without a license falls within the definition of misconduct and comes under the jurisdiction of the state Board of Medical Examiners.

- **Criminal behavior.** This is defined as "any conviction of an offense of moral turpitude, a felony, or a crime." When a physician takes advantage of his or her professional position to engage in criminal behavior, the circumstances move the case from a civil suit to a criminal court case.

Physician Impairment

Patient safety is the primary concern and the duty of all physicians. A physician impaired by alcohol, drugs, mental illness, or another affliction lacks the ability to exercise prudent medical judgment and the ability to practice medicine with reasonable skill and safety. When an impaired physician cannot exercise prudent medical judgment or is unable to practice with reasonable skill and safety, he or she should recognize the problem, stop seeing patients, and seek help.

However, the impaired physician often does not, or is unwilling to, recognize the problem. Staff members often are the first ones to see changes in behavior. It may fall to other doctors in the practice or in the community to address and confront the impaired physician. Those involved in the review must keep in mind the welfare of the patient, the physician, and the practice.

Obligation to Report

Physicians have an obligation to report impaired, incompetent, or unethical physician behavior. Those who allow an impaired physician to practice can be named as codefendants in any malpractice case involving that physician. This is an enormous risk for the practice and for the other physicians in the group. Information about the reporting process can be obtained from the state licensing board, listed on the Website for the Federation of State Medical Boards (www.fsmb.org). In addition, reports should be filed in line with the American Medical Association (AMA) policy E-9.031. It defines who and where the reports should be made. The policy can be obtained from the AMA at www.ama-assn.org.

Forms of Impairment

There are several causes for impairment:

- **Alcoholism or other substance abuse.** Alcoholism or other substance abuse affects physicians just as it affects the general population. Additionally, prescription drug use is higher among physicians because of the ease of access and the opportunity to self-prescribe.

- **Mental illness and behavioral disorders.** Mental illness and unpredictable and disruptive behaviors often cause high staff turnover and serious practice chaos.

- **Medical illness and advanced age.** Some physicians — like many other people — want to continue to work past the time they should quit, even if ill or aging. Such a physician should seek the counsel of his or her own physician as to the quality of care that he or she is capable of rendering.

Once impairment is recognized, steps can be taken for rehabilitation. If staff members notice that a physician or colleague appears to be having problems, they should sit down and talk candidly with the individual or go to his or her supervisor, department chief, medical director, or chief executive officer. One can also contact the state's physician health program or state medical society for help. These entities can provide diagnostic evaluation, treatment referrals, treatment monitoring, and support services for licensed physicians and physician assistants with health problems that, if left untreated, could adversely affect their ability to practice medicine safely. Physician health programs are listed by state on the Website for the Federation of State Physician Health Programs (www.fsphp.org).

Equipment Malfunction

Equipment failure can cause malpractice occurrences. It's the physician's responsibility to ensure that appropriate maintenance and testing is performed on all equipment and laboratory testing packages. Quality controls should be performed as soon as the testing packages are opened.

Equipment should also be tagged to confirm when routine maintenance is performed and equipment is certified for use. For example, a practice's electrocardiogram machine should have a regular maintenance schedule; the crash cart should be regularly reviewed for expired medications and a fully charged defibrillator.

Faulty equipment should not be used again until it has been repaired or replaced. The entire office should be reviewed periodically to ensure that its equipment and the facility do not pose any hazards to the patients or staff.

Inadequate Documentation

Although not a direct cause of malpractice, inadequate documentation can lead to losing a lawsuit. It also hinders communication among the treating physicians and can compromise patient safety and treatment. Often, it can be quite difficult, if not impossible, to defend a malpractice suit if there is little or no patient care documentation.

National Practitioner Data Bank Reporting Requirements

The U.S. Congress established the National Practitioner Data Bank (NPDB) as part of the Health Care Quality Improvement Act of 1986. It is an electronic repository of medical malpractice settlements, judgments, and payments. It includes adverse peer review actions against licenses, clinical privileges, and professional society memberships of physicians and other healthcare practitioners.

The NPDB (www.npdb.hrsa.gov) is required to make information available to hospitals, state licensure boards, and other healthcare entities. Patients, however, do not have access to this information.

Disciplinary actions related to competence and professional misconduct must be reported by the state medical board to the NPDB within 30 days of the incident. Hospitals are required to request information from the NPDB when a physician applies for hospital privileges. Without hospital privileges, many insurance companies will not contract with a physician.

State Board of Medical Examiners Investigations

The state Board of Medical Examiners is required to investigate every complaint it receives. The board sends notice to a physician when the physician is the subject of a complaint. The physician is required to respond to the board within the designated time frame. Do not ignore communications from the Board of Medical Examiners. It can and will take action on a failure to respond to the notice of complaint.

Patients can submit written requests to a state's Board of Medical Examiners for information about previous complaints about a physician.

::: Fostering Physician Leaders as Knowledgeable, Participative Stakeholders

The interactions of the group's physicians are an area of great concern for most organizations. It is important that physicians understand their role in the organization, the culture of the organization ("how we do things"), and what is expected of them individually as well as in a group. Effective management of these relationships will help to ensure that new physicians are successful in their practices and that members of the group who are experiencing difficulties are managed and mentored effectively.

Mentoring is becoming a popular way for groups to develop their staff. It also allows middle managers a forum to show that they are indeed blossoming leaders and can excel. Establishing and running a mentoring program is one of the best ways to help new members of the practice become a successful part of the group. It helps maintain the culture of the group and provides some guidance and expectations for performance and behavior. In addition, training and developing the group's staff will provide ample return on investment through increased skills, higher morale, and job satisfaction — all of which lead to happier patients.

Staff Training and Development

One area of the organization that is often neglected is staff training and development. Larger medical groups might have a human resource (HR) department for this task, but smaller medical groups often do not have an organized function or department, so it falls to the medical practice executive to lead this effort.

Peter Senge[4] discusses extensively how the successful and competitive organization is one that is a "learning" organization, or one that learns as it goes about its daily activities. Learning is a deep-seated organizational value in these entities. In his book *Good to Great*,[5] James Collins talks about having the right people on the bus. In his thesis, being able to adapt is critical to being competitive. Learning is essential to adaptation, especially within the highly complex and technical environment of healthcare. It takes a high-functioning and ever-developing workforce to make an excellent team. Teaming largely is a function of staff development, and it is the responsibility of the governing body to have these important functions clearly addressed. Every member of the group, whether employee or physician, should have:

- Development goals;
- Continuing professional education, either in-house or at away meetings; and
- Professional career goals that relate to organizational goals.

Every performance appraisal should include these goals, because what is rewarded and valued is what is usually received in the organization.

Adults learn in different styles and ways. Some prefer to go to a class, surrounded by others in similar situations, and discuss ideas and tasks in a group. Others prefer reading a how-to book, attending an online program, or listening to an audiotape. Still others believe that they cannot learn unless they perform the task at hand. Understanding which learning style is most effective for each staff member results in a higher retention rate.

Rewards

By their very nature, people respond to rewards. Motivational rewards, such as a day off, a staff outing, or a celebration of successes, whether for the team or for individuals, enhance the group practice morale. Not every reward must be centered on monetary bonuses, which tend to dominate many medical practices' ideals for rewarding good behavior. For example, promotions or title changes can be extremely motivational. In addition, removing a distasteful task from someone's job description for a job well done is a reward in itself. A note or letter of recognition and achievement, recognizing and announcing "star" behavior at staff meetings, or buying the staff lunchroom a new microwave or comfortable chairs for relaxing are all ways to show appreciation.

Human Dynamics

Healthcare institutions, like many organizations, often focus on competencies, talents, and skills rather than personality traits in determining the success of individuals in the job. All are necessary for a successful HR perspective, but personality has a significant influence on the governance and the organizational dynamics of the medical group. Today, this aspect of human dynamics receives a great deal of attention. A number of systems are currently being used to help evaluate personality and determine organizational fit. Two of these systems are the DiSC® system and the Predictive Index®, or PI.

DiSC System

The DiSC system[6] is based on the work of William M. Marston.[7] His work formed the foundation for a system of personality typing for:

- Dominance;
- Inducement;
- Steadiness; and
- Compliance.

The system has predictive value in determining how an individual will likely behave in a stressful situation. A personality type can be determined by testing individuals. The following nine associated behavioral styles of that personality type can be considered in this analysis:

1. Aggressive-Analytical;
2. Aggressive-Persuasive;
3. Persuasive-Forceful;
4. Persuasive-Diplomatic;
5. Persistent-Determined;
6. Conservative-Personable;
7. Cautious-Restrained;
8. Aggressive-Perfectionist; or
9. Persuasive-Persistent.

The Predictive Index

PI,[8] like the DiSC system, seeks to type an individual's personality by using four basic factors:

1. Factor A, or dominance;
2. Factor B, or introvert or extrovert;
3. Factor C, or patience; or
4. Factor D, or formal behavior.

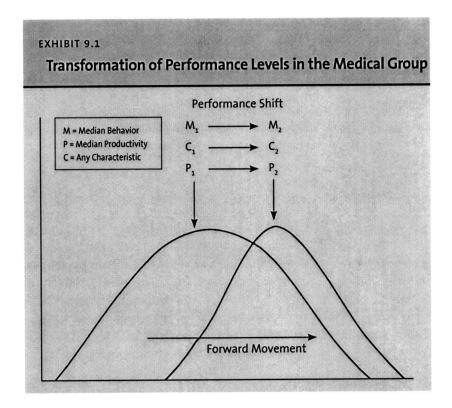

EXHIBIT 9.1

Transformation of Performance Levels in the Medical Group

Performance Shift

M = Median Behavior
P = Median Productivity
C = Any Characteristic

$M_1 \longrightarrow M_2$
$C_1 \longrightarrow C_2$
$P_1 \longrightarrow P_2$

Forward Movement

PI also includes two additional factors: M (energy level) and E (subjectivity and objectivity.) Through a testing process (not reviewed here), personality type can be determined, and an associated behavioral profile can then be created.

Understanding the personality types of a group and its members increases the opportunity to significantly improve the interaction of group members with one another and with the staff. This understanding provides a common language to discuss how individuals handle and express themselves differently in low-stress, or favorable, situations as well as in high-stress, or unfavorable, situations.

Understanding the behavioral characteristics of the group's membership will help to determine how best to motivate change. Change and improvement in the group has to move all members forward so that median behavior (M), median productivity (P), and any characteristic (C) has the effect of shifting the entire group's performance (see Exhibit 9.1).

Empowered Organizations

The governance structure of most medical groups is best characterized as professional and collegial. Although a central operating committee or board may be vested with specific authorities as outlined under the group's bylaws, a wise governance system provides ample opportunity for significant, meaningful collaboration with all members of the organization in the decision-making process. Governance structure must create the environment for constructive organizational dynamics. Legendary Notre Dame football coach Lou Holtz notes his three operating principles of life: "Do the right thing, do the best you can, and always show people you care."[9]

This also works for a medical group practice. Holtz describes the values of an empowered organization, which need to be the nature of the medical group practice because the governance structure of the group significantly influences the culture and the operations of the organization.

Many groups function as confederations of people, with little central leadership. Decisions are made by consensus, which often leads to poor decision making or no decisions at all. The modern group practice needs to move beyond this model. Strong, skilled leadership will result in better decision making.

More centralized systems of governance do not need to stifle input, but they must prevent the group from being stifled by a minority dissent that could delay or completely derail decision making. The phenomena of very small dissenting groups preventing change or decision making are very divisive and present a difficult way to run a substantial organization. This can be detrimental to the group because any individual who has a differing opinion about a topic, and sometimes completely vested in his or her own self-interest, can have a significant effect on the outcome of that decision through a filibustering or lobbying process.

Governance by consensus is frequently nonproductive and is antithetical to an effective operation. The board or governance body of the group exists only when it is in session. While in session, the board should act only to further the organization's mission.

Accountability for decisions in an opportunistic organization, such as a medical group, can be very problematic. In an article titled "7 Habits of Spectacularly Unsuccessful Executives,"[10] Sydney Finkelstein writes from the perspective of a large stock company, but his "habits" offer a number of apparent lessons for the medical group:

1. **Seeing themselves and their companies as dominating the environment — or the myth of preeminence.** Many medical groups believe they are the best because of credentials or reputation, but this perspective can change very quickly as new competitors innovate and supply the market with better services and a more caring delivery of the increasingly fungible "high-quality care."

2. **Mixing business with pleasure.** Group members identify so completely with the group that there is no clear boundary between their personal interests and their business interests. Although there certainly is much room for pride and ownership views in the medical group, physicians see themselves as the reason for the success of the group and do not see the efforts of the whole group as a team.

3. **"Knowing" all the answers.** As skilled as medicine is, there are usually proscribed ways of approaching diagnosis and decision making that are clearly and carefully learned in training from the earliest days of medical school. Unfortunately, many groups do not use good processes to make critical decisions about the business and rely too often on the quick judgment of the governing body. The environment of the medical group is faced with government issues, multiple payers, market forces, multiple stakeholders, changing technology, a changing workforce, and many other elements — all with their own dynamics, making uncertainty the norm and not the rule.

4. **Ruthlessly eliminating anyone who isn't 100 percent behind them.** Most medical groups are not good at incorporating dissent into the process of decision making and assessment. They tend to take dissent as a personal attack and reject it.

5. **Obsession with image.** Not wanting to discuss problems is normal, but that doesn't mean an issue should not be resolved. Group members often make too many excuses for colleagues who misbehave, or overlook a trait or behavior in a colleague that they would not tolerate in a competitor or in themselves.

6. **Underestimating obstacles.** The medical group is often in a position of not knowing what resources will be needed to accomplish a particular goal. Because the task is not fully understood, the group may underestimate the time and other resources needed to complete the task and then become impatient with its progress.

7. **Stubbornly relying on what worked in the past.** Another way to put this is resistance to change. Medical groups often see individual efforts as the key to success. That may have been true in the past, but today, group efforts and the team approach will more likely lead to success. The business model in healthcare is changing rapidly.

Conflict Resolution

Establishing effective employee relations and appropriate conflict resolution programs are necessary to work toward common goals. The word *team* is overused in healthcare: It conveys the expectation that everyone will work together to accomplish a common purpose. Often, employees and departments experience conflicts that thwart the attainment of high performance. When this happens, the supervisor needs to get involved and talk with the employees one-on-one or in groups to identify the problems and determine a resolution. Sometimes an objective third party may need to get involved if issues are plagued with cultural or historical resistance or the process of change isn't supported by the physicians. Also, another party may need to get involved if the conflict is between the employee and supervisor. Differences in problem-solving styles, information processing, and communication can create conflicts that, if not resolved soon after identification, may produce disastrous results.

Four Conflict Management Strategies

Few industries ask their employees to manage their bosses. But as a medical practice administrator, you're tasked with helping your practice's physicians become productive while reducing internal conflict that may arise between them (and you!).

Wendy Lipton-Dibner, president of Professional Impact, Inc., in Wilton, Conn., said at the Medical Group Management Association® (MGMA®) 2010 Annual Conference that you do this by making physicians aware of what conflict does to their business. She offers four practical strategies to help physicians help themselves by improving communication, cooperation, "colleagueship," and consensus, or what she refers to as the four C's:[11]

1. Align communication — encourage physicians to talk to one another;

2. Increase cooperation — get physicians on the same page about their business;

3. Encourage collegial activities — get physicians to spend time with one another outside the office; and

4. Facilitate consensus — encourage physicians to focus on facts, not feelings, to make efficient decisions.

Before you can motivate physicians to change how they interact as a team and with you as the practice administrator, you must know who you're working with. For this, Lipton-Dibner digs into sociology and psychology to identify four personality types. Although no person fits neatly into any category in which they are placed, Lipton-Dibner recommends teaching these concepts to your physicians. She asserts, "At least 50 percent of the conflict will be gone now because they have a language for it."[12]

- **Relator.** Relators are people-oriented and indirect in their mannerisms. These physicians talk softly, slowly, and avoid eye contact. They are 100 percent conflict averse and usually run behind schedule. Patients love these doctors (because the doctors spend so much time with them), which could mean lower productivity than their colleagues.

- **Enthusiast.** Enthusiasts are people-oriented and direct. "These are the fun docs," says Lipton-Dibner. They keep everyone laughing. They also dislike paperwork and often don't do it.

- **Thinker.** Thinkers are task-oriented and indirect. They dislike surprises or getting out of their routines and often need time to think before making a decision.

- **Commander.** Commanders are task-oriented and direct. They are highly goal- and result-oriented and tend to be highly productive but may seem aggressive or abrupt as they go about their work.

Relators and Enthusiasts get along least well with Thinkers and Commanders.

These personality types will get physicians talking, and it's important to continue to facilitate the conversation to promote colleagueship. Do this by scheduling a dinner for all the doctors once a month. Each month have one physician take the lead to pick a restaurant and a journal article and lead the discussion. Lipton-Dibner explains that she consulted for a practice whose physicians rarely talked to each other or got along. After three months of voluntarily setting these meetings, the physicians were all showing up and enjoying their time together.

Physicians are under enormous amounts of pressure, she says, and often suffer from low self-esteem, which is slowly taken from them in residency. "Nobody expects us [practice administrators] to be the kind of 'perfect' we expect doctors to be," Lipton-Dibner states.[13] The more you can have your physicians focus on the facts in a situation and less on feelings, the less conflict there will be in the workplace.

More Tips for Conflict Resolution

The following subsections offer some simple guidelines that can help you deal with difficult situations and, in some cases, prevent them.

Develop Self-Awareness and Self-Control

The self-aware group practice manager — someone who understands what triggers conflict and how to respond to it — is more emotionally and behaviorally prepared to deal with conflict. Gaining an understanding of conflict helps group practice managers avoid ineffective behaviors and consciously choose constructive ones that maximize productive resolution of differences. A number of approaches can be used to improve self-awareness. These include seeking feedback from colleagues by asking their perspective on how one behaves around conflict and using assessment instruments such as the Conflict Dynamics Profile,[14] an assessment instrument designed by Eckerd College to measure responses to conflict.

Understand Conflict Triggers

Certain situations or behaviors can trigger an emotional response and heighten conflict. Staff and other team members may possess characteristics that evoke strong reactions and exacerbate tense situations.

Examples include employees who are unreliable, overly analytical, unappreciative, aloof, self-centered, abrasive, untrustworthy, or downright hostile. This list does not exhaust the possibilities, but understanding these hot-button behaviors can help practice managers avoid being caught by surprise when encountering someone whose actions push these types of buttons.

Communication Is the Key to Success

"When we communicate effectively, it is more difficult to misunderstand or project unfavorable traits onto another person," says Donna Davis, a clinic supervisor for Premier Medical Group in Clarksville, Tenn. "There are always at least two points of view, and understanding the other person's perspective leads to empathy — a significant step in solving conflict. Empathy helps because it conveys a sense of caring or respect that in turn helps lessen tensions. While communication involves speaking and listening, it is the latter that is often most important. If you can listen to the other person, even if you don't agree with him or her, you will be better-positioned to suggest effective solutions to a problem."[15]

The Art of the Apology

The ability to apologize in a sincere fashion is an important skill. A genuine apology will often create patient and staff member loyalty and goodwill. In recent years, the art of the apology has gained prominence in graduate school curricula.

Lipscomb University in Nashville, Tenn., teaches a course on apology to students in the Master's Degree in Conflict Management Program. The university started the program, which draws on the fields of law, business, social sciences, and religion to address issues relating to interpersonal conflict, in 2006. Recently, the university held a summit on conflict in healthcare that attracted top industry executives and government decision makers.

⁝⁝ Personnel Policy

The personnel policy should state which representative will resolve the issue. It may be the HR representative, the medical practice executive, or an employee and labor relations consultant. If the practice is unionized, this role may fall to the union steward. This person will meet with the employee, supervisor, or both, as may be appropriate to the chain of command, to help in resolving their differences. This representative can provide advice on matters of policy interpretation, rights of management and employees, and information on the formal grievance process.

The personnel policy may have a statement on protection against retaliation of the employee for exercising his or her rights under the arbitration process. There may be time limits on the process to facilitate speedy resolution of the problem while providing appropriate time to collect, prepare, and present information. For example, if the employee fails to follow the time limits, the issue may be deemed to be resolved to the employee's satisfaction. If the medical practice fails to follow specific time limits, the employee may take the complaint to a higher level of resolution. Personnel policies should reflect current federal, state, and local employment laws.

Policy Interpretation for Grievance Procedures

For all disciplinary action, policy interpretation is an HR responsibility. The disciplinary action or progressive discipline process is meant to give appropriate feedback to the employee in a formal way. This constructive feedback for desired results is meant to provide the employee with measurable accomplishments, instill individual accountability and responsibility, and facilitate the desired behavior. The supervisor can serve as a mentor, coach, and facilitator of the process and help the employee understand the desired results.

If the communication requires multiple areas of behavior change, the supervisor may choose to give the employee a performance improvement plan (PIP). This tool focuses on below-average or substandard performance and provides an action plan for needed change. The plan is time specific and allows the employee to receive periodic feedback. For example, an employee may receive a PIP for inappropriate interactions with patients. The PIP would provide the employee with customer service training and weekly feedback sessions between the supervisor and employee on improvement in the desired results. Failure to achieve desired results can lead to additional disciplinary action up to and including termination. The PIP's intent is to help the employee be successful and shepherd the process along the way.

Mediation

In mediation, a professional mediator contacts the two parties involved and seeks to achieve agreement. Usually, each party meets individually with a mediator first to identify and discuss the concerns. The mediator will keep all information from these sessions confidential. Then the mediator will bring the two parties together to discuss the concerns and will work toward a win-win outcome. Sometimes a second session may be required, depending on the complexity of the issue. If the two parties reach an agreement, the mediator will work with them to create a written agreement listing the specific components of the agreement, which both parties will sign. Usually, these agreements do not change existing medical practice policies or union contracts.

Mediation lets the employer and employee troubleshoot issues and come to positive relations. It deals with problems promptly and provides an opportunity to address a problem before it escalates into an unworkable issue. Usually, mediation will move away from blame or judgment and allow a win-win situation, as opposed to a win-lose situation. The two parties, not the mediator, control the situation and the outcome.

Mediation can be used prior to a formal grievance process, such as arbitration. Using mediation, however, does not waive one's right to use a formal grievance process if the parties cannot reach a satisfactory outcome through mediation.

Arbitration

Nonbinding arbitration is a way of avoiding disputes because it provides a written guide on the practice used in employee grievances. The purpose of the arbitration policy is to establish a procedure for the fair, orderly, and speedy resolution of disputes that sometimes arise between management and employees. The policy will state to whom it applies (e.g., all members, unclassified employees) and how the policy is used. An employee may use the procedure to review an alleged violation of the medical practice's policy or rules pertaining to employment.

In a nonbinding arbitration process, two parties give a dispute to a neutral person to determine an advisory or nonbinding decision, meaning that neither party is required to accept the opinion. In the process, the two groups have input into the selection of the person arbitrating. Nonbinding arbitration is used when the parties want a quick dispute resolution, prefer a third-party decision maker, and want more control over the decision-making process if not resolved.

In binding arbitration, both parties present a dispute to an impartial arbitrator to determine a binding decision. The parties have the ability to decide who serves as the arbitrator. Binding arbitration is appropriate when the parties want a neutral third party to decide the outcome of the dispute and avoid a formal trial. The parties do not retain control over how their dispute is resolved and cannot appeal the arbitrator's decision.

Employee Grievance Procedures

Initially, there should be an attempt at an informal resolution of complaints. Regular communication between the practice managers and employees reduces the need for a more formal review and is in the mutual best interest of the medical practice and employees. Written resources materials, handouts, and guides should always be available to help management communicate information with employees. An employee who has a work-related problem should bring it to the medical practice executive's attention with the intent of resolving the problem. Management should discuss the concern with the employee in a timely manner in an effort to resolve the issue. If informal attempts at resolution are not satisfactory, employees may use a formal grievance process.

Listening to employees is key to ensuring excellent performance. Active listening will help to identify whether any issues or concerns are preventing the employee from performing the expected job duties. Early identification of problems can avoid serious problems later. If, through active listening, a supervisor recognizes that a problem exists that requires a higher level of problem solving or counseling, the supervisor needs to recognize his or her limitations and refer the employee to either the HR department or, if offered, an employee assistance program to help the employee sort through personal issues that are inhibiting acceptable performance levels.

Progressive Discipline

Corrective action strives to provide feedback to an employee to correct a behavior. Progressive discipline sets parameters on which behaviors are unacceptable and how the negative behaviors requiring change will be communicated with the employee. Large medical groups usually have a progressive discipline process that clearly establishes expectations and consequences of those behaviors if not met. The discipline process may be different for the staff and physicians. The purpose of having a constructive discipline process is to establish guidelines that will ensure an environment that is efficient, productive, and orderly to provide standards and rules governing performance and a procedure for consistent, nondiscriminatory application of the rules with the intent of providing quality patient care. The policy does not apply to employees who are in their new-hire period or per-diem or temporary employees. The personnel policy applies to part-time and full-time regular status employees.

Progressive discipline must be fair, consistent, well understood, and timely. Lack of a consistent process to administer discipline may ultimately lead to a disgruntled employee filing a lawsuit. A progressive discipline program provides the employee with feedback that clearly outlines unacceptable behavior and the consequences if this behavior is not changed. Usually progressive discipline involves a verbal warning followed by a written warning. If behavior doesn't change, a suspension or final written warning is the next level of discipline. Ultimately, if behavior doesn't improve, the employee may be terminated. Some behaviors may warrant a progressive level, and other behaviors may warrant more, or may skip a step and move into a higher level of discipline. For example, chronic tardiness would go through progressive discipline, whereas stealing money would result in immediate termination or suspension, pending an administrative investigation. Employees must understand that there is a process for discipline and consequences to bad behavior.

If a union is present in a practice, the union's progressive discipline process may require a union representative to be present with the union employee and manager when progressive discipline is administered.

Recorded Conference

For rule infractions considered less serious, a recorded conference may be the first step in the corrective action process. It consists of a verbal conference with, at a minimum, the employee and supervisor and will be documented in writing and placed in the employee's personnel file. Examples of behavior for which a recorded conference may be initiated as the first step of the correction action process include:

- Work area absence without permission (e.g., leaving work without clocking out);

- Extended lunch time or breaks without permission (e.g., taking a 30-minute break instead of a 15-minute break);

- Loitering during scheduled work time or during off-duty hours (e.g., staying in work area after shift and creating disturbances with employees);

- Smoking or eating in unauthorized areas (e.g., eating in surgical area that is a sterile environment);

- Conducting personal business on work premises (e.g., selling products during work time);

- Violation of parking rules (e.g., parking in a "no parking" or "patients only" zone for the duration of a work shift);

- Improper attire or appearance (e.g., wearing jeans or denim when not part of the dress code);

- Inefficiency or incompetence in work duties performed (e.g., failing to perform job duty during work shift);

- Unauthorized telephone use (e.g., making long-distance or extensive personal calls without permission); or

- Attendance problems (e.g., showing up late for work without prior notice or permission).

Written Corrective Action

The written corrective action is a document summarizing the performance problem or incident detrimental to the customer, inability to follow established policy, or the failure to respond to supervision. A written corrective action serves as notice that continued infractions will not be tolerated and/or that performance must improve to meet expectations. Examples of behavior for which a written corrective action may be initiated as the first step of the corrective active process include:

- Inappropriate treatment or behavior toward a customer;

- Conduct prejudicial to the best interest of the medical group;

- Careless, indifferent, or negligent job performance, including unsafe or unsanitary practices;

- Careless, neglectful, unauthorized, or improper use of company property or equipment;
- Collecting money or accepting gratuities for personal use;
- Failure of good behavior or neglect of duty; or
- Repeated or chronic infractions with no evident improvement in performance or conduct.

Suspension or Final Written Corrective Action

An unpaid suspension or final written corrective action in lieu of suspension may occur when performance continues to be detrimental to customer satisfaction or where a serious performance problem exists. Suspensions should be scheduled at a time as close to the infraction as possible but also so that patient care and consistency of service do not suffer. Depending on the seriousness of the incident or behavior, the employee may receive a suspension or final written corrective action as the first step of the corrective action process.

Examples of behavior warranting suspension include possession, use, or sale of alcohol, narcotics, or controlled substances on the medical group premises, or reporting to work under the influence of alcohol or narcotics, usually evidenced by one or more of the following behaviors:

- Inability to perform assigned work;
- Presentation of undesirable attributes (e.g., hygiene, attitude, uncooperativeness);
- Insubordination or refusal to perform a reasonable assignment after having been instructed by a supervisor to do so;
- Sleeping on the job;
- Disorderly conduct;
- Failure to conform to professional standards; or
- Any other critical failure of good behavior or serious neglect of duty.

Termination

Termination may occur as the final step in the corrective action process. Termination of an employee is never an easy task, but it is a necessary one if the employee does not consistently follow the medical group's policies and procedures. Termination may occur for serious offenses or for continued performance problems affecting the customer. Examples of behavior where immediate termination may be initiated as the first step of corrective action include:

- Threat of or actual physical or verbal abuse of patients, visitors, employees;

- Inappropriate treatment of any patient for any reason;

- Falsification of any official medical group records (e.g., medical records);

- Illegal or dishonest act;

- Damage or theft of property;

- Absence from work without justifiable reason or, in some practices, without reporting being off for two (or more, depending on the practice's variables) consecutive working days;

- Unauthorized possession, use, copying, or revealing of confidential information regarding patients, employees, or medical group activity;

- Unwelcome sexual advances, requests for sexual favors, or other verbal or physical conduct of a sexual nature with an employee, visitor, or patient;

- Harassment in any form, including that based on race, gender, religion, or national origin, which includes offensive jokes, ridicule, or racial, religious, sexual, or ethnic slurs;

- Improper use of leave of absence;

- Conviction of a felony relevant to the employee's position;

- Solicitation and/or distribution of literature (e.g., pornography, political campaigns, etc.); or

- Any other gross neglect of good behavior or gross neglect of duty.

⸬ Managing Internal Communication Pathways and Protocols

Clinical pathways are described as multidisciplinary plans of treatment that are developed to enable the implementation of clinical guidelines and protocols. While best known as clinical pathways, several other terms are used to describe this concept, including care maps, integrated care pathways, and collaborative care pathways. Clinical pathways are used to support clinical, resource, and financial management of a patient with a specific condition over a specified time period. The four major components to the clinical pathway include (1) a timeline, (2) the type of care, (3) the outcome criteria, and (4) the variance record for identifying deviations from the norms and/or expectations.

The goal of developing and implementing clinical pathways and clinical protocols is to attain a high level of quality of medical care by identifying, implementing, and adhering to specific medical standards by all physicians in a given specialty when treating a specific set of symptoms or identified illness or injury. Through the application of clinical pathways in the utilization of clinical protocols, a group practice will have the tools to generate clinical data that will enable the organization to prove to outside entities the level of clinical quality being provided by the practice.

Clinical pathways and protocols can be derived from multiple sources, including third-party payers, medical specialty societies, and the National Institutes of Health. Even though applying these protocols constitutes good clinical care on its own, the utilization of audits and external assessments to measure compliance with the protocols can be effectively used to confirm the quality of care being provided and therefore justify the negotiation of better contracts with third-party payers and improved relationships with local employers where direct contracting for medical services may be possible.

The effective development and implementation of clinical pathways within an organization requires a multidisciplinary approach, with input from all levels of clinical providers as well as input from nonclinical staff. The initial creation of this type of structure requires the full and unreserved endorsement and support of physicians as well as clinical and executive leadership of the organization. Preliminary meetings and discussions need to be held within the leadership structure to identify the organization-specific goals for the implementation of clinical pathways. In some cases, this may require the inclusion of various community collaborators who have involvement or responsibility for part of the care and treatment plan of the patient. Examples of this outside collaboration may include visiting-nurse services, rehabilitation facilities, and social services support agencies. In addition to being part of the leadership, administrative support goes further in the form of being advocates, facilitators, and champions to show that the organization is in favor of and supportive of the implementation of clinical pathways through both words and the identification and application of necessary financial and operational resources.

In addition, the development and implementation of clinical pathways may have significant effects that go beyond the simple goal of quality care. The development and application of clinical pathway structures, when properly communicated to staff, patients, and community stakeholders, sends a clear and effective message that the practice is committed to maintaining services at no less than industry norms and is effective at identifying and measuring those norms for improved patient care. Properly designed and implemented clinical pathways will also affect the cost of care through changes in the services that will be rendered based on specific presented symptoms and may have significant effect on insurance carrier–directed pay-for-performance models. The application of clinical pathways should also increase financial accountability through the elimination of redundancy and variations of clinical methods used by different providers.

In addition to developing and implementing this clinical pathway structure, an organization should create and implement a variety of quality assurance programs to measure the results of the implementation of the clinical pathways and ensure that the desired goals are being reached. Most quality assurance programs can be sized to meet the needs of both large and small medical practices. Dependent on the size of the organization, some practices complete their quality assurance programs internally, whereas other practices use outside consultants to complete the necessary reviews, audits, and surveys.

A key tool in evaluating adherence to clinical pathways and their effect on the patient population is through the use of various outcomes measures, including chart reviews, whereby a sample of medical records is reviewed to confirm that the proper care is being provided and properly documented in the medical record. Other measurements that can be used include patient and referring physician satisfaction surveys. These surveys, when completed properly and analyzed in a timely manner, can provide a wealth of information concerning how well the clinical pathways are being received and whether the pathways are in keeping with the standards in the community and the expectations of the patient. The results of these reviews and surveys should be presented to senior clinical and administrative management to enable them to address the issues raised by the results of the surveys and reviews. The data used to define the issues may be perceived differently when reviewed by clinical and administrative staff. Clinicians will be primarily seeking to improve the care being provided to enable the patient to reach the best possible outcome. This goal is important from the administrative point of review as well, but the medical practice administrator is also concerned that the care and service are being provided in the most cost-effective manner with the most efficient use of available resources. Finally, these data are critical to identifying and determining modifications that need to be made in both the strategic and operational planning processes.

Communicating with the Team

Problem solving and decision making require inquiry. One of the major areas of concern in decision making involves the factors that prevent decisions from being made, sometimes referred to as "decision paralysis" factors. Five paralyses factors are detrimental to the process:

1. Resistance to change (paradigm paralysis);
2. Lack of communication (no collaboration among departments or within some departments);
3. Lack of written guidance (policies and procedures);
4. Lack of employee empowerment; and
5. Lack of recognition of a need to change.

Many organizations fail to recognize the influence of "organizational culture" on the governance process within the entity. Governance flows from culture because the culture of the group will dictate how the group makes decisions.

Creating an Internal Communications Plan

For any practice to be functional, it needs a structured mechanism for ongoing communication about exposures, policies and procedures, systems improvements, and unanticipated events. Key audiences for internal communications include:

- **The board of directors**, which is ultimately responsible for the safety of patients and corporate compliance;
- **Administration**, which sets the corporate culture's tone;
- **Physicians**, who must understand the corporate expectations and culture within which they are working;
- **Staff members**, who take personal risks of retribution when they report an error or potential error and who must understand policies and how to implement them; and
- **Patients**, who are called on as partners in today's system to help report inaccuracies on their personal health records.

The communication plan for information management should include both verbal and written communication. Written communication should consider the issue of medical literacy and be written so that laypersons and all staff, including support staff, can understand it. A comprehensive internal communication plan will include the following:

- **Orientation presentations** for both the board and staff, including the role of information management, the responsibility of the staff and board, and the types of information management involvement expected of them. In addition, the orientation should communicate the philosophy of the organization about the expectation that all staff and the board will participate in ensuring that the organization complies with established standards of safety and corporate compliance.

- **Regular written reports to the administration and board,** including claims, suits, events, near misses, and identified exposures.

- **Regular written communication to staff members** to apprise them of exposure and acknowledge them for reporting exposures. Staff members are the eyes and ears of the information management process. Unless they are rewarded for exposing information management inefficiencies, deficiencies, and inaccuracies, their participation will be limited. Acknowledge and reward staff participation in communications activities. In addition, tell staff members about actions taken in response to their reports.

- **Corporate communication** through writing for internal newsletters, which should be the responsibility of the information manager whenever possible. The more widely the information management activities are known throughout the organization, the more corporate support is possible.

All staff should be educated about the need to avoid hearsay and gossip about unanticipated events. Speculation is damaging. Random musings become facts in the minds of those who share them. All staff, not just clinical staff, should be trained on the concepts of systems thinking in medical error and the notion of high reliability as an organizational goal. The more educated staff members are in thinking about safety and the notions of corporate compliance, the more they can believe the organization is just, fair, transparent, and striving to improve information and its flow, and the more they will grasp their role in damage control.

Internal Relations

It is important to maintain effective communications and relations with external customers such as patients, but it is also crucial to communicate with internal customers. Practice executives cannot overlook the importance of their employees and physician-owners. In other words, if the medical practice executive takes care of the employees, the employees will take care of the patients. Several methods ensure effective communications with employees, including writing a staff newsletter, holding regular staff meetings, establishing an intranet, and providing suggestion boxes.

Staff Newsletter

A staff newsletter can be a vehicle for regular communication with the staff and key stakeholders. Newsletters are an excellent method to reinforce organizational goals and objectives. By using targeted articles, practice executives can include employee success stories that highlight steps in the right direction. The stories not only act as reinforcements, but they also provide employees with recognition. Another purpose a staff newsletter serves is to provide employees with a periodic update on the current state of affairs. For example, if part of the practice's goals is to provide on-time service, each newsletter could show the trend toward that goal, along with ideas to help continue a positive trend or new ideas to turn around a negative trend. Another excellent idea is to provide a year-end report to show the practice's final results for each objective. The newsletter can be another method to communicate important information to staff, rather than the traditional meeting or memo.

Staff Meetings

Staff meetings can be an effective way to maintain communication within an organization. These meetings should be viewed as learning opportunities for practice executives and their staff. Meetings can increase the effectiveness and bottom line of both large and small practices; however, if not properly conducted, meetings can waste staff time.

Meetings should therefore have a purpose and a defined agenda. The practice executive should keep the meeting on task; otherwise, participants will lose focus and dread future meetings. Another method to increase the productivity of meetings is to provide staff members with the agenda in advance of the meeting, so they can research the topics for discussion. When staff members are properly prepared, meetings can be effective vehicles for problem solving. One last tip is to follow up all meetings with a thoughtful note to attendees to summarize meeting accomplishments and action plans. This note is more personal than simple meeting minutes sent by e-mail, which typically are deleted without ever being read.

⁝⁝ The Practice Administrator's Role in Governance

To understand what parts to play and when to play them, keep in mind the ultimate purpose of governance, suggests Richard D. Hansen, MS, MGMA Health Care Consulting Group vice president and managing principal.

"Governance is having a smaller but more efficient group making decisions on behalf of the whole," he says. "Your role as administrator is to facilitate that and speak up when there are problems in the decision-making process."

Speaking up doesn't mean taking the lead in decision making, however. Nonshareholders must use special skills and take caution when trying to influence group governance, says James Knight, MS, MGMA member, and CEO, Southwestern Ear, Nose & Throat Associates PA, Santa Fe, N.M.

"You're like an actor on stage," states Knight. "You have to pay attention to displaying your skills as a coach and mentor — in meetings and in private — but in ways that build trust, not just to show off."

In Knight's practice, all seven physician-owners sit on the board. He says that negotiation and oral skills can help head off potential conflicts. They also may help you maintain an image of neutrality, which in turn builds trust.

Elizabeth M. Wertz, FACMPE, MGMA member, and CEO, Pediatric Alliance PC, Pittsburgh, agrees. "The administrator can be the neutral party who helps the board see things from an organizational point of view," she says. "Physicians on a board need somebody who has more of a global outlook on the issues."

One role to avoid is that of a cheerleader, warns Tracie L. Jones, MGMA member and consultant at Today's Healthcare, Winter Springs, Fla. She says that rallying physicians can tarnish your image of neutrality and may devalue whatever decisions they reach.

"I wouldn't rally physicians to make a certain decision," Jones says. "They have to feel that the decision is theirs and that they own it."

A practice with corporate documents in disarray, poor planning processes, or conflicting values can endanger the administrator's career and peace of mind. Just ask Jones, who was administrator at a small surgical practice that broke up in 2003. She says that although the group had grown rapidly and consistently exceeded MGMA financial performance benchmarks, governance issues helped bring it down. Lurking beneath the group's appearance of success was a lack of common vision. Jones revealed that the practice quickly dissolved after the shock of a large increase in malpractice liability premiums. "The physicians could have reduced their incomes or taken other steps until they could expand the business, but they didn't share the same vision or have a group practice mentality," she says.

Governance will be tested in times of stress, says John A. Deane, MPA, MGMA member and CEO, Southwind Health Partners, Nashville, Tenn. Stresses can include new competition, hiring new physicians, merging with or acquiring other practices, opening new facilities, or growing rapidly.

"Restructuring or fixing the governance system also can be a stressor," he says. "People will say, 'We always decided things by a vote of all shareholders, but now I'm going to let a board of seven make important decisions on my behalf?'"

Deane suggests putting your practice under the microscope to spot brewing governance problems, such as the following examples.

Frequent about-faces. Deane calls this the red flag of faulty governance. It occurs when the administrator is later ordered to do the opposite of what the board decided. "It happens when the group has a weak leader who does not speak up during the meetings," states Deane. "Your best response is to explain to leaders the problems they create by doing that."

Union-shop steward mentality. Deane says it occurs when board members consider issues only in terms of their effect on them or their closest colleagues. "Board directors must have the greater good in mind regardless of personal or specialty loyalties," he says.

Meddling. Boards might dwell on minor administrative matters that are easier to grasp and solve than large strategic dilemmas. "It takes discipline to look after the policy issues, but some boards don't have it," admits Deane.

Shooting from the hip. Administrators should help boards make informed decisions by supplying them with critical data in easily digestible chunks. "The first responsibility of a board is to understand their reality, but this means giving them reliable, accurate, and timely information they can review quickly," Deane contends.

Doing end runs. When board members routinely bypass the CEO or administrator — or allow employees to do the same — they are giving the administrator a vote of no confidence, pursuing personal agendas, or just have bad management habits. "Since it is the administrator's job to execute board policy, this behavior becomes a governance issue," explains Deane.

Free-forming. Closely related to "shooting from the hip," this behavior occurs when the organization does little planning, fails to measure progress, and never assigns responsibility for achieving practice goals. Says Deane, "A board needs defined mission, vision and values; annual management plans; and people who have to know who owns each project or goal."

Avoiding Governance Mistakes

It may be a board of directors with a fuzzy sense of mission. It could be poorly written corporate bylaws. It might just be bad meeting habits. Regardless of the symptoms, asserts Richard D. Hansen, MS, poor governance and organizational dynamics will leave a host of problems on the administrator's doorstep. Here are common governance and organization problems that can trip up a medical practice administrator.

- **Failure to build a constituency.** Do leaders share the reasons for their decisions with other physicians? Those who feel left out may resist board decisions. Inevitably, the administrator is drawn into the conflict.

  Solution: Help physicians in governance roles build grassroots support for decisions. Remind them to share background information. If you don't take time to keep people updated, they will see it as a lack of respect and will resist.

- **Acting too independently.** Do you know the unwritten boundaries of your authority? Hansen recalls an administrator who invested a large amount of practice funds without asking the shareholders. Although she didn't need prior approval for the amount invested and the bet paid off, she was reprimanded anyway.

  Solution: Keep your job description up to date. Advise the executive committee or the board when making any major decision, even if advance approval is not required.

- **Not speaking up enough.** Are you speaking up often enough? Administrators who fail to offer any opinions will appear indecisive, which could lead to a loss of credibility.

  Solution: Provide opinions and perspectives backed by good data, notes Stephen L. Wagner, PhD, FACMPE. "At the senior level you have to be willing to say what you think; if not, you're in the wrong job," he says.

- **Not knowing where you stand.** How long has it been since your last performance evaluation? Fewer than half (42.9 percent) of 259 medical groups responding to a recent MGMA Information Exchange said they had a formal performance appraisal process for the administrator. Just 16.3 percent of administrators said they received annual appraisals.[16]

Solution: Insist on meeting with physician leaders annually to set your goals. "Setting mutually agreed-on goals and evaluating performance are major responsibilities of a board, and you should hold leaders to it," declares Hansen.

- **Ignoring conflicts.** Are you doing anything about conflicts between physicians? Unresolved conflicts can lead to operational hassles and eventually depress financial performance. The blame will often fall on the administrator. Also watch out for situations that put you in the middle of physician disagreements.

Solution: Polish mediation skills. Help physician leaders understand where conflicts occur and guide them in conflict resolution, maintains Hansen. "You are not a clinician, so you won't know or be able to respond credibly to all of the extenuating circumstances a dissenting physician might cite in his or her defense."

- **Meandering strategy.** Do board decisions seem inconsistent with practice culture? This can occur when board members don't share a common vision. "The practice will appear to be adrift. But it could look like you — the administrator — are the cause," Hansen confides.

Solution: Work with a physician leader or meet with physicians individually to initiate a broader discussion of group direction. Knight states, "The discussions can be cathartic experiences, but you will end up with a group that is discussing its core values."

- **Failure to follow through.** Do board decisions go by the wayside? Failing to conduct leaders' initiatives will quickly shorten your tenure as an administrator, notes Hansen.

Solution: Make sure board members get solid information before decisions are made. Guide them to encourage other physicians to participate in committees or ad hoc groups. Know when a simple majority won't do and full consensus is needed, such as when buying an electronic health record system.

- **Forgetting to reach out to informal leaders.** Do board decisions often meet resistance?

  Solution: Remember to consult opinion leaders who are not board members, such as respected senior physicians, the physicians who bring in the most revenue, or perhaps younger shareholders who will soon be on the board. "You have to listen because they have power, too, even if their roles aren't defined on corporate documents," says Hansen.

Legal Considerations of Governance

A medical group's basic legal paperwork will consist of articles of incorporation, bylaws, employment contracts for stockholders and nonstockholders, buy-sell agreements, minutes of meetings, and similar documents.

A key issue is currency: Are these documents reviewed periodically by your attorney to ensure that they are legally up to date and consistent with how the group is structured and operating? To find out, ask the following questions:

- Is there a current employment agreement on file for every physician?

- Is the pathway to becoming a stockholder crystal clear?

- Does the buy-sell agreement define the buy-sell process and the valuation method? Does a new physician know at the time of employment how much it will cost to buy into the group and related entities?

- Can retiring physicians learn the amount they will receive?

- Is the income distribution plan consistent with the current legal and regulatory environment?

::: Intranet Communication

An intranet is an internal network belonging to an organization and is typically accessible only by the organization's members. Like the Internet, intranets provide access to information, but they are secure from unauthorized users and provide organizations with their own personal information resource. Intranet sites can be used to inform stakeholders of what is happening in the practice, changes in practice procedures, upcoming training sessions, continuing education opportunities, and updates on new governmental regulations. They can also provide links for help.

Intranet Case Study

If you've ever been frustrated by outdated forms, lack of consistent protocols, or ineffective staff communication, an intranet could solve your problems. One seven-doctor endocrinology group built its own and improved efficiency, patient education, and staff satisfaction.

Identifying the Problem

In taking stock of the group's processes, the new administrator found few written procedures or protocols, and those that did exist were often outdated. As a result, staff members were completing tasks in different ways and often missing steps, including some patient education. In fact, patient forms were inaccurate or incomplete in many cases. In addition, some long-time staff members complained that policy changes had never been communicated to all parties in a timely manner.

Investigating the Options

The administrator presented three options to the board of directors:

1. Keep doing things the same way;

2. Implement different solutions for different types of communication; or

3. Create an intranet.

All parties agreed that the current system was no longer viable. Implementing bulletin boards, holding more frequent staff meetings and providing staff notebooks was another option. It would be quicker and cheaper than an intranet but had several drawbacks, including continued confusion about the location of current documents.

Creating an intranet would:

- Give immediate and sustained access to important dates, policy changes, and other new information;

- Serve as a repository for all updated forms; and

- Collect all procedures, protocols, job descriptions, and policies in one place, and make them available to anyone at any time.

Costs included a more expensive Internet connection so that the satellite location could access the intranet, a minimal amount of lost productivity as staff got used to the new system, and the replacement of old computers.

Implementing the Solution

The board of directors agreed to move forward with developing an intranet. After undergoing a proposal process that generated bids from $800 to $2,500, the administrator built the intranet using Microsoft® Expression Web software at a cost of $400 plus her time.

The administrator collected copies of all forms and policies in use, including 23 different fax cover sheets, and created a standard template for each form type. Old forms were either recycled or used up. The administrator added a shortcut to the intranet to each computer desktop and asked staff members to check the site daily for updates and announcements.

Staff members gave input on what other resources they would like on the intranet, such as patient education forms, lists of referral sources by specialty, and weekly and monthly staff schedules.

Assessing the Benefits

In addition to solving the problem of unprofessional and inaccurate communication, the intranet offered other benefits. The clinic saved money by not using outside vendors to print forms, and the intranet was a secure place to archive old versions of documents. The destruction of old form stock reclaimed enough space to create a new work station. And once they were used to accessing the computer for all types of information, providers and staff members were less resistant to the adoption of electronic medical records. Ultimately, using the intranet not only increased efficiency, it resulted in enhanced patient and staff satisfaction.

Suggestion Boxes

Suggestion boxes no longer have to be of the wooden variety. Currently, electronic suggestion boxes are often located on an organization's Website and may also be found on its intranet. The suggestion box located on the external Website, which is accessible via the Internet, can serve to solicit opinions, experiences, and perceptions of customers.

Perhaps more important is the suggestion box located within the organization's intranet. Frequently, employees have the knowledge and information necessary to improve the organization; however, they withhold the information for fear of reprisal. This method of communication, if anonymous, can overcome that objection.

::: Matrix Reporting Principles

Merging or integrating a practice with a larger health system or hospital means an increased chance for organizational silos and decreased collaboration. Matrix reporting structures, which involve employees reporting to more than one supervisor to provide more effective management, are a remedy for streamlining information and improving communication after integration. Although matrix reporting can help eliminate the miscommunication and inefficiencies that arise in larger, more complicated organizations, it isn't just for large systems. Small and midsize private practices can implement aspects of matrix reporting to enhance communication among staff and ultimately improve patient care.

Direct Line Supervisors vs. Dotted Line Supervisors

Direct line supervisors are traditional supervisors who manage the performance of their direct reports and who determine job responsibility and compensation. Dotted line supervisors are horizontal connections between two staff members, and one may not technically report to another. Horizontal connections usually imply mutual reporting, with both people working together to achieve similar goals. Examples of horizontal connections could be two front-office staff members or two nonphysician providers. One doesn't report to the other, but they're accountable to each other to improve their areas.

Identify where dotted line supervisors reside in your practice. Direct line supervisors should be aware of their employees' dotted line supervisors to understand the scope of their staffs' workload and accountability.

Encourage Communication among All Supervisors

Miscommunication and accountability concerns are common when staff members get direction and feedback from their direct line supervisor, their dotted line supervisors, and other staff members. For example, your billing personnel may work regularly with the front-office staff on patient payment plans, but you, the administrator, may not know that.

They may each report to you, but they are dotted line supervisors to one another. Make sure they communicate to you the protocols they establish together. You can accomplish this through regular staff meetings, huddles, or one-on-one appointments.

Consider Cross-Training

Staff members of smaller medical practices are more to likely to have jobs that overlap with one another since there are fewer internal resources and staff members often have to cover for one another. In larger groups or integrated delivery systems, however, staff members tend to have more clearly defined positions and less opportunity to understand their colleagues' roles. If time allows, have staff members train, or shadow, workers from other areas of the practice for a day.

By experiencing firsthand what their coworkers do every day, staff members may be able to identify new solutions for common problems and reduce interdepartmental misunderstandings. This could be especially true for schedulers and front-office staff to learn more about the clinical processes in a practice, and vice versa. It's also a chance to see how their two jobs intersect and find out ways to work together more effectively.

⠿ Emotional Labor

When faced with winding down a practice she had managed for 16 years, Dea Robinson, FACMPE, used a tool called emotional labor to keep staff and providers engaged for 10 months. Here's how she did it.

Early in 2013, the private practice Robinson had managed for 16 years had to close its doors because it lost a bidding process for services at local hospitals. It had just hired two new associates: One had just finished a residency program and gotten married; the other had just moved to the area and was expecting a baby. Administration knew five months before the announcement that the practice would not be a viable company by the end of the year, but had to maintain a "business as usual" attitude in terms of regular physician and staff meetings, which caused emotional stress for those who knew the practice was in jeopardy.

Managing emotions in the workplace, a concept known as emotional labor, will become an increasingly popular topic as industry members recognize that the Patient Protection and Affordable Care Act presents unknown implications to every model, facility, and/or medical practice across the nation.

Robinson describes her behavior during that time as "surface acting," which refers to outward emotional expressions that do not match your true emotions. Staying positive in light of the immense pressure of losing is an example of surface acting (not really feeling the emotion).

Robinson's role was to keep the staff and physicians engaged with their jobs as if everyone would be there indefinitely. She had to force herself to smile and rally every day for more than 10 months. She quickly realized that her workday changed drastically with the constant departure of physicians from her group, and the real work she was doing was emotional labor, which refers to situations when workers are unable to display their true emotions on the job. Finally the word was out, and the physicians, staff, and Robinson had to face the reality that they would all lose our jobs in a matter of months.

In contrast, it was almost required that Robinson show her true feelings and emotions when she met with key physicians before the bidding process had been completed regarding the practice's strategy and the consequences if it lost the proposal. Sharing their feelings helped them act cohesively. Robinson reports it was a relief to be herself and reveal the concern she had for the corporation and individuals involved.

Rethinking Emotions in the Workplace

It is a commonly accepted notion that emotions don't belong in the workplace because they are too subjective and not based on reality or fact. There is a time for a poker face, but researchers have found that the more we depersonalize and distance ourselves from our current obstacles, projects, or situations, the less we can identify and adopt a strategy.[17] And the less we employ a strategy, the more difficult or laborious work becomes. Expressing emotions appropriately is important for leaders because there are positive effects for those they lead. Some benefits of displaying emotions to staff or physicians in the workplace include:

- Emotions reveal authenticity;

- Emotions shown by leaders reveal the capacity to empathize, a desirable characteristic when working with others in patient care; and

- Emotions show transparency.

Why is this important to medical executives? These professionals are industry change agents. They have knowledge of every aspect of patient care except for the clinical aspects of treating a patient. If they strike a balance and allow their emotions to be part of their daily narrative, they are more likely to keep, retain, and motivate their staff and physicians despite what is going on in their environment.

Research shows that one of the important functions of leaders is to instill feelings of optimism; convince associates, physician partners, and staff that challenging goals are obtainable; and influence employee performance.[18] The ultimate goal is preserving the patient care experience and increasing positive outcomes. Further research shows that emotional labor is found to be at higher levels for workers in any kind of leadership position, and a refined area of research has evolved into the advantages and effects of leading with emotional labor.[19]

Humphrey, Pollack, and Hawver created a complex qualitative emotional labor scale, which involves a multifaceted approach including emotions experienced, frequency, intensity, variety, duration of social interaction, and other categories.[11] The work group categories in their study consisted of customer service, caring professions (e.g., healthcare), social control, and leaders. The medical management industry has complexities that challenge the most highly educated individual and might make it difficult to lead if you avoid using or displaying any emotion. Some leadership theories have generally focused on the personality of the leader rather than how the environment affects the leader.

Change Agents

Picture the following scenario: Your physician leadership decides the best course of action for your group is to merge with your local hospital and participate in a Medicare Shared Savings Program by the end of your next fiscal year. The physicians have been good to you and your staff, however, current times require this change. The future of employment for the entire group is unknown and the roles your physicians had as leaders will change as well. You are a leader in your organization and some of this news was not a surprise, but hearing it spoken had an emotional effect on you.

The first step is to explain to your physician leaders what is involved and realistically achievable, and what a better-performer timeline would look like. The second option is to smile and say, "No problem" while inside you are completely overwhelmed with how to accomplish the task in front of you. Seasoned executives know that the task is typically achievable and the timeline is almost always impossible. The latter choice is what is identified as emotional labor. This process helps us negotiate enormous stress in the workplace because we smile and, in a sense, become actors because our behavior is contrary to our real emotions.

⠿ Servant Leadership

The first priority of a leader is putting service and others first, including employees, customers, and the community, according to the article "Needed: Servant-Leaders" by David Peete.[20] In other words, a servant leader serves followers, creating an organizational culture of community by elevating and exalting the dignity of staff.

Servant leadership begins with personal connections among a leader and his or her followers. He or she recognizes the need for emotional ownership among staff members, who are stakeholders in the success of a medical practice. You, as a medical practice leader, must show genuine interest in each staff member as an individual, setting the bar higher for a proficient employee and mentoring an employee who is working on identified weaknesses. Elevating the dignity of one individual elevates the dignity of everyone in the group and demonstrates that the practice values each employee. Likewise, servant-leaders openly communicate their belief that staff is highly capable and will achieve the organization's goals.

Building Trust

Trust in a medical practice leader is the most important ingredient in the leader–follower relationship. To earn it, you must communicate respectfully with staff members who are encouraged to give open and respectful feedback. A successful servant-leader demonstrates a high level of integrity and honesty.

Building trust also involves soliciting ideas for process improvement and prioritization from staff members. Involve them in implementing these plans.

The authentic servant-leader understands that "rounding" with staff is more than making an appearance. Servant-leaders spend time, side by side, with staff with their sleeves rolled up to participate in the daily responsibilities of patient care. For example, when you receive an order of supplies, don't leave them out for staff members to stow them — put them away yourself. This demonstrates that every task is everyone's task.

Give staff members clear directions on what is expected of them and why. Ensure they have the information needed to perform their jobs well. When they have difficulty identifying what they should do, a servant-leader facilitates staff discussion to help them discern what they need to do.

You must continually prove your worthiness as a leader. Holding yourself to higher standards and levels of accountability is one way to do this. Your worth as a leader also gains credibility when you show respect for everyone you interact with, including physicians, staff, patients, vendors, and maintenance staff.

Follow-through on issues also bolsters your worthiness. Sometimes it means admitting that an issue cannot be solved or that you need to research it further, which validates the importance of fulfilling all of one's responsibilities.

Servant leadership is not "soft management." It forces you to give direction, guide with values, define purpose, and set high expectations for all staff members. It's about service excellence.

Defining Roles

Administrators who work successfully with physician leaders to run group practices talk about the need to establish clearly defined roles and have the confidence to reinforce them.

"It's sometimes hard for physicians to let administrators do what they were hired to do," says John Brown, CMPE, CEO, Medical Specialists of the Palm Beaches, Inc., Lake Worth, Fla. "Physicians are taking on more of the administrator's role [and that's] a unique dynamic because the physician can take on administrative duties but I cannot take on physician duties."

The key, he states, is to recognize what issues are best suited for administrators and what issues require a doctor's attention to optimize skill sets.

"Physicians naturally go to [Brown's physician counterpart] first, and they shouldn't always," Brown admits. Redirecting inquiries that fall into an administrative realm helps reinforce boundaries. "We both understand and respect each other's roles," Brown says. "It helps us keep egos in check."

Identifying and managing egos are important components to successful practice management, confirms Timothy Coker, Lt. Cmdr., USN, MSC, FACHE, MGMA member, division head, Healthcare Operations, U.S. Navy, Falls Church, Va.

"I think administrators often want to manage [doctors] as employees and not as another member of the team," says Coker. "This is something to avoid. Additionally I think administrators don't demand and command respect for their position in a given practice. They are often employees themselves but hold a unique role on the team. Don't let a doctor push you around as a subjugated subordinate and not a valued member of the team."

To establish boundaries between medical and administrative areas and delegate accordingly, Brown suggests the following steps:

1. Set defined roles between the two leaders;
2. Educate the physician staff and management team on those roles;
3. Communicate frequently;
4. Give constant feedback; and
5. Accept the limitations of each role.

Brown's partnership, which has evolved during the last two years as he has co-managed 30 locations and 76 doctors with a physician leader, relies on a willingness to hold each other in check. "We have to ask, 'Why are you dealing with that? That's something I should be doing,'" Brown says. The underlying message: I can help you with that.

The two meet weekly and talk daily, which helps to ensure good communication, though Brown admits that an equally important piece of the partnership is the confidence to hold his own, assert his opinion and back it up with facts to establish trust with physician leaders and, in his case, a board of directors.

"As an administrator, you're always going to make unpopular decisions," allows Brown. "You're always going to have someone who's unhappy." But fear of upsetting physicians can stymy innovation and tie a practice manager's hands. "As an administrator, it's difficult to practice appropriately if you're afraid for your job," he says. If that's the case, he adds, it's important to ask yourself if you're in the right place.

Coker concurs and adds that he has had success with engaging physicians early in the process. "I find doctors make better partners (or thought leaders) than employees," he contends. "Engage them early and often and you won't have much of an issue establishing and maintaining an effective partnership."

⠶ Improving Physician Attendance at Meetings

One of the more common refrains from practice administrators is, "I can't get my doctors to attend meetings! What can I do?"

Time is a limited resource. Especially for physicians, given their clinic time, surgery schedules, hospital rounds, call schedules, and so forth. Boosting meetings attendance requires a multilevel approach, and the following guidelines can help.

1. Set Expectations for New Physicians

When recruiting physicians, discuss governance participation requirements at the practice. Ensure the new doctor understands that partnership comes with the responsibility for attending meetings and participating in decisions related to group governance. Once the new physician is on site, include this information in the orientation session.

2. Refresh Expectations for Current Physicians

Take time to educate — or reeducate — current physician partners on the roles and responsibilities of board members. Talk about the board's governance duties of care, obedience, and loyalty. It's difficult to meet those obligations if one does not participate in the practice's governance.

You can have this conversation at an annual orientation session for new physicians, present it as part of the preliminary work-up to a strategic planning meeting, or take it piece by piece and discuss it at consecutive board meetings. For example, you can discuss these duties with the physicians during individual interviews as well as in the preliminary presentation at a retreat.

3. Set Clear Goals for Each Meeting

If a meeting doesn't have a written agenda, physicians will have no incentive to attend because they won't know why their input is needed. Always begin planning meetings with a clear goal in mind, making sure agenda items follow that goal.

4. Discuss Items That Are Worth Their Time

This is critical to securing good attendance. Ensure all agenda items are relevant. For example, during a gastroenterology practice board meeting, the physicians spent 45 minutes arguing whether or not Sally, one of the nurses, should get a 45-cents-per-hour raise even though everyone else was receiving a 30-cents-per-hour raise. Nobody controlled the conversation, and nobody suggested this was not the appropriate forum for the discussion.

Was this an appropriate conversation for a board meeting? Did the physicians believe the discussion was valuable and therefore the meeting worthwhile? Of course not. Will the practice be able to get those physicians back to another meeting? Not any time soon. If raises are handled by the administrator within limits established by the board, future meetings will be shortened, agendas will be more carefully constructed, and attendance will increase.

5. Provide Materials in Advance

Make sure minutes from the previous meeting, financial reports, or documents for discussion are provided to physicians prior to the meeting — not just an hour before, but several days.

Make sure these documents are well presented and formatted. Is the important information highlighted? Does the agenda indicate what decisions the board will be asked to make? It's not just a matter of supplying information; it has to be the right information, properly presented and formatted for easy review and assessment. Don't print out an entire report for everyone attending if an executive summary will suffice.

6. Start Meetings on Time

If you don't begin promptly, participants will continue to arrive later and later, allowing less time for board governance work. And for those physicians who do show up on time, is it fair for them to wait 25 minutes for the meeting to start? If you want to keep attendance up, start and end on time.

7. Review Your Meeting Format and Schedule

Do you schedule meetings at the end of the day when everyone's ready to go home or at times when you know participants will be most alert? Examine how often you hold meetings and ask the team if they think the schedule is appropriate. Giving them input will demonstrate your flexibility in meeting their needs.

8. Maintain Focus at Meetings

This may seem easy, but there are many ways participants can derail a meeting. Consider a board meeting attended by a consultant where there were two agenda items, one a relatively complex financial issue and the other a personnel issue. The meeting lasted nearly two-and-a-half hours, but could have been completed in far less time. There was no direction, and discussion rambled from participant to participant.

Following the meeting, the consultant talked to the physician and raised the issue of how to chair a meeting. The physician acknowledged he probably wasn't very good at it, but this was how all his predecessors ran meetings. The two discussed a few of the tools required to facilitate an effective and efficient meeting, and the next meeting was shorter and more effective. As the president improves his skills and the group gets used to the process, they can all accomplish more in less time.

◼ Conclusion

A professional code of conduct sets the ethical and behavioral benchmark for staff across the organization. As such, it is the living and breathing manifestation of practice culture and mission and the day-to-day embodiment of practice values. The effective medical practice leader will facilitate the implementation of these standards through ongoing administration of policies that support professional behavior, the effective communication of performance expectations, and the growth of physicians as leaders within the organization.

Notes

1. Romano 2005, as cited in *Rx for Business Success: Joining a Medical Group Practice*, (Englewood, CO: Medical Group Management Association, 2005).

2. Rade B. Vukmir, *Physician Contract Guidebook* (Englewood, CO: MGMA, 2014), 11.

3. Peter G. Teichman and Anne E. Caffee, "Preventing Errors in Your Practice: Prescription Writing to Maximize Patient Safety," *Family Practice Management* 9, no. 7 (2002): 27–30.

4. Peter Senge, *The Fifth Discipline: The Art and Practice of the Learning Organization* (New York: Currency, 1999), 233–272.

5. James Collins, *Good to Great: Why Some Companies Make the Leap…and Others Don't* (New York: HarperCollins, 2001).

6. DiscProfile, "What is DiSC®? The DiSC Personality Test Explained, www .discprofile.com/what-is-disc/overview/.

7. William M. Marston, *The Emotions of Normal People* (New York: Harcourt, Brace & Company, 1928). This book in its entirety is the basis for the DiSC system.

8. "Behavior and Skill Assessments, Analytics, Consulting Services," PI Worldwide, www.piworldwide.com/.

9. BrainyQuote, s.v. "Lou Holtz," www.brainyquote.com/quotes/authors/l/ lou_holtz.html.

10. Sydney Finkelstein, "7 Habits of Spectacularly Unsuccessful Executives," *Fast Company* (July 2003): 84–89.

11. Caren Baginski, "4 Strategies to Manage Conflict among Physicians," MGMA *In Practice* Blog (Nov. 1, 2010), www.mgma.com/blog/4-strategies -to-manage-conflict-among-physicians.

12. Baginski, "4 Strategies."

13. Baginski, "4 Strategies."

14. Wendy Lipton-Dibner, M.A. *M.A.D. Leadership for Healthcare: Proven Strategies to Get People to Do What You Want Them to Do: Motivate–Align– Differentiate* (Phoenix, MD: Greenbranch, 2009), 11.

15. Jim Usry. "Managing Discord," *MGMA Connexion* 10, no. 7 (2010): 38–40.

16. R. Hansen, "Transforming Group Practice Governance: Three Instructional Case Studies Show You How," *MGMA Connexion* 5, no. 4 (2005).

17. Dea Robinson, "Showing Strength: Reasons to Lead with Emotions," *MGMA Executive View* 10, no. 1 (Summer 2014): 30–33.

18. R.H. Humphrey, J.M. Pollack, and T. Hawver, "Leading with Emotional Labor," *Journal of Managerial Psychology* 23, no. 2 (2008): 151–168.

19. Humphrey, Pollack, and Hawver, "Leading with Emotional Labor."

20. David Peete, "Needed: Servant-Leaders," *Nursing Homes: Long-Term Care Management* 54, no. 7 (2005): 8.

Resource List

The following resources are available on the Medical Group Management Association® (MGMA®) Website. Please visit the MGMA Store at www.mgma.org/store for updates and new products. Members of MGMA seeking assistance locating articles and industry resources on operations management may contact the MGMA Knowledge Center at infocenter@mgma.org.

MGMA Books and Reports

- *Assessment Workbook for Medical Practices*, by Carolyn Pickles, Alys Novak, and Darrell L. Schryver (2011). Item # 8259.

- *Better Data, Better Decisions: Using Business Intelligence in the Medical Practice*, by Nate Moore and Mona Reimers (2013). Item # 8706.

- *Data Sanity: A Quantum Leap to Unprecedented Results*, second edition, by Davis Balestracci (2015). Item # 8803.

- *Experts Answer 95 New Practice Management Questions*, by Mary Mourar, with Kenneth T. Hertz, Cynthia L. Dunn, Nick A. Fabrizio, and Jeffrey B. Milburn (2012). Item # 8369.

- *Physician Contract Guidebook*, by Rade B. Vukmir (2014). Item # 8777, # E8777 (download version).

- *Physician Policies: A Practical Guide to Governance Issues*, by Marshall M. Baker and Kenneth M. Hekman (2011). Item # 8260.

- *RVUs: Applications for Medical Practice Success*, third edition, by Frank Cohen (2013). Item # 8539.

- *Star-Studded Service: Six Steps to Winning Patient Satisfaction*, second edition, by Kevin W. Sullivan and Meryl D. Luallin (2012). Item # 8595.

- *Strategies for Value-Based Physician Compensation*, by Jeffrey B. Milburn and Mary Mourar (2013). Item # 8652.

MGMA Practice Resources Topics and Tools Sections
See the following topic-focused sections on the MGMA Website:

- Operations Management
- Physician Compensation
- Quality Management

MGMA Connection Magazine — Operations Management Focus

- *Medical Practice Today*, published each July, is a review of the annually updated "What Members Have to Say" research, focusing on challenges faced by MGMA members and what they're doing to survive and thrive in today's healthcare environment.

- *Operations Management* issue, published each October, is an array of articles that drill down into specific Body of Knowledge domain topics.

- *The State of Medical Practice*, published each January, is an annual update to the myriad issues medical practice executives will grapple with in the coming year.

MGMA Annual Survey Data Reports
The following reports can be obtained from www.mgma.com/store/surveys-and-benchmarking:

- *Academic Practice Compensation and Production*
- *Best Practices of Successful Medical Groups*
- *Cost and Revenue Module for Integrated Delivery Systems*
- *Cost, Revenue and Staffing*

- *Medical Directorship and On-Call Compensation*
- *Medical Management Compensation*
- *MGMA DataDive*

MGMA Education — Self-Study Courses

- Essentials of Group Practice Management
- Essentials of Information Management
- Essentials of Operations Management
- Essentials of Quality Management

Index

NOTE: *ex.* indicates exhibit.

CPSIA information can be obtained
at www.ICGtesting.com
Printed in the USA
FFOW01n0215170318